INTRODUCTION
TO
STATISTICAL
MECHANICS

INTRODUCTION
TO
STATISTICAL
MECHANICS

BY

G. S. RUSHBROOKE

SENIOR LECTURER IN THEORETICAL PHYSICS
IN THE UNIVERSITY OF OXFORD

OXFORD
AT THE CLARENDON PRESS

*Oxford University Press, Ely House, London W.*1

GLASGOW NEW YORK TORONTO MELBOURNE WELLINGTON
CAPE TOWN SALISBURY IBADAN NAIROBI LUSAKA ADDIS ABABA
BOMBAY CALCUTTA MADRAS KARACHI LAHORE DACCA
KUALA LUMPUR HONG KONG TOKYO

FIRST PUBLISHED 1949
REPRINTED LITHOGRAPHICALLY IN GREAT BRITAIN
1951, 1955, 1957, 1960, 1962, 1964, 1967

PREFACE

THIS book has been written in an attempt to provide an introduction to statistical mechanics suitable for students who, while of limited mathematical experience, require, nevertheless, to appreciate something of the content and importance of modern statistical theories, especially in the field of physical chemistry. It is based on lectures given during the past two or three years, while I was a member of the Department of Physical and Inorganic Chemistry in the University of Leeds, to third-year Honours chemistry students and young research workers. I could have wished no better audience, and should like here to acknowledge my indebtedness to the lively discussions which often followed these lectures and contributed very greatly to my own understanding of the subject.

The emphasis of the book is on the fundamental principles and techniques of statistical mechanics, rather than on their application to specific physical or chemical problems. Inevitably, however, some application of these principles to definite experimental phenomena must be made: both in order to confirm the validity of the basic statistical postulates and to illustrate the kind of understanding which statistical interpretations afford. I hope that my choice of these illustrations will not seem too arbitrary. For the most part the examples chosen are of quite fundamental importance (as, for instance, the statistical interpretation of the specific heats of gases): others have been included either on account of their mathematical suitability or because of current interest within the department in which I was lecturing. For this latter reason I have dealt in some detail with the theory of non-ionic solutions. But I must emphasize that these lectures were not intended in any way to cover the ground in theoretical chemistry. Nor is this book. Its aim is simply to take a student with no previous knowledge of statistical mechanics, and little mathematical equipment, sufficiently far for him afterwards to be able to read original papers and standard treatises (see bibliography) with some understanding and not too much effort.

Until the last chapter, when something is said, briefly, of their interconnexion, statistical mechanics and thermodynamics are regarded as largely independent disciplines both bearing on our field of inquiry: some acquaintance, therefore, with the basic concepts of thermodynamics is presupposed. Nevertheless, I think that all the thermodynamic formulae which have been used have been derived from first principles either in the text or in appendixes at the end of the book. Mathematically, no knowledge is presupposed apart from that which is indispensable to any scientist: acquaintance with logarithmic and exponential functions, elementary algebra, and the fundamentals of differential and integral calculus. Although there are problems of statistical mechanics which require for their satisfactory solution very powerful instruments of pure mathematics, it is quite surprising how much progress is possible with the help only of simple and elementary tools.

Any book which makes no special claim to originality necessarily owes much to current standard treatises, and while I have tried to avoid conscious plagiarism my indebtedness to the works listed in the bibliography will be apparent to all who are familiar with them. I only hope that the result of this present text will be that many others are enabled to enjoy those weightier publications, indispensable to serious research workers. It has seemed inappropriate, in an exposition which is primarily theoretical, to make detailed reference to the origin of experimental values listed in the half-dozen tables of physical measurements. Most of these tables, which give the experimental values that I quoted in my lectures, were derived from miscellaneous sources: in so far as many of these can be traced in the reference books already mentioned, I hope that this expression of my indebtedness to them may be taken as sufficient acknowledgement. Table II is rather exceptional in that its columns were taken as they stand from the corresponding table on p. 90 of Fowler and Guggenheim's *Statistical Thermodynamics*. I am very grateful to Professor Guggenheim, F.R.S., and the Syndics of the Cambridge University Press, for their kind permission to use this table.

It gives me much pleasure to express my gratitude to the many friends who have helped me in this work. Particularly must I thank Professor C. A. Coulson, who was not only responsible for my starting to write the book but has read the whole manuscript and corrected many of its errors, and Professor M. G. Evans, F.R.S., with whom I have had countless invaluable discussions: for their kind encouragement I am especially grateful. I must also thank by name Dr. N. B. Slater and Mr. J. S. de Wet for their help in correcting the proofs and checking the examples.

Finally, I am much indebted to the officers of the Clarendon Press for their unfailing patience and helpfulness, which have made my share in the business of publication so agreeable and pleasurable a task.

G. S. R.

OXFORD
January 1949

CONTENTS

APPENDIXES

I

INTRODUCTION

1. STATISTICAL mechanics is concerned with interpreting and, as far as possible, predicting the properties of macroscopic physical or chemical systems in terms of the properties of the microscopic systems (atoms, molecules, ions, electrons, etc.) of which these aggregates are composed. It is, moreover, primarily concerned with the equilibrium properties of macroscopic systems and not with the velocity with which this equilibrium is reached. The theory of rate-processes is called kinetic theory and, although of great importance, is still very much in process of development and hardly yet on as sound or final a basis as is the theory of the properties of thermodynamic systems which have attained complete equilibrium. This book will deal only with the latter field, in which the rules are already well established.

The field is, of course, by no means an unimportant one. For we shall be concerned with the theory underlying the interpretation, in terms of molecular structure and intermolecular forces, of such diverse physical or chemical properties as the specific heat of a gas, the partial vapour pressures of a solution or the melting-point of a solid. We shall not, however, attempt to deal with all existing applications of statistical mechanics. Some of these, e.g. to the melting-point of a solid, are necessarily either superficial or mathematically very involved: and most are already easily available either in standard treatises (such as Fowler and Guggenheim; see Bibliography) or in original papers. The present book aims rather at preparing the ground so that such more detailed and elaborate works may be read with profit. The basic concepts and principles of statistical mechanics are introduced, it is hoped, both simply and systematically, and the examples chosen to illustrate the application of the principles, and to further a clear understanding of them, are generally of quite fundamental importance. Some examples of rather minor interest, however, have been included when these have served to extend the mathematical technique. For statistical mechanics is essentially a mathematical

B

science, and besides introducing the basic concepts and principles of the theory an elementary book must also develop some of the necessary mathematical tools. Here, however, we have deliberately kept to the very simplest methods.

The theory is called *statistical* mechanics because it evidently has to do with average behaviour, in much the same way as an actuary is concerned with average behaviour when dealing with population statistics. The pressure of a gas, for example, on the walls of its container, is clearly some kind of *average* rate of destruction of the momenta of the gas molecules on collision with the walls. For, by definition, pressure is force per unit area and, by Newton's laws of motion, force is rate of change of momentum. Strictly, the pressure will be subject to fluctuations, but these will usually be too small to measure. The existence of local fluctuations in the pressure, or density, of a gas is revealed by the blue colour of the sky (Rayleigh); the Brownian movement of colloidal suspensions and the shot effect in electronics are other well known instances of fluctuation effects. The theory of fluctuation phenomena is a branch of statistical mechanics, but one with which we cannot start off: it constitutes a rather specialized field, which is largely outside the scope of this book.

2. Before the development of statistical mechanics, there were two major theoretical sciences which dealt with the behaviour of bulk matter: classical mechanics and thermodynamics. These, associated respectively with the names of such men as Newton, Euler, and Hamilton on the one hand and Carnot, Joule, and Planck on the other, formed well-established sciences, valid in their own proper domains, but with little or nothing by way of a link between them.

By classical mechanics we mean mechanics based on Newton's laws of motion, in distinction to the more recent quantum or wave mechanics which, we now know, replaces the older theory when very small bodies, of atomic size, are considered. Although one of our main concerns in subsequent chapters will be to emphasize the differences in macroscopic properties resulting from quantal rather than classical behaviour (of the atomic systems of which bulk matter is composed), in the present paragraph it will be sufficient to confine attention to the more familiar classical concepts. These concepts of classical mechanics are simply time, displacement, mass, velocity, energy, force, etc., and the equations of classical mechanics describe the motion, in time and space, of bodies, generally macroscopic bodies, acted upon by given forces. The equations can be solved accurately only when very few bodies, such as those of a planetary system, are involved.

Thermodynamics, by contrast, deals with the general laws governing heat effects: the total conservation of energy, whether mechanical or thermal, the existence of entropy, the phase rule, and so on: a field having at first sight no intimate connexion with classical mechanics. It is concerned only with very general properties of bulk matter: a typical thermodynamic formula, for instance, being that connecting the difference between specific heats at constant pressure and constant volume, respectively, with compressibility and the coefficient of thermal expansion, i.e.

$$C_p - C_v = -T \left(\frac{\partial P}{\partial V}\right)_T \left(\frac{\partial V}{\partial T}\right)_P^2.$$

A certain familiarity, on the part of the reader, with the basic concepts of thermodynamics and some knowledge of the more important formulae, are assumed throughout this book. For easy reference, however, most of the formulae required, together with a concise derivation of them from statements of the first and second laws of thermodynamics, are collected together in Appendix I.

Now just because the fundamental laws of thermodynamics are so general, applying equally to a litre of hydrogen and a block of ice, thermodynamics, as such, is completely unconcerned with specific molecular behaviour. Why, at the same temperature and external pressure, H_2O molecules can form a solid while H_2 molecules form a gas, is a question thermodynamics alone cannot answer.† Yet the limitations of classical mechanics are equally profound. It is easy to suppose that *if* we could solve the 3.10^{23} formulae of Newtonian mechanics for a thermodynamic system

---

† It is, however, not quite true to say that thermodynamics is altogether unconcerned with molecular models: cf. the last chapter.

of 10^{23} atoms we should possess a complete description of the properties of the bulk matter. Quite apart from the possibility of so doing, this is not true. Our answer would still be in terms of space–time concepts (mass, position, velocity of each atom, etc.) and not in terms of thermodynamical concepts such as heat content, entropy, or specific heat. There is a gap here which has to be bridged by some entirely new ideas. It is the theory of Statistical Mechanics, due to Boltzmann, Gibbs, Fowler, and others, which provides the bridge.

3. Before stating the fundamental problem of statistical mechanics explicitly, we must give rather more precision to our terminology. So far, as the reader will have observed, we have employed the word *system* to denote two very different entities.

In the first place it has been used, e.g. in the phrase thermodynamic system, to describe any collection of macroscopic bodies (solids, liquids, or gases) among which thermal, physical, or chemical changes can occur. Secondly, it has been used, e.g. in the phrase microscopic system, to describe one of the basic particles (atom, molecule, ion, or electron) the statistical behaviour of a very large number of which gives rise to the measurable properties of a macroscopic body. Such dual usage is liable to produce confusion, and we shall, therefore, use the word *assembly* to denote what we have so far called a thermodynamic, or macroscopic, system; and we shall reserve the word system, by itself, for what we have hitherto called an atomic, or microscopic, system. This terminology is not universal, in the literature of statistical mechanics, though it is used in the writings of Fowler and Guggenheim and has a great deal to commend it. More precisely, then:

(i) We shall refer to a thermodynamic system, no matter how many, or few, phases and constituents it comprises, as an assembly.

(ii) We shall reserve the word system as a generic term for any of the atoms, molecules, ions, etc., of which the assembly is composed.

There are two other related words which we shall use in a restricted technical sense, and it is convenient to give their definitions here. They are the words *species* and *components*. The systems of an assembly can be of differing species. Thus we may take for our assembly a piece of brass: the systems then comprise two species, copper atoms and zinc atoms (or, if we wish to be more precise, there are three species, copper ions, zinc ions, and electrons). Alternatively, we might consider a quantity of gaseous HCl. In this assembly HCl systems preponderate, but there are also necessarily some H_2 and Cl_2 molecules in dissociative equilibrium with them. When these traces of H_2 and Cl_2 can be ignored, as, for instance, in the theory of the specific heat of gaseous HCl, we shall say that there is only one species present, namely HCl molecules. But if we are particularly interested in the value of the equilibrium constant between HCl, H_2, and Cl_2 then we must recognize that our assembly contains (at least) three types of system, and we shall refer to each distinct type of system as a distinct *species*. In the present instance we should recognize (probably) three species in the assembly: H_2 molecules, Cl_2 molecules, and HCl molecules. Quite generally,

(iii) The number of species present is the number of different types of system which we recognize as existing as distinct entities in the assembly. Each distinct type constitutes a species.

In the above example, however, the numbers of systems of the three species, H_2, Cl_2, and HCl, are not independent. If we add more systems of the type H_2, then the number of HCl systems will also change, on account of the chemical reaction. We shall refer to the *independent* chemical constituents of an assembly as its *components*. Thus, in the above example, there are two components: though whether we regard H_2 and Cl_2 or Cl_2 and HCl or HCl and H_2 (molecules) as specifying these components does not matter. Actually we should, in this case, probably not choose any of the three species as components, but take the two components of the assembly to be H atoms and Cl atoms, from which all three species are built up. In general,

(iv) the number of components of an assembly is the number of independent types of system from which we may regard all the species present as built up or deriving. Which species, or types of system, we choose to regard as the primary components, and which as simply derivative species, is a matter of convenience.

This particular nomenclature, however, will not concern us again until Chapter XII.

After these preliminary definitions, we return to a statement of the fundamental problem of statistical mechanics. This is *to derive the properties of assemblies from those of the systems which compose them.* Or, in terms of our bridge metaphor,

THE MECHANICAL PROPERTIES		THE THERMODYNAMIC PROPERTIES
Velocities or momenta	have	Temperature
Positions	to be	Pressure
Kinetic and potential energies	linked	Entropy
etc.	with	Specific heat
		etc.
OF THE SYSTEMS		OF THE ASSEMBLY.

The substitution of quantum mechanics for classical mechanics does not seriously affect this problem. It merely changes the 'mechanical' description of the systems, precise assessments of position and velocity having to be replaced by probability distributions or wave-functions.

In building this bridge, we shall not hesitate to work from both sides. In the last chapter of this book we shall look at the possibilities of building from one side only—which, of course, must be from the side of mechanics since we cannot pass from statistical averages to a precise knowledge of individual behaviour—but to start that way is only to add unnecessary difficulties to our task. Because statistical mechanics bridges the gap between mechanics and thermodynamics, the analogous term *statistical thermodynamics* is nowadays coming into use. It is possibly less forbidding but also, perhaps, less satisfactory, since it is mechanical and not thermodynamical properties which have to be averaged.

4. At first sight, the most obvious link between mechanics and thermodynamics is to be found in the similar properties of the average kinetic energy, per system, of an assembly consisting of a very large number of interacting systems and the temperature of the assembly itself. We can, indeed, advance the following arguments in support of a connexion between the two concepts:

(i) If an isolated assembly radiates heat its temperature falls: since heat is a form of energy, we may conclude that the average kinetic energy of each of its systems falls too.

(ii) The kinetic energy of all the systems will, due to collisions, tend to become more or less uniform† throughout the assembly, just as temperature also tends to become uniform throughout an assembly.

The mechanical aspect of (ii), though subject to theoretical proof, can be nicely demonstrated by a mechanical model due to Bohr. The model employs a number of small balls and a shallow basin (ball-bearings and a large watch-glass are quite suitable). If one ball is placed at rest in the bottom of the basin, and another is shot down the side so as to collide with it, then, on collision, the stationary ball may well acquire the momentum of the moving one and be ejected from the basin. But if several balls are placed in the basin, it is then possible to shoot another into them with considerable velocity without any of the originally stationary balls acquiring sufficient momentum to be ejected. The demonstration is most striking if the base of the basin is flat and the balls placed in it are not quite in contact with each other.

(iii) The specific heats of assemblies tend to assume values independent of the temperature. Though this requires a lot of qualification, there is sufficient truth in the statement to suggest a linear relationship between mean kinetic energy and temperature.

We shall later derive the relation between mean kinetic energy and temperature quite rigorously, and shall then find that such a linear dependence is frequently valid. In fact, we shall find that the mean kinetic energy corresponding to any particular momentum of a system, e.g. the average value of $\frac{1}{2}m\dot{x}^2$ corresponding to motion in the x-direction, is often given by

$$\overline{K.E.} = \tfrac{1}{2}kT,$$

where T is the temperature and k is Boltzmann's constant, i.e.

† We shall find that there is an equilibrium distribution of kinetic energies: see § 5 below and later.

the gas constant per molecule, equal to $1·3805.10^{-16}$ erg/deg. It follows at once that gases whose systems are complex molecules will tend to have larger specific heats than those whose systems are simple atoms. For since complex molecules possess vibrational and rotational modes of kinetic energy as well as kinetic energy of translational motion, a given addition of heat to the assembly will cause a smaller increment in the average kinetic energy of any particular mode, and hence a smaller rise in the temperature of the assembly.

Despite the ease, however, with which we can make out a strong case for an intimate connexion between average kinetic energy and temperature, this line of argument will not take us very far. The main reason is that the simplicity of relationship breaks down when classical mechanics gives place to quantum mechanics. The rather premature discussion above has been included solely to accustom the reader to thinking in terms both of mechanics and thermodynamics, and to show the kind of insight we may hope to gain from a properly founded statistical theory. We shall now proceed to develop a very much more useful line of approach.

5. Thermodynamically, we know that entropy tends to increase, and never decreases, in an isolated assembly.

As we shall illustrate below, this is a property also of the 'mechanical' concept of disorder, or randomness, among the very many systems of the assembly. And a full exploitation of this analogy, between entropy and randomness, provides the link that we are seeking.

Before attempting to give a precise measure to the 'mechanical' concept of randomness or disorder, it will be well to explain qualitatively what is meant by these terms. The general idea is clear enough. When, for instance, a liquid evaporates to give a gas it is well known that the entropy, per mole, of the gas is considerably greater than that of the liquid. It is also evident that the evaporation of the liquid has destroyed a limited knowledge that we had about the positions of the systems of the assembly. Randomness and disorder are almost synonymous with uncertainty and ignorance. Moreover, any further expansion of the gas, say at constant temperature, increases our ignorance of the whereabouts of the molecules and simultaneously produces an increase in the entropy of the assembly.

As a second illustration, we may consider the interdiffusion of two different gases. If, by the removal of a partition between them, two different gases, let us suppose originally at the same temperature and pressure, are allowed to diffuse into each other we again have an increase of entropy in the whole assembly. Again, too, we have lost a certain knowledge about the molecules, though this is not of quite the same kind as in the case of the expansion of a gas into a vacuum. We are more ignorant now in that whereas before the removal of the partition knowledge that a molecule was at a certain place gave us also knowledge of the nature of the molecule, after the removal of the partition this is no longer true: even if we have 'located' a molecule we still have no *a priori* knowledge of the species to which it belongs.

As the last example shows, it is sometimes not most helpful to think of entropy as associated simply with uncertainty or ignorance of *position*, although, in that case, since every system is somewhere we can reduce the uncertainty to ignorance of position if we so wish. Consider, for instance, the increase in entropy of a gas which results from an increase in temperature, the volume being kept constant. Increasing the temperature implies that we have increased the kinetic energy of the systems of the assembly. If all these systems had exactly the same energy, i.e. had precisely the mean energy (given by the total energy divided by the number of systems), then merely increasing the total energy would not add to our ignorance of the microscopic state of the assembly. But this is not so. We shall find that the systems possess a distribution of energies about the mean, some having more than the average energy and others less; and increasing the total energy does, indeed, increase our ignorance as to which systems have a high energy and which have a low energy. Deviations from the equilibrium *distribution* of energies are actually unimportant and do not, in general, contribute to the entropy: consequently, if we so wish, we can again think of the entropy as associated with the positions of systems having various energies.

Nevertheless it is wiser, and certainly sounder at the present stage, to associate entropy with total ignorance or uncertainty, rather than merely with ignorance or uncertainty about the spacial positions of the systems.

Having now a qualitative idea of what we mean by randomness or disorder, ignorance or uncertainty, as applied to the microscopic state of an assembly, it remains to give the concept a precise quantitative measure.

To do so it is useful to consider, by way of analogy, the shuffling of a pack of cards. If these are originally in their correct order (corresponding to a state of zero entropy) and we start to shuffle them (corresponding to thermal agitation due to a rise in temperature) then, at any later stage, we are uncertain of the order of the cards (corresponding to a gain in entropy). Obviously a *measure* of our uncertainty, or of the state of disorder in the pack, is given by the number of a priori *equally probable arrangements* of the cards at the stage that we have reached. Let us denote this number by ϖ.

Now consider two packs of cards shuffled independently. Then the number of equally probable arrangements of the cards in both packs (ϖ) is the product of the respective numbers of arrangements for the two packs separately (ϖ_1 and ϖ_2): for any particular arrangement of the cards in one pack can occur with any of the possible arrangements of the cards in the other pack, i.e.

$$\varpi = \varpi_1 \varpi_2. \tag{1}$$

On the other hand, thermodynamically, the entropy (S) of an assembly consisting of two independent parts is the sum of the entropies (S_1 and S_2) of the two parts separately, i.e.

$$S = S_1 + S_2. \tag{2}$$

Thus we may contrast:

(i) The increasing property of ϖ with the increasing property of S.

(ii) The multiplicative property of ϖ with the additive property of S.

This suggests a relationship of the form†

$$S = k \ln \varpi, \tag{3}$$

where k is a constant:‡ for then (2) follows from (1), i.e.

$$S = k \ln \varpi = k \ln \varpi_1 \varpi_2 = k \ln \varpi_1 + k \ln \varpi_2 = S_1 + S_2.$$

Equation (3) forms the basis of our first serious approach to statistical mechanics, except only that when dealing with an assembly we shall replace the symbol ϖ, introduced in the example above, by the more customary symbol Ω. The equation then reads

$$S = k \ln \Omega \tag{3'}$$

and connects S, the entropy of the assembly, with Ω, the number of *a priori* equally probable *complexions*, or micromolecular states, of the assembly.

6. Before we proceed to the evaluation of Ω for particular assemblies there are two final points, concerning equation (3'), which must be made.

The first is that, since in any isolated assembly the total internal energy (E), the volume (V), and the number of systems which it contains (N) are fixed, E, V, and N must be supposed fixed, i.e. given quantities, when we evaluate Ω. The argument may not be entirely convincing but a further, and more cogent, reason is provided by a consideration of the thermodynamical equation (see Appendix I, § a)

$$T \, dS = dE + P \, dV - \mu \, dN. \tag{4}$$

This equation connects the small changes in entropy, internal energy, volume, and the number of systems in an assembly (assuming that only one species is present) consequent upon any small change in the thermodynamic state of the assembly. It shows that a change in S is governed by changes in the three independent quantities E, V, and N which, fortunately, are all 'mechanical' concepts. Our problem, then, is to evaluate Ω, not as a mere number which would be quite uninteresting, but as a function of the number of systems in the assembly, the volume within which these are contained, and their total energy. The

---

† We use ln in place of the more cumbersome $\log_e$ to denote natural logarithms.

‡ It is not difficult to show that this is the only possible relationship for which (2) will follow from (1).

total energy, of course, includes contributions from all types of potential energy as well as from all types of kinetic energy. That Ω depends explicitly on E, V, and N is most simply expressed symbolically by the equation

$$\Omega = \Omega(E, V, N)$$

to be read as 'Ω depends on (or, is a function of) the variables E, V, and N'.

The second point, following from this, is that once we know Ω as an explicit function of E, V, and N we know not only S but *all* the thermodynamic properties of the assembly. For, by equation (4), the temperature (T), the pressure (P), and the chemical potential† (μ) are given by

$$\left(\frac{\partial S}{\partial E}\right)_{V,N} = \frac{1}{T}, \tag{5a}$$

$$\left(\frac{\partial S}{\partial V}\right)_{E,N} = \frac{P}{T}, \tag{5b}$$

and

$$\left(\frac{\partial S}{\partial N}\right)_{E,V} = -\frac{\mu}{T}. \tag{5c}$$

In terms of Ω, by equation (3'), these formulae read

$$\left(\frac{\partial \ln \Omega}{\partial E}\right)_{V,N} = \frac{1}{kT}, \tag{6a}$$

$$\left(\frac{\partial \ln \Omega}{\partial V}\right)_{E,N} = \frac{P}{kT}, \tag{6b}$$

and

$$\left(\frac{\partial \ln \Omega}{\partial N}\right)_{E,V} = -\frac{\mu}{kT}. \tag{6c}$$

Therefore when we know Ω explicitly as a function of E, V, and N we can, by partial differentiation, derive also expressions for T, P, and μ; and thence obtain any other thermodynamic quantities that we may require.

We shall, later, prove that the constant k, occurring in equations (3') and (6), is simply Boltzmann's constant, **k** (see § 4 above).

---

† Since N denotes the number of systems, μ is the chemical potential *per system* (not per mole). To obtain the partial molar Gibbs free energy we must multiply μ by Avogadro's number, N_0.

Meanwhile, however, we shall leave k an unknown constant and proceed to the evaluation of Ω for certain simple, but very important, assemblies.

EXAMPLES

1. A perfect gas satisfies the equation of state $PV = RT$, per mole, where R is a constant. Use the thermodynamic formula quoted in section 2 above to prove that for any such assembly

$$C_p - C_v = R \quad \text{(per mole)}.$$

2. For any thermodynamical assembly, the Helmholtz free energy, F, is defined by the equation $F = E - TS$. Use equation $(6\,a)$ to prove

$$F = E^2 \frac{\partial}{\partial E}\left(\frac{\ln \Omega}{E}\right)_{V,N} \Big/ \left(\frac{\partial \ln \Omega}{\partial E}\right)_{V,N}.$$

3. For any thermodynamical assembly, of one component,

$$E - TS + PV = N\mu.$$

Use this equation to prove that for any such assembly Ω must satisfy the differential equation

$$E\left(\frac{\partial \ln \Omega}{\partial E}\right)_{V,N} + V\left(\frac{\partial \ln \Omega}{\partial V}\right)_{E,N} + N\left(\frac{\partial \ln \Omega}{\partial N}\right)_{E,V} = \ln \Omega.$$

AN ASSEMBLY OF INDEPENDENT LOCALIZED SYSTEMS

1. IN Chapter I we indicated a basis for statistical mechanics in the equation

$$S = k \ln \Omega \qquad (1)$$

connecting the entropy of an assembly with the number of *a priori* equally probable complexions, or micromolecular states (of the assembly) corresponding to given values of E, V, and N. We certainly did not pretend to derive equation (1) at all rigorously, but merely indicated the field of statistical mechanics and gave plausible grounds for expecting an equation of this type to hold. For the present we must regard the validity of equation (1) as ultimately resting on the agreement of theoretical results deduced from it with experimental data.

To proceed to derive these theoretical results, we have to calculate $\Omega(E, V, N)$, i.e. Ω as a function of E, V, and N for the assembly. Now Ω, by definition, is the number of *a priori* equally probable complexions of the assembly corresponding to given values of E, V, and N. In the absence of any indication to the contrary, we can only assume that

all conceivable different micromolecular states of the assembly *(complexions) corresponding to the same values of E, V, and N,* *are equally probable.* (a)

This hypothesis underlies the whole of statistical mechanics and, like equation (1), must, for the present, be regarded as justified *a posteriori*, by the success of the theory based on it. In the last chapter of this book we shall consider again the foundations of the statistical mechanics which we shall now commence to develop on the basis of these assumptions.

We shall work, to start with, in terms of quantum mechanics and not classical mechanics. For not only is quantum mechanics frequently more applicable to the systems of an assembly, but also the resulting formulae are simpler and more easily interpreted.

We shall make the transition to classical mechanics in Chapter IV and then, of course, use whichever theory is appropriate.

The simplest of all assemblies to consider is one that consists of N systems, all alike, which are localized in space and independent of each other. Both these terms, however, require a little explanation. By *localized* we mean that though the systems may vibrate about their mean positions these mean positions are themselves fixed in space and there is only one system in the neighbourhood of each of them. Clearly a crystalline phase, in which the systems are more or less located at certain fixed lattice-points, falls in this category. By the second epithet, *independent*, we mean that, at any instant, the state of any one system is entirely unaffected by the state of any of the other systems. There is, of course, one condition making the above statement not quite precise, namely that the total energy of the assembly, E, is fixed. But, apart from this one condition, we mean by independent systems that the energy, or any other property, associated with any one system is entirely independent of the simultaneous characteristic properties of the other systems.

Now the distinctive feature of quantum mechanics is that, for any single system moving in a potential field, there is generally a set of discrete energy levels to each of which belongs one stationary wave-function.† In terms of quantum mechanics, then, the condition of independent systems implies that for any one system there is a set of permissible energies, ϵ_1, ϵ_2,..., ϵ_i,... say, and whichever energy the system has is entirely unaffected by the energies of the other systems provided that the energy of the whole assembly is E.

Our problem, now that we have defined an assembly of N independent localized systems, is to evaluate Ω, the number of distinguishable states of the assembly. We have first to decide just what states to include; for any system, of course, need not be in a quantum-mechanically *stationary* state. Since, however, the energy of a system is not definite for a non-stationary state and, moreover, non-stationary quantum states are simply built up of

† We do not exclude *degenerate* levels, but shall refer to them more particularly below.

linear combinations of stationary states, we are led to modify, or particularize, assumption (a) above so as to read, in terms of quantum mechanics,

all distinguishable stationary states of the assembly, corresponding to given values of E, V, and N, are equally probable; and the number of them is $\Omega(E, V, N)$. (b)

The evaluation of Ω now involves a straightforward algebraic calculation.

The problem is simple. We have N systems, each having one of its permissible energies, $\epsilon_1, \epsilon_2, ..., \epsilon_i, ...$, and the total energy is E. In how many ways can this occur ? Suppose that, in any particular state of the assembly,

$$\begin{array}{ll}
n_1 & \text{systems have energy} \quad \epsilon_1 \\
n_2 & \text{systems have energy} \quad \epsilon_2 \\
\cdot \quad \cdot \quad \cdot \quad \cdot \quad \cdot \quad \cdot \quad \cdot \quad \cdot \\
n_i & \text{systems have energy} \quad \epsilon_i \\
\cdot \quad \cdot \quad \cdot \quad \cdot \quad \cdot \quad \cdot \quad \cdot
\end{array} \quad (2)$$

then the set of numbers $n_1, n_2, ..., n_i, ...$ gives a certain specification of the state of the assembly, but does not fix it completely. Even when the numbers $n_1, n_2, ..., n_i, ...$ are known, we still do not know just *which* of the N systems have energies ϵ_1, or ϵ_2, etc.; we only know that n_1 of them have energy ϵ_1, n_2 of them have energy ϵ_2 and so on. But the number of different states of the assembly *corresponding to a given set of numbers* $n_1, n_2, ..., n_i, ...$ is simply the number of ways of dividing N things into groups with $n_1, n_2, ..., n_i, ...$ members in each group, which is (see Appendix II)

$$\frac{N!}{n_1! \, n_2! \, ... \, n_i! \, ...}$$

or, as we shall write it, $\qquad \dfrac{N!}{\prod\limits_i n_i!}$. (3)

Thus the *total* number of different states of the assembly is given by the *sum* of expressions of the form (3) for all possible sets of the numbers $n_1, n_2, ..., n_i, ...$, i.e.

$$\Omega = \sum_{\substack{\text{(all possible sets of} \\ \text{values of } n_1, n_2, ..., n_i, ...)}} \frac{N!}{\prod\limits_i n_i!}. \qquad (4)$$

There are, of course, two restrictions on the permissible values of the numbers $n_1, n_2,..., n_i,...$. The assembly contains N systems and their total energy is E: consequently

$$n_1 + n_2 + ... + n_i + ... = \sum_i n_i = N, \qquad (5)$$

and
$$n_1 \epsilon_1 + n_2 \epsilon_2 + ... + n_i \epsilon_i + ... = \sum_i n_i \epsilon_i = E. \qquad (6)$$

We have, therefore, to sum the right-hand side (r.h.s.) of (4) subject to these two conditions, (5) and (6).

We combine (4), (5), and (6) by writing briefly

$$\Omega = \sum_{\substack{n \\ \left(\substack{\sum_i n_i = N \\ \sum_i n_i \epsilon_i = E}\right)}} \frac{N!}{\prod_i n_i!}. \qquad (4')$$

Before we proceed to evaluate this sum, there is one comment to be made. The numbers n, n without a suffix standing for the set of numbers $n_1, n_2,..., n_i,...$, do not occur in the answer, i.e. in Ω. They are introduced only for convenience and, since we sum over all possible values of them, do not appear in the final result. Nevertheless, we shall find their use most important, and they are known as *distribution* numbers. Conditions of the form of (5) and (6) we call *restrictive conditions* on the distribution numbers.

2. The explicit evaluation of the sum (4'), in closed algebraic form, is difficult owing to the restrictive conditions on the distribution numbers. Yet if there were no such restrictive conditions we should not be much better off, for then the sum would diverge.†

Moreover, it is through the restrictive conditions that the quantities E and N enter into Ω, so that $\Omega = \Omega(E, V, N)$ as we require. As we shall see later, V enters into Ω through the energy levels $\epsilon_1, \epsilon_2,..., \epsilon_i,...$.

Actually the evaluation of (4') in closed algebraic form is impossible unless N is very large. But *when N is very large* it can be shown that *only the largest term in the sum makes any effective contribution to* Ω. We shall discuss the meaning of this in more

† The number of permissible energy levels for any one system is usually infinite, and, without the restrictive condition (6), the sum (4') is simply the number of levels raised to the power N.

detail, and attempt some justification of the statement, in paragraph 6 below: meanwhile we shall proceed, on the basis of this postulate, to pick out the greatest term in the sum on the r.h.s. of (4'), and equate Ω to it. The number of systems in a thermodynamic assembly is customarily of the order of 10^{23}, which is certainly a very large number.

Now the general term in (4') is

$$t(n) = \frac{N!}{\prod_i n_i!} \tag{7}$$

and we require the greatest value of t for any permissible values of $n_1, n_2, ..., n_i, ...$. The problem, therefore, is simply that of finding the n's which make $t(n)$ a maximum. At first sight, then, we might expect to have to satisfy $\partial t(n)/\partial n_i = 0$ for all i. But owing to the restrictive conditions on the n's these are not all independent variables, and we must be rather more careful.

For any small changes, $\delta n_1, \delta n_2, ..., \delta n_i, ...$ in $n_1, n_2, ..., n_i, ...,$ producing a corresponding small change δt in $t(n)$, we have

$$\delta t = \frac{\partial t}{\partial n_1} \delta n_1 + \frac{\partial t}{\partial n_2} \delta n_2 + ... + \frac{\partial t}{\partial n_i} \delta n_i + ... \tag{8}$$

where $\partial t/\partial n_i$ denotes the partial differential coefficient of $t(n)$ with respect to n_i, $t(n)$ being regarded as a function of independent variables $n_1, n_2, ..., n_i, ...$. This is true whatever the small changes $\delta n_1, \delta n_2, ..., \delta n_i, ...$. Owing, however, to the restrictive conditions (5) and (6), t and $t + \delta t$ are both terms of the sum in (4') only if

$$\delta n_1 + \delta n_2 + ... + \delta n_i + ... = 0 \tag{9}$$

and $$\epsilon_1 \delta n_1 + \epsilon_2 \delta n_2 + ... + \epsilon_i \delta n_i + ... = 0. \tag{10}$$

Here (9) and (10), the differential forms of (5) and (6), assure the constancy of N and E, respectively, and restrict the small changes, $\delta n_1, \delta n_2, ..., \delta n_i, ...$ among the n's to those which correspond to passing from one to another of the terms of the sum in (4').

If we multiply (9) by α and (10) by β and add these to (8), we obtain

$$\delta t = \left(\frac{\partial t}{\partial n_1} + \alpha + \beta \epsilon_1\right) \delta n_1 + \left(\frac{\partial t}{\partial n_2} + \alpha + \beta \epsilon_2\right) \delta n_2 + ... + $$
$$+ \left(\frac{\partial t}{\partial n_i} + \alpha + \beta \epsilon_i\right) \delta n_i + ... \tag{11}$$

whatever the values of α and β.

Now if the n's have values which make $t(n)$ a maximum, then $\delta t = 0$ for all small changes δn. Since we are looking for these particular n's, we require the r.h.s. of (11) to vanish for all small values of δn_1, δn_2,..., δn_i,... consistent with (9) and (10). But equations (9) and (10) may be regarded as giving δn_1 and δn_2 in terms of the *independent* small quantities δn_3, δn_4,..., δn_i,.... If we choose α and β so that

$$\frac{\partial t}{\partial n_1} + \alpha + \beta \epsilon_1 = 0$$

and

$$\frac{\partial t}{\partial n_2} + \alpha + \beta \epsilon_2 = 0,$$

then
$$\delta t = \left(\frac{\partial t}{\partial n_3} + \alpha + \beta \epsilon_3\right)\delta n_3 + ... + \left(\frac{\partial t}{\partial n_i} + \alpha + \beta \epsilon_i\right)\delta n_i + ...$$

and $\delta t = 0$ for *any* values of the independent small quantities δn_3, δn_4,..., δn_i,... only if

$$\frac{\partial t}{\partial n_3} + \alpha + \beta \epsilon_3 = 0,$$

$$\frac{\partial t}{\partial n_4} + \alpha + \beta \epsilon_4 = 0,$$

$$. \quad . \quad . \quad . \quad . \quad . \quad .$$

$$\frac{\partial t}{\partial n_i} + \alpha + \beta \epsilon_i = 0,$$

$$. \quad . \quad . \quad . \quad . \quad .$$

i.e. the equations we have to satisfy, to find the n's which make $t(n)$ a maximum, are

$$\frac{\partial t}{\partial n_i} + \alpha + \beta \epsilon_i = 0 \quad \begin{array}{l} \text{for all } i, \\ \text{i.e. } i = 1, 2, 3,.... \end{array} \tag{12}$$

As we should expect, these equations are all of the same form; i.e. all values of i enter on the same footing. The restrictive conditions (9) and (10) may be regarded as giving any two of the δn's in terms of the others, and the argument above then modified accordingly, to give the same set of equations (12) for all values of i.

The method which we have outlined here, and of which a more general discussion is given in Appendix III, is known as Lagrange's method of undetermined multipliers. The 'undetermined multipliers' are α and β, the unknown constants by which we multiplied the restrictive conditions (9) and (10) before adding them to equation (8). They do not, however, remain undetermined, for, as we shall see below, the equations (12) *together with the restrictive conditions* (5) *and* (6) are sufficient to determine α and β as well as the n's for which $t(n)$ has its greatest value.

3. Having secured the requisite mathematical tool, we have now to use it in the case when $t(n)$ is given by equation (7). The evaluation of $\partial t/\partial n_i$ looks difficult, but is greatly simplified if we consider not t but $\ln t$. When $t(n)$ is greatest so also is $\ln t(n)$: we are therefore justified in seeking those n's which satisfy the equations

$$\frac{\partial \ln t}{\partial n_i} + \alpha + \beta\epsilon_i = 0 \quad (i = 1, 2, 3,...) \tag{13}$$

instead of equations (12).† This makes things easier, since

$$\ln t = \ln N! - \ln n_1! - \ln n_2! - ... - \ln n_i! - ...$$
$$= \text{constant} - \sum_i \ln n_i!$$
$$= \text{constant} - \sum_i (n_i \ln n_i - n_i).$$

In the last step, we have used the well-known mathematical formula known as Stirling's formula‡ (see Appendix IV). Then differentiating with respect to (w.r.t.) n_i,

$$\frac{\partial \ln t}{\partial n_i} = -\frac{\partial}{\partial n_i}(n_i \ln n_i - n_i)$$
$$= -\ln n_i - 1 + 1$$
$$= -\ln n_i. \tag{14}$$

Putting (14) into (13) we have, finally,

$$\ln n_i = \alpha + \beta\epsilon_i \quad (i = 1, 2, 3,...). \tag{15}$$

The equations (15) are the equations we were looking for, giving us the values of $n_1, n_2,..., n_i,...$ satisfying the restrictive conditions (5) and (6) and leading to the greatest term, $t(n)$, in the sum in

---

† Though the n's are the same whether we satisfy (13), (5), and (6) or (12), (5), and (6), α and β are, of course, altered. We shall, below, regard (13), (5), and (6), and not (12), (5), and (6), as defining α and β. (12) was introduced only for convenience in explaining the method of undetermined multipliers.

‡ $\ln n! \sim n \ln n - n$: read, $\ln n!$ *can be replaced by* $n \ln n - n$ *when n is sufficiently large.*

(4′). That the term corresponding to these n's is indeed the greatest, and not the least, term in the sum, can be proved without much difficulty, but we shall not go into the proof here. The necessary satisfaction of the restrictive conditions is ensured by the, as yet, undetermined constants α and β.

By good fortune the equations (15) are already *separated* equations, i.e. only one n occurs in each equation. Their solution is immediate, i.e.

$$n_i = e^{\alpha} e^{\beta \epsilon_i} \quad (i = 1, 2, 3, ...)$$

or $\qquad\qquad n_i = A e^{\beta \epsilon_i} \quad \text{where} \quad A = e^{\alpha}.$

These, then, when α and β are chosen to satisfy equations (5) and (6), are the values of the n's which correspond to the greatest of the terms in the sum in (4′), i.e. in Ω. For the present, and for the sake of clarity, we shall denote these particular n's by $n_1^*, n_2^*, ..., n_i^*, ...$ (later we shall sometimes drop the stars when no confusion is likely to arise without them). Then

$$t_{\max} = t(n^*) = \frac{N!}{\prod_i n_i^*!} \tag{16}$$

where $\qquad n_i^* = e^{\alpha} e^{\beta \epsilon_i} = A e^{\beta \epsilon_i} \quad (i = 1, 2, 3, ...),$ $\qquad$ (17)

and $\qquad\qquad \sum_i n_i^* = N,$ $\qquad\qquad\qquad\qquad\qquad\qquad$ (5′)

and $\qquad\qquad \sum_i n_i^* \epsilon_i = E.$ $\qquad\qquad\qquad\qquad\qquad\qquad$ (6′)

At the end of paragraph 1 of this chapter, we remarked that the distribution numbers, n, could not occur in $\Omega(E, V, N)$ since we summed over all possible values of them. But since then we have assumed, so far without proof, that when N is sufficiently large (as is the case for all thermodynamic systems) only the greatest term in the sum representing Ω makes any effective contribution to Ω. That being so, i.e. if we are equating Ω to $t_{\max}$, certain particular values of the distribution numbers do occur in the simplest expression for Ω (equation (16))—although, of course, we could avoid their appearance, by getting rid of the n^*'s between equations (16), (17), (5′), and (6′), if we so wished. Actually, owing to their physical interpretation, this particular set of distribution numbers, $n_1^*, n_2^*, ..., n_i^*, ...$, is very important for a clear understanding of the properties of the assembly, and we shall call it the *equilibrium* set of distribution numbers. Our unproved postulate is that there are overwhelmingly more distinct microscopic states of the assembly corresponding to this particular set of distribution numbers than there are for all other possible sets of distribution numbers put together.†

Since (assumptions (a) and (b) above) all distinct microscopic states of the assembly are, for thermodynamic equilibrium, counted as equally probable, it follows that the assembly is overwhelmingly more likely to be found in a state corresponding to the distribution numbers n_1^*, n_2^*,..., n_i^*,... than in any other state: and therefore these particular distribution numbers are appositely described as equilibrium distribution numbers. Alternatively, we may refer to them as the distribution numbers corresponding to the *most probable* distribution (of energy among the many systems of the assembly).

4. The thermodynamic properties of our assembly are now given by

$$S = k \ln \Omega$$
$$= k \ln t_{\text{max}}$$
$$= k \ln N! - k \sum_i \ln n_i^*!$$
$$= k \Big\{ N \ln N - N - \sum_i (n_i^* \ln n_i^* - n_i^*) \Big\}$$

(by Stirling's formula)

$$= k \Big(N \ln N - \sum_i n_i^* \ln n_i^* \Big) \qquad \text{by (5')}$$
$$= k \Big\{ N \ln N - \sum_i n_i^* (\alpha + \beta \epsilon_i) \Big\} \quad \text{by (17)}$$
$$= k(N \ln N - \alpha N - \beta E) \qquad \text{by (5') and (6').}$$

We can easily get rid of α since, by (17) and (5'),

$$N = e^\alpha \sum_i e^{\beta \epsilon_i},$$

or
$$\alpha = \ln N - \ln \sum_i e^{\beta \epsilon_i}.$$

Consequently,
$$S = k \Big(N \ln \sum_i e^{\beta \epsilon_i} - \beta E \Big). \tag{18}$$

† To be interpreted in the light of paragraph 6 below.

It is more difficult to get rid of β, but we shall find that this is not necessary. For, by equation (5 a) of Chapter I,

$$\left(\frac{\partial S}{\partial E}\right)_{V,N} = \frac{1}{T}$$

and, from (18)

$$\left(\frac{\partial S}{\partial E}\right)_{V,N} = -k\beta + k\frac{\partial}{\partial \beta}\Big(N\ln\sum_i e^{\beta\epsilon} - \beta E\Big)\frac{\partial \beta}{\partial E}. \tag{19}$$

The first term on the r.h.s. of (19) is self-evident: the second arises from the fact that β itself depends on E on account of the equations (17), (5'), and (6'). In the partial differentiation with respect to β everything else has, of course, to be kept fixed, and we have

$$\frac{\partial}{\partial \beta}\Big(N\ln\sum_i e^{\beta\epsilon_i} - \beta E\Big) = N\frac{(\partial/\partial\beta)\sum_i e^{\beta\epsilon_i}}{\sum_i e^{\beta\epsilon_i}} - E$$

$$= N\frac{\sum_i \epsilon_i e^{\beta\epsilon_i}}{\sum_i e^{\beta\epsilon_i}} - E$$

$$= N\frac{\sum_i n_i^* \epsilon_i}{\sum_i n_i^*} - E \text{ (introducing } e^\alpha \text{ in both numerator and denominator)}$$

which $= 0$, on account of (5') and (6').

Consequently $$\left(\frac{\partial S}{\partial E}\right)_{V,N} = -k\beta \tag{20}$$

and β, in equation (18), could equally well have been regarded as a constant.

Equation (20), combined with (5 a) of Chapter I, shows us at once that β has a physical meaning. In fact

$$\frac{1}{T} = -k\beta$$

or $$\beta = -1/kT. \tag{21}$$

β is simply a measure of the *temperature* of the assembly, and equations (17), (5'), and (6') tell us that the temperature is fixed when E, V, and N are known—which is certainly true.

Returning to equation (18), we have now

$$S = kN \ln \sum_i e^{-\epsilon_i/kT} + E/T. \tag{18'}$$

But $E - TS$ measures the Helmholtz free energy of the assembly, which we shall denote by[†] F. Consequently (18') can be written

$$F = -NkT \ln \sum_i e^{-\epsilon_i/kT} \tag{22}$$

which, remembering that the ϵ's depend on the volume of the assembly, expresses F not in terms of E, V, and N but in terms of T, V, and N. This, however, is a much better choice of variables as far as F is concerned. For, thermodynamically (see Appendix I, § b)

$$dF = -S\,dT - P\,dV + \mu\,dN \tag{23}$$

so that, in dealing with F, T, V and N are certainly the most appropriate variables to use.

5. Thus, for an assembly of independent localized systems, the bridge between the mechanical properties of the systems and the thermodynamical properties of the assembly is complete, or at least sufficiently complete for us to be able to cross without difficulty. Equation (22) generally provides the simplest route, though the equations (17), with β interpreted as $-1/kT$, are also of fundamental importance. We shall later find that α, as well as β, has a direct physical, or thermodynamical, significance.

Equation (22) directs particular attention to the sum

$$\sum_i e^{-\epsilon_i/kT},$$

ϵ_1, ϵ_2,..., ϵ_i,... being the various quantum-mechanically permissible energies for any system of the assembly. It is known as the *sum-over-states* (German, *Zustandsumme*) or *partition function* for a system of the assembly. The former name calls for no explanation: the latter, which is more generally used and which we shall employ in this book, is not quite so obviously suitable. The reason for it lies in equations (17) and (5'). For we have

$$N = \sum_i n_i^* = A \sum_i e^{-\epsilon_i/kT},$$

$$n_i^* = A e^{-\epsilon_i/kT},$$

† Sometimes denoted by A.

and therefore, getting rid of A,

$$n_i^* = N \frac{e^{-\epsilon_i/kT}}{\sum\limits_i e^{-\epsilon_i/kT}};$$ (24)

so that the various terms in the partition function are proportional to the numbers of systems in the corresponding energy states (in those states which correspond to the equilibrium values of the distribution numbers), i.e.

$$\frac{n_i^*}{n_j^*} = \frac{e^{-\epsilon_i/kT}}{e^{-\epsilon_j/kT}}.$$ (25)

Consequently the partition function tells us how, in the equilibrium distribution, the systems are partitioned, or divided up, among the different energy levels. For the most part we shall not employ any particular symbol for the partition function, but simply refer to it as (p.f.).

So far we have supposed that for any system there is just one stationary wave-function corresponding to each energy level: i.e. we have supposed that all the energy levels are non-degenerate. It is quite customary, however, for quantum mechanics to allow several alternative wave-functions all corresponding to the same energy level. When this is so we speak of a *degenerate* energy level, and the number of independent† wave-functions, ω, corresponding to any particular energy, ϵ, is called the degeneracy or *weight-factor* of that level. For our equations to be completely general we have, therefore, to introduce these weight factors and allow each energy, ϵ_i, to have a degeneracy ω_i.

The proper way to do this is to go back to equation (3). Each of the n_i systems with energy ϵ_i can now be in any one of ω_i different wave states: therefore (3) now becomes

$$\frac{N!}{n_1!\,n_2!\dots n_i!\dots} \omega_1^{n_1} \omega_2^{n_2} \dots \omega_i^{n_i} \dots \quad \text{or} \quad \frac{N!}{\prod\limits_i n_i!} \prod\limits_i \omega_i^{n_i}.$$ (3′)

With this more general expression for $t(n)$, $\ln t(n)$ becomes

$$\ln t(n) = \ln N! - \sum_i (n_i \ln n_i - n_i) + \sum_i n_i \ln \omega_i,$$

† Not counting linear combinations of these which, of course, also satisfy the wave-equation.

and carrying through precisely the same analysis as before (which is left as an exercise for the reader) we now obtain

$$t_{max} = t(n^*) = \frac{N! \prod_i \omega_i^{n_i^*}}{\prod_i n_i^*!} \tag{16'}$$

where

$$n_i^* = \omega_i e^{\alpha} e^{\beta \epsilon_i} = \omega_i A e^{\beta \epsilon_i} \tag{17'}$$

and, of course, equations (5') and (6') are unchanged.

The equation $S = k(N \ln N - \alpha N - \beta E)$

is also unchanged, but (18) now reads

$$S = k\Big(N \ln \sum_i \omega_i e^{\beta \epsilon_i} - \beta E\Big). \tag{18'}$$

We still obtain $\beta = -1/kT$, but now (22) becomes

$$F = -NkT \ln \sum_i \omega_i e^{-\epsilon_i/kT} \tag{22'}$$

and equations (24) and (25) are now

$$n_i^* = N \frac{\omega_i e^{-\epsilon_i/kT}}{\sum_i \omega_i e^{-\epsilon_i/kT}} \tag{24'}$$

and

$$\frac{n_i^*}{n_j^*} = \frac{\omega_i e^{-\epsilon_i/kT}}{\omega_j e^{-\epsilon_j/kT}}, \tag{25'}$$

respectively.

We find, in fact, that the only changes in our formulae produced by the degeneracy of energy levels are those given by replacing the partition function $\sum_i e^{-\epsilon_i/kT}$ by its more general form

$$(\text{p.f.}) = \sum \omega_i e^{-\epsilon_i/kT}. \tag{26}$$

We could also, though less convincingly, have seen this by allowing the previously non-degenerate energy levels to become equal in appropriate groups.

While in actual applications of the theory we shall frequently have to deal with degenerate energy levels, and so use the more general formulae with the weight factors included, we shall, for the sake of simplicity, usually omit them when developing the theory itself. As we have just seen, the introduction of the requisite weight factors, when necessary, gives rise to no difficulty.

6. Before we proceed to illustrate the usefulness of the formulae which we have so far derived, by considering their application to the theory of the specific heat of a solid, we ought to pause a moment to make a few comments on the nature of our postulate that, when N is sufficiently large, only the greatest term in the sum over all possible sets of distribution numbers, giving the number of distinguishable states of the assembly, makes any significant contribution to that sum, i.e. to Ω. The principle of picking out the greatest term in such a sum is basic to our whole method of approach in this book, and we must attempt some justification of it.

It is important to realize clearly that the principle at stake is purely a mathematical one: either the whole sum can be replaced by its greatest term without sensible error, or it cannot; and the mathematical answer is that, to all intents and purposes, the sum can be so replaced when N is sufficiently large. The assumptions (a) and (b) above are of a quite different character: they are ultimately physical hypotheses and can only be justified either *a posteriori*, by the success of the theory based on them, or by deducing them rigorously from more fundamental physical principles—which, of course, we shall not attempt to do.

But, one may well ask, How can the present step be justified mathematically: we have treated $t(n)$ as a continuous function of $n_1, n_2,..., n_i,...$ and found its maximum value; will there not then be other values of $t(n)$, in the immediate neighbourhood of t_{max}, which, while not quite equal to, are only a little less than this greatest term and which, added together, will make a much greater contribution to the whole sum?

The criticism is sound and valid; but the answer is that it does not matter. For we are interested not in Ω but in $\ln\Omega$. Let us suppose that there are m terms in the sum all equal to t_{max}, and that all the rest put together are negligible. Then we shall have

$$\Omega = mt_{max}$$

and $$S = k\ln\Omega = k\ln t_{max} + k\ln m,$$

and even if m were as large as N the new term would be only

$k \ln N$, which is quite negligible compared with the first term which (see equation (18)) contains N as a factor.†

In general, the various distributions (sets of values for n_1, n_2,..., n_i,...) which contribute appreciably to Ω are all very much alike. It is difficult to prove this when the distribution is specified by a whole set of numbers, n_1, n_2,..., n_i,..., but we may consider, in support of the statement, the simpler case of, say, N atoms distributed among the two alternative states, A and B, of a single energy level of degeneracy two. In paragraph 5 above, we have included *all* such distributions by means of a factor 2^N. Alternatively, we might have introduced a new distribution number, n say, giving the number of atoms in state A, there being then $N-n$ atoms in state B. The number of such arrangements, differing only in which atoms are in which state, is simply

$$\frac{N!}{n!\,(N-n)!}$$

and the *total* number of arrangements, for all n, is

$$\sum_{(n)} \frac{N!}{n!\,(N-n)!} = 2^N. \tag{27}$$

But if we had decided to pick out the *greatest term* in the sum in (27) we should have had

$$\ln t(n) = N \ln N - n \ln n - (N-n)\ln(N-n) \tag{28}$$

and, on differentiating, the value, n^*, of n for which $t(n)$ is greatest is given by

$$\ln n^* - \ln(N-n^*) = 0$$

i.e. $n^* = N/2$. Putting this into (28) we have

$$\ln t(n^*) = N \ln 2$$

or

$$t(n^*) = 2^N$$

as before! At first sight it is surprising that we should seem to have *exactly* the same result, but the explanation is that we have dropped certain second-order terms in using Stirling's formula and, were they included, we should have a correction term in the expression for $\ln t(n^*)$ of the order of $\ln N$. This, of course, is quite negligible compared with the term which we have retained: when $N \sim 10^{23}$, $\ln N \sim 53$.

Moreover, we can now ask, What is the probability of having a deviation x from $n = n^*$ or, more precisely, what fraction of arrangements corresponds to $n = (N/2)-x$? Putting $n = (N/2)-x$ in the above expression for $t(n)$ and using Stirling's formula, we easily find that the fraction of arrangements corresponding to $n = (N/2)-x$ is given, when x/N is small, by

$$e^{-2x^2/N}.$$

The root-mean-square value of x is thus of the order of $\sqrt{N}$ which, when $N \sim 10^{23}$, is negligible compared with $N/2$.

† So also for N^p 'large' terms, provided p is 'small' compared with N.

A more complete discussion is beyond the scope of this book, and the reader must take it on trust that the principle of picking out the greatest term in the sum for Ω is indeed always mathematically valid provided that N is sufficiently large, that is, for all actual thermodynamical assemblies. It is only in certain very difficult problems of statistical mechanics (such as the complete theory of the condensation of an imperfect gas), for which a distribution is not easily specified, that a more elaborate and rigorous mathematical technique needs to be employed.

After this digression we can proceed, with justifiable confidence, to apply the formulae which we have obtained in paragraphs 4 and 5 to a particular assembly of independent localized systems.

7. In order to illustrate the usefulness of the formulae of paragraphs 4 and 5, let us consider, for our assembly, a simple atomic crystal of N identical atoms regularly spaced in a lattice formation. And let us aim to calculate the specific heat of this assembly.

We can regard the energy of the crystal (assembly) as comprised of two parts,
$$E = E' + E''$$
where $E' = $ energy when atoms are placed in their mean (average) positions,

and $E'' = $ energy of displacements of the atoms from their mean (average) positions.

For, of course, in a crystal the atoms are not rigidly fixed, but are free to oscillate, or vibrate, about lattice-points which are simply their average positions. The state of lowest energy corresponds to the atoms being at rest at the lattice-points ($E'' = 0$),[†] but, due to thermal motion, the assembly is not in its state of lowest energy.

We shall assume that E' is a constant, independent of the temperature. Since we are primarily interested in calculating the specific heat of the crystal, C_v, given by
$$C_v = \left(\frac{\partial E}{\partial T}\right)_V,$$

† We shall discover that, on account of quantum requirements, E'' as defined above is never quite zero: and shall later incorporate the lowest possible value of E'' into E'.

E' will not concern us further. E'', however, the contribution to
the internal energy arising from the vibrations of the atoms about
their mean positions, has yet to be calculated as a function of
temperature—which is equivalent to saying that we have to find
the connexion between the temperature of the assembly, T, and
the energy E''.

The simplest assumption to make, which is due to Einstein
(1907, 1911), is that each atom behaves as if tethered to its mean
position by a very short elastic spring or, more accurately, is
pulled back to its mean position by a restoring force proportional
to its displacement therefrom. We shall further suppose that each
atom can vibrate in three independent directions (which is reasonable for isotropic solids) and that the vibrations of neighbouring
atoms do not interfere with each other. In other words, as far
as E'' is concerned we regard our assembly as an assembly of $3N$
independent localized harmonic-oscillators, and Einstein assumed
that these $3N$ harmonic-oscillators all have the same frequency
(in classical mechanics) ν.

Now, to apply the formulae of paragraphs 4 and 5, we require
to know the permissible energies, ϵ_1, ϵ_2,..., ϵ_i,..., of each system.
Quantum mechanics, however, tells us that an harmonic-oscillator
of (classical) frequency ν can have energies ϵ_1, ϵ_2,..., ϵ_i,... given by†

$$\epsilon = (n+\tfrac{1}{2})h\nu \quad (n = 0, 1, 2,...) \tag{29}$$

where h is Planck's constant ($6\cdot62.10^{-27}$ erg. sec.); and that each
energy level is non-degenerate.

Combining equations (24) and (6′) above, we thus obtain

$$E'' = 3N\frac{\sum (n+\tfrac{1}{2})h\nu e^{-(n+\frac{1}{2})h\nu/kT}}{\sum e^{-(n+\frac{1}{2})h\nu/kT}}, \tag{30}$$

the summation being over all values of n from 0 to infinity.
$3N$ replaces N in (24) since we are concerned with an assembly
of $3N$ harmonic-oscillator systems.

The r.h.s. of (30) can be simplified: we divide numerator and

† n here, of course, denotes a quantum number (and has nothing to do with
a distribution number).

denominator by $e^{-\frac{1}{2}h\nu/kT}$ and also remove the $\frac{1}{2}h\nu$ part from the first factor in the numerator, so obtaining

$$E'' = \frac{3N}{2}h\nu + 3N \frac{\sum\limits_{n=0}^{\infty} nh\nu e^{-nh\nu/kT}}{\sum\limits_{n=0}^{\infty} e^{-nh\nu/kT}},$$

i.e.
$$E'' = \frac{3N}{2}h\nu + 3NkT^2 \frac{\partial}{\partial T}\ln \sum_{n=0}^{\infty} e^{-nh\nu/kT} \tag{30'}$$

(performing the differentiation in (30′) we recover the r.h.s. of the previous line). Now

$$\sum_{n=0}^{\infty} e^{-nh\nu/kT} = 1 + e^{-h\nu/kT} + e^{-2h\nu/kT} + \ldots$$

$$= \frac{1}{1 - e^{-h\nu/kT}}$$

the series being a simple geometrical progression. Therefore

$$E'' = \frac{3N}{2}h\nu - 3NkT^2 \frac{\partial}{\partial T}\ln(1 - e^{-h\nu/kT})$$

$$= \frac{3N}{2}h\nu + 3N \frac{h\nu e^{-h\nu/kT}}{1 - e^{-h\nu/kT}},$$

i.e.
$$E'' = \frac{3N}{2}h\nu + 3N \frac{h\nu}{e^{h\nu/kT} - 1}. \tag{30''}$$

The first term in the r.h.s. of (30″) is a constant, and is the value of E'' when $T = 0$. It is known as the zero-point energy, and can be assimilated into the other constant part of the energy, E'. The only temperature-dependent internal energy is given by

$$E(T) = 3N \frac{h\nu}{e^{h\nu/kT} - 1}, \tag{31}$$

and, differentiating w.r.t. T, we obtain

$$C_v = 3Nk \left(\frac{h\nu}{kT}\right)^2 \frac{e^{h\nu/kT}}{(e^{h\nu/kT} - 1)^2}. \tag{32}$$

Before discussing this result, there are two comments to be made.

First, instead of using equations (24) and (6′) we could equally well have calculated F from equation (22), i.e.

$$F = -3NkT \ln(\text{p.f.}),$$

and then found E from F by means of the Gibbs–Helmholtz thermodynamic formula

$$E = F - T\left(\frac{\partial F}{\partial T}\right)_V = -T^2 \frac{\partial}{\partial T}\left(\frac{F}{T}\right)_V$$

(cf. equation (30′)). Indeed, the method of first calculating F and then deriving, thermodynamically, all other quantities from F is, perhaps, generally the most straightforward. On the other hand it rather obscures the essentially simple structure of the underlying statistical formulae, and for that reason we have not used it in the present instance.

The second comment is of a rather different nature. It is that, instead of regarding the crystal as an assembly of $3N$ linear harmonic-oscillators we could, equally well, have regarded it as an assembly of N three-dimensional harmonic-oscillators, and should have obtained the same result.

By a three-dimensional harmonic-oscillator we mean a particle in a spherically symmetrical potential field producing a restoring force proportional to the displacement of the particle. Quantum mechanically the allowed energies of a [3]-oscillator are given by

$$\epsilon_n = (n+\tfrac{3}{2})h\nu \quad (n = 0, 1, 2,...)$$

and have degeneracies, ω_0, ω_1,..., ω_n,... given by

$$\omega_n = \tfrac{1}{2}(n+1)(n+2) \quad (n = 0, 1, 2,...).$$

Consequently the partition function for a [3]-oscillator is given by

$$\begin{aligned}
(\text{p.f.}) &= \sum_{n=0}^{\infty} \tfrac{1}{2}(n+1)(n+2)e^{-(n+\frac{3}{2})h\nu/kT} \\
&= e^{-\frac{3}{2}h\nu/kT}(1 + 3e^{-h\nu/kT} + 6e^{-2h\nu/kT} + 10e^{-3h\nu/kT} + ...) \\
&= \frac{e^{-\frac{3}{2}h\nu/kT}}{(1 - e^{-h\nu/kT})^3} \\
&= \left(\frac{e^{-\frac{1}{2}h\nu/kT}}{1 - e^{-h\nu/kT}}\right)^3,
\end{aligned}$$

which is simply the cube of the partition function for a linear, or

[1]-harmonic-oscillator. Therefore an assembly of N independent localized [3]-oscillators has precisely the same thermodynamic properties as an assembly of $3N$ independent localized [1]-oscillators.

After these digressions, we return to discuss equation (32). Both $E(T)$, equation (31), and C_v, equation (32), are shown as functions of T by the full curves in Fig. 1.

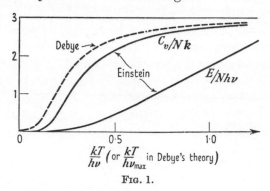

$$\frac{kT}{h\nu} \left(\text{or } \frac{kT}{h\nu_{\max}} \text{ in Debye's theory} \right)$$

Fig. 1.

When kT is large compared with $h\nu$, (31) gives

$$E(T) \sim 3N \frac{h\nu}{(1+h\nu/kT+...)-1} \sim 3NkT \quad (kT \gg h\nu)$$

and (32) gives
$$C_v \sim 3Nk \quad (kT \gg h\nu).$$

Therefore, at sufficiently high temperatures, the specific heat becomes constant, independent of the temperature. Moreover, this high-temperature value of the specific heat is independent of ν and should, therefore, be the same for all atomic crystals. This is in agreement with the experimental law of Dulong and Petit, according to which many solids (atomic crystals) have a constant specific heat of about 6 cal./deg./mole, or $3R$, where R is the gas constant: and, as we have said already, k will later be identified with Boltzmann's constant, k, so that $Nk = R$ if N is Avogadro's number, i.e. if we are considering one mole of solid.

At lower temperatures, however, equation (32) predicts that C_v will fall, approaching zero at very low temperatures. This also is in qualitative agreement with experimental behaviour, although, quantitatively, equation (32) does not fit experimental data at all well at very low temperatures. The reason is that our model, replacing the crystal by an assembly of $3N$ harmonic-oscillators each of the same frequency ν, is far too crude to do justice to all conceivable vibrations of an actual crystalline solid: it does not discriminate between low frequency lattice vibrations, which become important at low temperatures, and high frequency lattice vibrations. Nevertheless this Einstein theory of the specific heat of a solid was one of the early triumphs of quantum mechanics, since classically, as we shall see in Chapter IV, we obtain $C_v = 3Nk$ at all temperatures, and the experimentally observed fall in C_v at lower temperatures is quite inexplicable.

A much better theory of the specific heat of a crystalline solid, taking fuller account of the whole range of lattice vibration frequencies, is that due to Debye (1912). We shall not discuss Debye's theory in detail since it is mathematically more complicated and readily available in standard works. We mention it here, however, since we shall have occasion to refer to it again in Chapter IX in connexion with the extrapolation of specific heat data to very low temperatures. Experimentally determined specific heats generally approximate closely to the broken curve in Fig. 1, which represents C_v as a function of T according to Debye's theory.

Finally, equation (32) predicts that the specific heats of all atomic crystals ought to follow the same curve if we plot C_v against not T but $kT/h\nu$, where ν is the appropriate frequency for each solid. There is a similar 'law of corresponding states' for Debye's theory, and it is found to be satisfied experimentally. The appropriate values of ν range from about 2.10^{12} sec.$^{-1}$ ($h\nu/k \sim 100°$ K.) for soft solids like lead to 4.10^{13} sec.$^{-1}$ ($h\nu/k \sim 2,000°$ K.) for hard substances like diamond, and, as Fig. 1 shows, the temperature at which the specific heat starts to fall away from the classical value of $3R$ (cal./deg./mole) is proportional to the corresponding value of ν.

EXAMPLES

1. From the expression (3′) for $t(n)$, and the restrictive conditions (5) and (6), derive the equations (16′) and (17′) by use of the method of Lagrange's undetermined multipliers.

2. Prove that, if the ϵ's are treated as constants, equation (18) leads to the formula $\mu = -kT \ln(\text{p.f.})$ for the chemical potential of a system in the assembly. (Whilst not strictly accurate, this equation is, as we shall see later, satisfactory for almost all practical purposes.)

3. Derive equation (32) from the equation $F = -3NkT \ln(\text{p.f.})$ and the Gibbs–Helmholtz thermodynamic formula.

4. Derive the equation

$$S = -3Nk \frac{\partial}{\partial T}[T \ln(1 - e^{-h\nu/kT})]$$

for the vibrational entropy of an Einstein solid. (Note that this shows that the zero-point motion does not contribute to the entropy.) Show that when $kT \gg h\nu$ this formula gives

$$S = 3Nk\left\{\ln\frac{kT}{h\nu} + 1 + \text{terms of order}\left(\frac{h\nu}{kT}\right)^2 + ...\right\}.$$

5. The allowed energy levels for a two-dimensional harmonic-oscillator, of classical frequency ν, are given by

$$\epsilon = (n+1)h\nu \quad \text{with degeneracies } \omega = n+1.$$

Show that the partition function for such a [2]-oscillator is the square of the partition function for a [1]-oscillator having the same classical frequency.

AN ASSEMBLY OF INDEPENDENT NON-LOCALIZED SYSTEMS

1. In the last chapter we solved the problem of the evaluation of $\Omega(E, V, N)$ for an assembly of N identical, independent, localized systems. That, in order for the formulae there obtained to be relevant, the systems of the assembly must be both identical systems and independent systems requires no further emphasis. The restriction to identical systems, i.e. to only one species of independent systems, can, of course, be removed without much difficulty (see Chapter XI), and it is only for convenience that we have chosen to deal first exclusively with one-component assemblies. The restriction to independent systems is much more profound. Not only does the method of Chapter II entirely break down, but the whole algebraic procedure becomes enormously more complicated when this condition of independence is not fulfilled. In the later chapters of this book we shall consider in some detail particular cases of assemblies of non-independent systems, when the new difficulties introduced will be sufficiently apparent.

Accepting, for the present, that the assembly comprises identical and independent systems, it may not be quite so evident that the formulae of Chapter II apply only when these systems are *localized*. The simplest way to make clear the necessity for this condition is to consider an assembly of N identical, independent but non-localized systems, and to examine the additional features of this new assembly which may, and indeed do, give rise to a different expression for $\Omega(E, V, N)$. Assemblies of identical, independent, and non-localized systems are actually of greater physical, or chemical, interest than are assemblies of independent localized systems: for any single component gas, at a sufficiently low pressure, fulfils all the theoretical requirements.

It is commonly, but erroneously, supposed that the essential distinction, in the present connexion, between a gas and a crystal is that the systems of a gaseous assembly are forever changing, or interchanging, their positions while those of a crystalline assembly are not. Even if true, this difference is, as we shall see, quite beside the point: and more frequently it just is not true. The real distinction between localized and non-localized systems lies deeper and, though not difficult to detect, calls for a little care in its revealing.

Returning to the assembly of localized systems of Chapter II, we recognize that there is a difference between, for instance, the

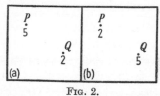

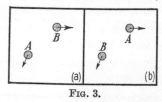

FIG. 2.   FIG. 3.

state of the assembly in which two systems, located at P and Q say, have energies ϵ_5 and ϵ_2, respectively, and the state in which these systems, at P and Q, have energies ϵ_2 and ϵ_5 respectively. (We may suppose that all the other systems have the same energies in both of the states under consideration.) The two states, shown schematically in Fig. 2 (a) and (b), are certainly physically distinguishable, and both go to make up the sum total of distinguishable states which is Ω.

If, on the other hand, we consider a gaseous assembly of, for simplicity, just two systems, A and B say, and, concentrating on the translational motion of these systems, we try to count the distinguishable microscopic states of the assembly on the basis of the positions and velocities of the systems, we are confronted with a very different situation. As A moves about, taking up all its possible positions and velocities, it will get into the state, both as regards position and velocity, now occupied by B: and simultaneously B can take up the position and velocity now possessed by A. This is illustrated schematically in Fig. 3 (a) and (b). But these two states, (a) and (b), are *not* in any way physically distinguishable: for the labels, A and B, attached to the two systems have no existence in reality. Physically the two systems are identical and, therefore, mutually indistinguishable. Consequently, if we first hypothetically label the systems (A and B) and then count up the complexions of the assembly which are distinguishable with the systems labelled, we have thereby counted all the physically distinguishable complexions twice over.

Before generalizing this result in respect of an assembly of N systems, we should notice that there was no question of artificially labelling the systems of the former, crystalline, assembly. Here we can recognize from the start that the systems are identical: it is only the *lattice sites* which are labelled. The atoms of a crystal can, and constantly do, change places,† as is evidenced by the phenomenon of diffusion in solid phases: but if the atoms are all of the same kind (and if we ignore distortions of the lattice structure, as pertaining to a class of complexion which does not contribute appreciably to Ω) then such an interchange of atoms does not produce anything new (and is really meaningless). All we can say is that the system *at P* is in its ith energy level, the system *at Q* is in its jth energy level, and so on. But there just is not an underlying permanent lattice to which to assign the quantum numbers for the systems of a gaseous assembly.

Proceeding now to consider an assembly of N non-localized identical systems, we may suppose first that these are hypothetically labelled, 1, 2,..., N. Then any particular microscopic state of the assembly is just one member of a set of $N!$ such states obtained from this one by permuting the labels, 1, 2,..., N (cf. Fig. 3): and these $N!$ states of the assembly are mutually distinguishable provided that the labels are attached. Thus all the distinguishable microscopic states of the hypothetical assembly of labelled systems fall into sets of $N!$ states, the members of any set being mutually distinguishable only on account of the labels artificially attached to the systems. Consequently, if we enumerate the complexions of an assembly of N identical non-localized systems by the expedient of attaching hypothetical labels to the systems, then we count all the truly distinguishable states of the assembly $N!$ times: and the true number of complexions is the apparent number (for an assembly of labelled systems) divided by $N!$.

We see, then, that the results of Chapter II do apply only to an assembly of localized systems, which are effectively labelled

† When this has any meaning.

by the lattice sites† themselves. It is only on the basis of this assumption that the number of complexions corresponding to the set of distribution numbers, $n_1, n_2,..., n_i,...$, is correctly given by

$$\frac{N!}{n_1! \, n_2! \dots n_i! \dots} \quad \text{(see Appendix II).}$$

To obtain the corresponding formulae for an assembly of non-localized systems, we have to divide the expression for $\Omega(E, V, N)$ in Chapter II by $N!$

It remains to add here only that there is nothing *quantum mechanical* about this result.‡ The division by $N!$ is an essentially classical necessity, produced by the indistinguishability of the systems. In fact the arguments of this section do not do full justice to the proper quantum-mechanical treatment of the translational motion of a gas, a matter to which we shall refer again briefly in paragraph 3 below.

2. Before applying our new formulae to an actual assembly of non-localized systems, it will be well to list them explicitly, so as to emphasize the modifications introduced by the new factor $1/N!$ in Ω. The most important formulae of Chapter II (with degeneracy included) were

$$\left.\begin{aligned} S &= k(N \ln \sum_i \omega_i e^{\beta \epsilon_i} - \beta E) \\ \text{or} \qquad \Omega &= \left(\sum_i \omega_i e^{\beta \epsilon_i} \right)^N e^{-\beta E} \end{aligned}\right\}, \tag{1}$$

$$\beta = -1/kT, \tag{2}$$

$$\begin{aligned} \text{and} \qquad F &= -NkT \ln \sum_i \omega_i e^{-\epsilon_i/kT} \\ &= -kT \ln \left(\sum_i \omega_i e^{-\epsilon_i/kT} \right)^N, \end{aligned} \tag{3}$$

while the equilibrium values of the distribution numbers were given by

$$\left.\begin{aligned} n_i^* &= N \frac{\omega_i e^{-\epsilon_i/kT}}{\sum_i \omega_i e^{-\epsilon_i/kT}}, \\ \text{with} \qquad \sum_i n_i^* \epsilon_i &= E. \end{aligned}\right\} \tag{4}$$

† We have spoken of lattice sites but there is, of course, no need for these to be *regularly* arranged in space.

‡ I take Heisenberg's uncertainty principle (see next chapter) as the starting-point of quantum theory.

If now we divide Ω (see equation (4′), Ch. II, p. 17) by $N!$, it follows at once that the changes introduced into these equations affect only (1) and (3). In fact, (1) becomes

$$\left.\begin{aligned}
\Omega &= \frac{\left(\sum_i \omega_i e^{\beta \epsilon_i}\right)^N e^{-\beta E}}{N!} \\
S &= k\left(N \ln \sum_i \omega_i e^{\beta \epsilon_i} - \beta E\right) - k \ln N!
\end{aligned}\right\}, \qquad (1')$$

(2) is unchanged, and (3) becomes

$$F = -NkT \ln \sum_i \omega_i e^{-\epsilon_i/kT} + kT \ln N!$$

$$= -kT \ln\left\{\frac{\left(\sum_i \omega_i e^{-\epsilon_i/kT}\right)^N}{N!}\right\}. \qquad (3')$$

Since the equations (4), giving the equilibrium values of the distribution numbers are, like (2), quite unchanged, it is convenient still to refer to $\sum_i \omega_i e^{-\epsilon_i/kT}$ as the partition function of a system. The modifications introduced by the new factor $1/N!$ in $\Omega(E, V, N)$ concern only the external thermodynamical properties of the assembly, S, F, etc., and have no influence on the *internal* distributive properties of the assembly, determined by $n_1^*, n_2^*, ..., n_i^*, ...$.

Having listed the new formulae, let us now apply them to the simplest conceivable assembly of independent non-localized systems, namely a *perfect gas of structureless particles*. By a perfect gas of structureless particles we mean an assembly of N identical systems, having mass but no other distinctive feature, which are free to move at random in a certain volume, V, and sufficiently few per unit volume (i.e. at sufficiently low pressure) for them legitimately to be regarded as independent.

We let the container, of volume V, be a rectangular box having sides of length a, b, and c. Then, according to quantum mechanics, the allowed energies of a particle of mass m confined within this box are given by

$$\epsilon_{p,q,r} = \frac{h^2}{8m}\left(\frac{p^2}{a^2} + \frac{q^2}{b^2} + \frac{r^2}{c^2}\right), \quad \begin{array}{l} p \\ q \\ r \end{array} = 1, 2, 3, ...$$

and $\qquad \omega_{p,q,r} = 1,$

i.e. the energy levels are non-degenerate† (unless the particle has spin).

It is convenient to distinguish the levels by three suffixes and not just one, i.e. to write $\epsilon_{p,q,r}$ rather than ϵ_i, because there are ∞^3 levels altogether. But, of course, this is just a notational convenience: in forming the partition function we still have to sum over every level, i.e. over all values of p, q, and r.

Consequently

$$(\text{p.f.}) = \sum_{p=1}^{\infty} \sum_{q=1}^{\infty} \sum_{r=1}^{\infty} \exp\left\{ -\left(\frac{p^2}{a^2} + \frac{q^2}{b^2} + \frac{r^2}{c^2} \right) \frac{h^2}{8mkT} \right\}$$

$$= \sum_{p=1}^{\infty} \sum_{q=1}^{\infty} \exp\left\{ -\left(\frac{p^2}{a^2} + \frac{q^2}{b^2} \right) \frac{h^2}{8mkT} \right\} \sum_{r=1}^{\infty} \exp\left(-\frac{r^2}{c^2} \frac{h^2}{8mkT} \right)$$

(since, with given values of p and q, we have to sum over all values of r)

$$= \sum_{p=1}^{\infty} \exp\left(-\frac{p^2}{a^2} \frac{h^2}{8mkT} \right) \sum_{q=1}^{\infty} \exp\left(-\frac{q^2}{b^2} \frac{h^2}{8mkT} \right) \sum_{r=1}^{\infty} \exp\left(-\frac{r^2}{c^2} \frac{h^2}{8mkT} \right)$$

$$(5)$$

(by the same argument applied to the first sum, over p and q).

The partition function therefore factorizes into the product of three sums, each of the same form. We need consider only one of them in detail, say the first:

$$\sum_{p=1}^{\infty} \exp\left(-\frac{p^2}{a^2} \frac{h^2}{8mkT} \right) \equiv \sum_{p=1}^{\infty} \exp(-\alpha^2 p^2) \quad \text{where‡} \quad \alpha^2 = \frac{h^2}{8ma^2kT}.$$

Now suppose m is the mass of a hydrogen atom, $1\cdot67.10^{-24}$ gm., that a is 1 cm., $T = 300°$ K., and let us provisionally identify k with Boltzmann's constant having the numerical value $1\cdot38.10^{-16}$ erg/deg. h is Planck's constant, with the value $6\cdot62.10^{-27}$ erg sec. Then

$$\alpha^2 = \frac{(6\cdot62.10^{-27})^2}{8.1\cdot67.10^{-24} \, 1\cdot38.10^{-16} \, 300} \approx 10^{-16}$$

which is very small. And for actual gases m will generally be

† We are assuming, for simplicity, that a^{-2}, b^{-2}, and c^{-2} are incommensurable quantities.

‡ This α has nothing to do with the α of Chapter II or paragraph 5 below: α is used in the present paragraph as a convenient shorthand symbol only.

greater than the mass of a hydrogen atom, while a may well be greater than 1 cm.: α^2 becoming still smaller on both counts.

If α^2 is very small, the sum $\sum_{p=1}^{\infty} e^{-\alpha^2 p^2}$ can, without sensible error, be replaced by an integral: i.e. we may write

$$\sum_{p=1}^{\infty} e^{-\alpha^2 p^2} = \int_0^{\infty} e^{-\alpha^2 p^2} \, dp. \tag{6}$$

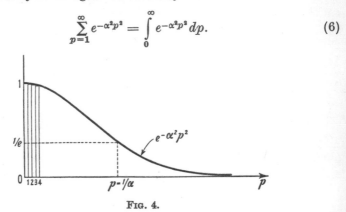

Fig. 4.

Fig. 4 shows $e^{-\alpha^2 p^2}$ as a continuous function of p, and it is evident that α merely determines the horizontal scale of this curve. When α is small this horizontal scale is small, in the sense that a large value of p is required to correspond to an appreciable move along the curve from the peak at $p = 0$ towards the tail at $p \to \infty$. The points on the curve corresponding to integer values of p are therefore very close together and, as we see by considering the area beneath the curve, the sum may legitimately be replaced by the integral in equation (6).

Now the integral on the r.h.s. of (6) is a well-known standard definite integral of pure mathematics. In fact

$$\int_0^{\infty} e^{-\alpha^2 x^2} dx = \frac{\sqrt{\pi}}{2\alpha}. \tag{7}$$

A simple proof, though ignoring questions of rigour, is as follows:

$$I = \int_0^{\infty} e^{-\alpha^2 x^2} \, dx = \int_0^{\infty} e^{-\alpha^2 y^2} \, dy$$

since the variable of integration is only a dummy variable. Therefore

$$I^2 = \int_0^{\infty} e^{-\alpha^2 x^2} \, dx \int_0^{\infty} e^{-\alpha^2 y^2} \, dy = \int_0^{\infty} \int_0^{\infty} e^{-\alpha^2 (x^2 + y^2)} \, dx \, dy$$

since $e^{-\alpha^2 x^2} e^{-\alpha^2 y^2} = e^{-\alpha^2 (x^2 + y^2)}$ and the double integral implies the limit of a double summation of the integrand over all elements of area of the positive quadrant of the (x, y)-plane. Changing to polar coordinates, r and θ, the corresponding element of area becomes $r \,.\, d\theta \,.\, dr$ and the integrand becomes $e^{-\alpha^2 r^2}$. Consequently

$$I^2 = \int\limits_{r=0}^{\infty} \int\limits_{0}^{\frac{1}{2}\pi} e^{-\alpha^2 r^2} r \, d\theta dr.$$

Performing the θ-integration, we obtain

$$I^2 = \tfrac{1}{2}\pi \int\limits_{0}^{\infty} e^{-\alpha^2 r^2} r \, dr$$

and, on substituting s for r^2, we have

$$I^2 = \tfrac{1}{4}\pi \int\limits_{0}^{\infty} e^{-\alpha^2 s} \, ds = \frac{\pi}{4\alpha^2}.$$

Therefore $I = \dfrac{\sqrt{\pi}}{2\alpha}$, as we stated in (7).

Using this formula, we have

$$\sum_{p=1}^{\infty} \exp\left(-\frac{p^2}{a^2}\frac{h^2}{8mkT}\right) = \frac{\sqrt{\pi}}{2}\sqrt{\left(\frac{a^2 8mkT}{h^2}\right)} = a\frac{\sqrt{(2\pi mkT)}}{h}$$

and, since the other summations in (5) may be performed analogously,

$$\begin{aligned}
\text{(p.f.)} &= \sum_{p=1}^{\infty} \exp\left(-\frac{p^2}{a^2}\frac{h^2}{8mkT}\right) \times \\
&\qquad\qquad \times \sum_{q=1}^{\infty} \exp\left(-\frac{q^2}{b^2}\frac{h^2}{8mkT}\right) \sum_{r=1}^{\infty} \exp\left(-\frac{r^2}{c^2}\frac{h^2}{8mkT}\right) \\
&= a\frac{\sqrt{(2\pi mkT)}}{h} \; b\frac{\sqrt{(2\pi mkT)}}{h} \; c\frac{\sqrt{(2\pi mkT)}}{h} \\
&= abc\left(\frac{2\pi mkT}{h^2}\right)^{\frac{3}{2}}
\end{aligned}$$

or, since $abc = V$, the volume of the container,

$$\text{(p.f.)} = V\left(\frac{2\pi mkT}{h^2}\right)^{\frac{3}{2}}. \tag{8}$$

Equation (8), giving the partition function for the translational motion of a structureless particle of mass m confined to a volume V, when the temperature is T, is of quite fundamental importance. Although we have derived it only for volumes having the shape of a rectangular box, the formula is equally valid, as we shall show in the next chapter, whatever the shape of the volume within which the assembly is contained. We shall not, however, prove the general result on the basis of quantum mechanics, but from classical mechanics. A quantum-mechanical treatment as in this section and the derivation from classical mechanics lead to precisely the same expression, equation (8), for the partition function for translational motion.

On the basis of equations (8) and (3′) we obtain, for the Helmholtz free energy of a perfect gas of structureless particles,

$$F = -NkT \ln V \left(\frac{2\pi mkT}{h^2}\right)^{\frac{3}{2}} + kT \ln N!$$

or, using Stirling's formula,

$$F = -NkT \ln V + NkT \ln N - \tfrac{3}{2}NkT \ln\left(\frac{2\pi mkT}{h^2}\right) - NkT; \quad (9)$$

but before discussing the consequences of this formula we must, as indicated at the end of paragraph 1 above, first say a little more about the range of validity of equation (8).

3. This digression, although necessary, must be brief. A detailed discussion would not only involve us in mathematical complexities but lead us into a field of statistical mechanics of comparatively little importance to the physical chemist. On the other hand it is desirable to recognize the limitations of the argument in paragraph 1, and to know at least the range of validity of equation (8) above.

First let us be quite clear that any limitations in formula (8) are *not* introduced by the mathematical device of replacing the sum by the integral in (6). The mathematical condition, $\alpha^2 \ll 1$, warranting this step is justifiable, not only for atomic or molecular gases but even for a gas of free electrons down to temperatures at which our formulae already fail on other grounds.[*] To discover these other grounds, we must return to the argument in paragraph 1.

The argument was sound as far as it went, but did not really go far enough. It led us, when dealing with non-localized systems, to divide the number of complexions as evaluated for localized, or labelled, systems by $N!$. Now in terms of the notation of Chapter II, this appears to give

$$\Omega = \sum_{\substack{(\sum_i n_i = N \\ \sum_i n_i \epsilon_i = E)}} \frac{1}{\prod_i n_i!} \tag{10}$$

which is difficult to understand, since each term is numerically less than unity—and so can hardly represent a number of complexions or stationary wave-functions. The explanation is that when we use equation (10), we are actually *underweighting* those complexions, if any (see below), which correspond to integer values of the distribution numbers $n_1, n_2, ..., n_i, ...$, other than the values 0 and 1. And for the translational motion of an atomic or molecular gas the complexions which are thus underweighted are so improbable anyway that they could equally well be omitted from consideration entirely. (Treating the distribution numbers as continuous variables we find that their equilibrium values are very small fractions. The use of Stirling's formula is really not permissible but, as we shall see later, leads, surprisingly, to the correct result.) To enumerate the complexions correctly we must do more justice to the quantum mechanics of the problem.

For non-localized systems, the discussion in paragraph 1 was couched in classical terms (position and velocity). This was because it is difficult to visualize quantum-mechanical stationary states for several non-localized systems. But according to quantum theory, if we have N identical systems moving independently in the same field and $\epsilon_1, \epsilon_2, ..., \epsilon_i, ...$ are the permissible energies for any one system, then there is only *one* stationary wave-function for a given set of distribution numbers $n_1, n_2, ..., n_i, ...$, i.e. we ought to have

$$\Omega = \sum_{\text{(allowed } n\text{'s)}} 1. \tag{11}$$

If the only restrictions on the n's are $\sum_i n_i = N$ and $\sum_i n_i \epsilon_i = E$ then we speak of the assembly as satisfying *Einstein–Bose* statistics, and this is the case, according to quantum theory, for photons or black-body radiation. On the other hand, for electrons or protons Pauli's exclusion principle further restricts the n's by allowing to each n only two possible values, 0 or 1. In this case we speak of *Fermi–Dirac* statistics. And we see that, in general, equation (10) corresponds to neither Einstein–Bose nor Fermi–Dirac statistics.

Nevertheless equation (10) is by no means useless. The statistical mechanics founded on it is said to be based on *classical* statistics, as distinct from quantum statistics which can be of either Einstein–Bose or Fermi–Dirac type. Statistical mechanics based on quantum statistics is outside the scope of this book, but it can be shown that for N particles each of mass m and confined to a volume V, the thermodynamic properties of the assembly are identically the same whether calculated by classical statistics, Einstein–Bose statistics or Fermi–Dirac statistics, provided that

$$\frac{N}{V} \frac{h^3}{(2\pi mkT)^{\frac{3}{2}}} \ll 1. \tag{12}$$

This is a much more restrictive condition than the condition $\alpha^2 \ll 1$ discussed above. It implies that the energy levels for translational motion in the volume V are so close together, compared with kT, that, even with N systems in the assembly, those distributions of the systems among the levels for which there is more than one system in any one level make an entirely negligible contribution to Ω as calculated by equation (10). It is then evident that the requirements of Einstein–Bose and Fermi–Dirac statistics are equally well satisfied with those of classical statistics.

When the condition (12) fails we speak of a *degenerate* gas. Nevertheless (12) is generally satisfied for the assemblies of physical chemistry, and it is usually only for assemblies of electrons or photons that quantum statistics are needed. An ordinary atomic or molecular gas will always satisfy (12) at N.T.P. and would continue to do so, as the temperature is reduced, down to very low temperatures of only a few degrees absolute but for the fact that before then it would have condensed, and so could no longer be regarded as an assembly of independent non-localized systems.

This brings us to a final point concerning the validity of equation (8). Equations (8) and (9) have been derived on the assumption that the gas behaves as an assembly of *independent* non-localized systems: and long before any atomic or molecular gas becomes degenerate, in the sense above, it will become *imperfect* due to the effects of intermolecular, van der Waals', forces. But we are not yet in a position to discuss the statistical mechanics of imperfect gases; we must first deal with the very simplest assemblies and proceed to derive the thermodynamic consequencies of equations (8) and (9).

4. Equation (9), which we derived from (3') using equation (8'), reads

$$F = -NkT \ln V + NkT \ln N - \tfrac{3}{2}NkT \ln\left(\frac{2\pi mkT}{h^2}\right) - NkT$$

which may be rewritten

$$F = -NkT\left\{\ln V - \ln N + \tfrac{3}{2}\ln T + \tfrac{3}{2}\ln\left(\frac{2\pi mk}{h^2}\right) + 1\right\}. \qquad (9')$$

With F in this form, it is at once apparent that if we had not included the factor $1/N!$ in Ω then F would not have been a properly *extensive* property of the assembly in the thermodynamic sense. F is an extensive property if, for example, doubling both N and V, keeping T constant, also doubles F. This is, experimentally, true of the Helmholtz free energy of a single phase assembly (ignoring surface effects), and it is a necessary consequence of equation (9'); but it would not have been true if we had dropped the factor $1/N!$ in Ω—as the reader will easily verify.

Now, from the thermodynamic equation (equation (23) of Chapter II)

$$dF = -S\,dT - P\,dV + \mu\,dN,$$

we can derive the other thermodynamic properties of the assembly.

First,
$$P = -\left(\frac{\partial F}{\partial V}\right)_{T,N} = \frac{NkT}{V}$$

which gives the *equation of state*, connecting P, V, and T, i.e.

$$PV = NkT. \qquad (13)$$

Equation (13) shows that an assembly of independent non-localized structureless particles (satisfying the requirements of classical statistics) obeys Boyle's law. It also suggests an identification of k with the gas constant per system, or Boltzmann's constant, **k**.

Secondly,
$$S = -\left(\frac{\partial F}{\partial T}\right)_{V,N} = -\frac{F}{T} + \tfrac{3}{2}Nk \qquad (14)$$

whence
$$E = \tfrac{3}{2}NkT \quad \text{(since } E = F + ST\text{).} \qquad (15)$$

Equation (15) shows that the average energy per system of the assembly is $\frac{3}{2}kT$. Since the systems are independent systems, and structureless, this must be all kinetic energy and the result provides a verification of our statement in Chapter I that the average kinetic energy per system corresponding to any particular type of momentum is frequently given by $\frac{1}{2}kT$. In the present case there are three degrees of freedom, corresponding to motion in the x-, y-, and z-directions.

Moreover, from equations (13) and (15), we derive

$$C_v = \left(\frac{\partial E}{\partial T}\right)_V = \tfrac{3}{2}Nk$$

and

$$C_p - C_v = Nk,$$

whence

$$\gamma = C_p/C_v = 5/3. \tag{16}$$

Equation (16) provides a certain experimental verification of equation (15). For γ, the ratio of the specific heats, is fairly easily determined experimentally from the velocity of sound through the gas. Table I shows the experimental values of γ (at room temperature, extrapolated to zero pressure) for the inert monatomic gases Neon, Argon, Krypton, and Xenon, and it is seen that these lie very close to the theoretical value of 1·67.

TABLE I

Gas	γ
Ne	1·64
A	1·66
Kr	1·69
Xe	1·67

Also from equation (14) we derive

$$S = Nk\left\{\ln V - \ln N + \tfrac{3}{2}\ln T + \tfrac{3}{2}\ln\left(\frac{2\pi mk}{h^2}\right) + \tfrac{5}{2}\right\}$$

or, using the equation of state, equation (13),

$$S = Nk\left\{\tfrac{5}{2}\ln T - \ln P + \ln\left(\frac{2\pi m}{h^2}\right)^{\frac{3}{2}}k^{\frac{5}{2}} + \tfrac{5}{2}\right\}. \tag{17}$$

For one mole of gas Nk becomes R, the gas constant, equal to 1·987 cal./deg. Equation (17) is the Sackur–Tetrode equation for the translational entropy of a perfect gas; we shall refer to it in more detail later (Chapter IX).

Finally, from (9′) we derive the chemical potential,

$$\mu = \left(\frac{\partial F}{\partial N}\right)_{T,V} = -kT\left\{\ln V - \ln N + \tfrac{3}{2}\ln T + \tfrac{3}{2}\ln\left(\frac{2\pi mk}{h^2}\right) + 1\right\} + kT$$

$$= -kT\left\{\ln V - \ln N + \tfrac{3}{2}\ln T + \tfrac{3}{2}\ln\left(\frac{2\pi mk}{h^2}\right)\right\} \tag{18}$$

or, in terms of the pressure,

$$\mu = kT\left\{\ln P - \tfrac{5}{2}\ln T - \ln\left(\frac{2\pi m}{h^2}\right)^{\frac{3}{2}}k^{\frac{5}{2}}\right\}, \tag{19}$$

showing that, at constant T, μ varies linearly with $\ln P$. Again we postpone any detailed discussion of the result till later (see especially Chapter XII): here we remark only that comparison of (18) with (9′) provides the equations

$$N\mu = F + NkT$$
$$= F + PV \quad \text{(by (13))}$$
$$= G. \tag{20}$$

Thus the chemical potential is indeed the Gibbs free energy per system: a thermodynamical requirement for any one-component assembly. Equation (20) would not have been satisfied, as the reader will easily verify, had we not included the factor $1/N!$ in Ω.

5. In commenting on equation (13) above, we said that it suggested identity between k, the unknown factor in our statistical theory, and k, the gas constant per molecule also known as Boltzmann's constant. Although (13) does certainly support such a conjecture, it is not very satisfactory that so important a matter as the proper identification of k should rest only on our treatment of an assembly as hypothetical and particularized as a perfect gas of structureless particles. We shall, therefore, conclude this chapter with a more general proof of this identity.

Returning to equation (1′) and, for simplicity, putting $\omega_i = 1$, $(i = 1, 2, 3,...)$, i.e. dealing only with non-degenerate energy levels, we have

$$\Omega = \frac{\left(\sum_i e^{\beta\epsilon_i}\right)^N e^{-\beta E}}{N!}.$$

E

Therefore $\qquad \ln \Omega = N \ln \sum_i e^{\beta \epsilon_i} - \beta E - \ln N!$

or, by Stirling's theorem,

$$\ln \Omega = N \ln \sum_i e^{\beta \epsilon_i} - \beta E - N \ln N + N \tag{21}$$

and, as we have already shown (Chapter II, paragraph 4)

$$\frac{\partial \ln \Omega}{\partial E} = -\beta, \tag{22}$$

the terms depending on the variation of β with E vanishing on account of the distributive equations

$$n_i^* = e^{\alpha} e^{\beta \epsilon_i}, \quad (i = 1, 2, 3 \ldots)$$

and the restrictive conditions

$$\left. \begin{aligned} \sum_i n_i^* &= N \\ \sum_i n_i^* \epsilon_i &= E \end{aligned} \right\}. \tag{23}$$

These equations, (23), are, of course, quite unaffected by the new factor $1/N!$ in Ω.

Now we can also derive from (21) the equation

$$\frac{\partial \ln \Omega}{\partial N} = \ln \sum_i e^{\beta \epsilon_i} - \ln N$$

or, by (23), $\qquad = \ln \sum_i e^{\beta \epsilon_i} - \ln \sum_i n_i^*$

$$= \ln \sum_i e^{\beta \epsilon_i} - \ln \left(e^{\alpha} \sum_i e^{\beta \epsilon_i} \right)$$

$$= -\ln e^{\alpha}$$

$$= -\alpha \tag{24}$$

and just as comparison between (22) and equation $(6\,a)$ of Chapter I led to $\qquad \beta = -1/kT$

so now comparison between (24) and equation $(6\,c)$ of Chapter I leads to

$$\alpha = \mu/kT, \tag{25}$$

where μ is the chemical potential of a system in the assembly. Consequently $\qquad \mu = kT\alpha$

$$= -kT\left(\ln \sum_i e^{-\epsilon_i/kT} - \ln N \right)$$

so that

$$N\mu = -NkT \ln \sum_i e^{-\epsilon_i/kT} + kTN \ln N$$

$$= F + NkT \text{ by (3') and Stirling's theorem.}$$

Thermodynamically, however, we must always have

$$N\mu = G$$

and

$$G = F + PV.$$

Therefore, quite generally, any thermodynamical assembly of N identical non-localized independent systems confined to a volume V, and obeying classical statistics, satisfies the equation of state

$$PV = NkT$$

which, by comparison with the equation of state of a perfect gas

$$PV = NkT \tag{26}$$

identifies k with k.

There are three final comments to be made. First, it will have been evident to the reader that two or three lines in the above proof, those involving n_i^* and α, could equally well have been omitted. They were inserted in order to obtain, *en passant*, equation (25) which supplies, for the present problem, the physical interpretation of α. The very fundamental importance of equation (25) makes it worth introducing here; but we shall deal with its full implications much more thoroughly in later chapters.

Then, secondly, it should be noticed that we take the equation of state, (26), as the definitive equation of a perfect gas. This does not imply anything about the constancy of the specific heat C_v: indeed we shall find that C_v, calculated on the basis of the equations of this chapter, often varies markedly with temperature.† *Every assembly of the type considered in this chapter is, according to our definition, a perfect gas*: for every such assembly satisfies the equation of state $PV = NkT$.

Lastly, remembering that the energies ϵ depend, in general, on

---

† The other well-known 'perfect gas condition', $(\partial E/\partial V)_T = 0$, follows thermodynamically from (26) on the basis of the first and second laws.

the volume, V, of the assembly, we derive, analogously with (22) and (24),

$$\frac{\partial \ln \Omega}{\partial V} = N \frac{\partial}{\partial V} \ln \sum_i e^{\beta \epsilon_i}, \text{ with } \beta \text{ treated as a constant,}$$

$$= N \frac{\sum_i \beta (d\epsilon_i / dV) e^{\beta \epsilon_i}}{\sum e^{\beta \epsilon_i}}$$

$$= -\frac{1}{kT} \left(\frac{\partial F}{\partial V} \right)_{T,N} \qquad \text{by equation (3').}$$

But, according to (6 b) of Chapter I,

$$\frac{\partial \ln \Omega}{\partial V} = \frac{P}{kT},$$

and thence we verify the well known thermodynamical equation

$$P = - \left(\frac{\partial F}{\partial V} \right)_{T,N}.$$

In future we shall replace k everywhere by Boltzmann's constant, $\boldsymbol{k}$.

EXAMPLES

1. Prove that for any assembly of identical, independent systems, localized or non-localized,

$$E = NkT^2 \frac{\partial}{\partial T} \ln(\text{p.f.}),$$

and verify that when $(\text{p.f.}) = \left(\frac{2\pi mkT}{h^2} \right)^{\frac{3}{2}} V$ then $E = \frac{3}{2} NkT$.

2. Show that for a perfect gas of structureless particles,

$$\Omega(E, V, N) = \left[\left(\frac{-2\pi m}{\beta h^2} \right)^{\frac{3}{2}} V \right]^N \frac{e^{-\beta E}}{N!}$$

where β is given by $\partial \Omega / \partial \beta = 0$ (formally; keeping E, V, and N constant). Deduce the equation of state $PV = NkT$ from the formula

$$S(E, V, N) = k \ln \Omega(E, V, N).$$

(See equation (6 b) of Chapter I.)

3. A perfect gas of structureless particles has its temperature raised from 300° K. to 400° K. Show that if this is done at constant volume the increase in entropy of the gas is $0\cdot43R$ (per mole), whilst if it is done at constant pressure the increase in entropy is $0\cdot72R$ (per mole).

4. Prove that for a perfect gas of structureless particles the entropy change between any two temperatures when the pressure is kept constant is 5/3 times the corresponding entropy change when the volume is kept constant.

5. Show that, if $V = 1$ c.c., $T = 300°$ K., and $m = 40m_H$ (Argon), where m_H is the mass of a hydrogen atom, then the absolute value of (p.f.) as given by equation (8) is approximately $2 \cdot 5 \cdot 10^{26}$.

TRANSITION TO CLASSICAL DYNAMICS

1. ALL our theory, so far, has been developed in terms of quantum-mechanical concepts or, more accurately, it has been erected on a quantum-mechanical foundation. Our basic problem, for any assembly, was to evaluate Ω, the number of distinguishable complexions or micromolecular states corresponding to given values of E, V, and N (the total energy, volume, and number of systems, respectively, of the assembly). On the assumption that we count as complexions only quantum-mechanically stationary states, the evaluation of Ω presents little difficulty when the systems of the assembly are independent systems. For the different permissible states of any one system are then easily enumerable, and the evaluation of $\Omega(E, V, N)$ devolves, as we have shown, on the essentially simple problem of counting the number of ways in which the total energy of the assembly can be distributed between the N systems.

The above method, however, entirely depends for its simplicity on the easy enumeration of the different permissible states for any one system. Quantum-mechanically, of course, this easy enumerability is generally assured. In almost all the interesting cases we do find, on solving the quantum-mechanical equations governing the motion of a single system, that the stationary states for this system pertain to certain definite discrete energy values (energy levels), each energy level corresponding to a definite number of independent stationary states (the degeneracy of that level). But if each single system is supposed governed by classical, rather than quantal, mechanics we are faced with a different, and less tractable, situation. Not only do we now have to deal with a *continuous* range of permissible energies, generally ranging from zero to infinity, instead of with discrete energy levels, but also the other simple notion of weight, or degeneracy, associated with any particular energy, is now much more vague. We cannot, for instance, any longer think of two energy levels coinciding to give a degeneracy factor two. It is, indeed, obvious that a system can, according to classical mechanics, exist in very many recognizably different states with the same energy; for example, a particle in a box can have infinitely many recognizably different positions in the box, and different directions of motion at these positions, and still have the same kinetic energy for all these distinguishable states.   But we have still to decide how to give a numerical measure to this degeneracy, or classical analogue of degeneracy.

Since our present theory is quite appropriate for quantum mechanics, we shall most profitably cross from quantum mechanics to classical mechanics from the quantum-mechanical side.   Historically, of course, the step was made in the reverse direction, and we shall later say a word about the entirely classical derivation of the formulae we obtain.

2. The foundation stone of quantum mechanics is Heisenberg's Uncertainty Relation (Born–Jordan (1925), Heisenberg–Bohr (1927))†

$$\Delta x \, \Delta p_x \sim h \tag{1}$$

where Δx = accuracy with which we can measure a positional coordinate, x,

Δp_x = accuracy with which we can simultaneously measure the corresponding momentum, p_x,

and $h = 6\cdot62.10^{-27}$ erg. sec. (Planck's constant).

The general meaning of this equation is nowadays well known: with the relation expressed as in (1), Δx and Δp_x stand for the best possible simultaneous accuracies in measurements of x and p_x. More generally, with measurements which are not necessarily of optimum accuracy, we have, of course,

$$\Delta x \, \Delta p_x \geqslant h.$$

Moreover it is this relationship, holding between any pair of *conjugate* dynamical variables, which is the source of all specifically quantal effects. If the small, but finite, h in (1) is replaced by *zero*, we regain the equations, and predictions, of classical dynamics.

† We have written $\sim$ and not $=$ in (1) since we have not precisely defined Δx or Δp_x. A numerical factor, of the order of unity, is introduced into the r.h.s. of (1) according to the definition of these quantities.

It is, perhaps, advisable to stress that p_x, the momentum corresponding or conjugate to the spacial coordinate x is not, in general, $m\dot{x}$. If x, y, z are rectangular Cartesian coordinates, then $p_x = m\dot{x}$, $p_y = m\dot{y}$, and $p_z = m\dot{z}$. But if, instead, we are using spherical polar coordinates, r, θ, ϕ (Fig. 5), then

$$p_r = m\dot{r}; \quad p_\theta = mr^2\dot{\theta}; \quad p_\phi = mr^2\sin^2\theta.\dot{\phi},$$

and with cylindrical polar coordinates, ρ, ϕ, z (Fig. 5) we have

$$p_\rho = m\dot{\rho}; \quad p_\phi = m\rho^2\dot{\phi}; \quad p_z = m\dot{z}.$$

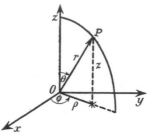

Fig. 5.

When in doubt of the correct momenta corresponding to a given set of configurational coordinates any reasonably advanced text-book of mechanics should be consulted. The customary notation is to denote positional coordinates by q_1, q_2,..., q_i,... and the corresponding momenta by p_1, p_2,..., p_i,.... . The complete set, q_1, q_2,..., q_i,..., p_1, p_2,..., p_i,... are said to constitute the coordinates of the *representative point* in *phase space*.

We have, then, an equation of the form

$$\Delta x \, \Delta p_x \sim h$$

for every coordinate x, y, z,.... This uncertainty relationship shows up in a quite definite and striking way if we compare the classical and quantal solutions of any particular mechanical, or dynamical, problem. To take the simplest possible case, let us consider a particle constrained to move on a straight line. There is then only one positional coordinate, x say, and the corresponding momentum, p_x, is given by $m\dot{x}$. Again for simplicity, we will suppose that there is no potential field, other than that confining the x-coordinate to the region, or range,

$$0 \leqslant x \leqslant a,$$

i.e. we consider the problem of a particle in a 'one-dimensional box'.

Since a constant potential energy may be ignored, the energy of the particle is given, according to classical dynamics, by

$$E = \tfrac{1}{2}m\dot{x}^2 = \frac{p_x^2}{2m} \quad \text{where} \quad -\infty \leqslant p_x \leqslant \infty, \tag{2}$$

whereas quantum dynamics gives (see paragraph 2 of Chapter III)†

$$E = \frac{h^2}{8m}\frac{p^2}{a^2}, \quad p = 1, 2, 3, \ldots. \tag{3}$$

We can compare these two results most easily if we think in terms of *phase space*, a concept to which we have already referred

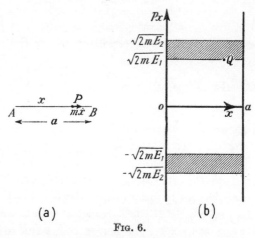

(a)   (b)

Fɪɢ. 6.

above. Fig. 6 (a) shows P, the point defining the position of the particle in ordinary displacement space; and Fig. 6 (b) shows Q, the *representative point* of the system in phase space, the figmentary or conceptual space in which any point is defined by the two coordinates x and p_x. It is evident that any position of Q in phase space determines, uniquely, not only the position of P in displacement space, but also the magnitude and direction of the momentum, or velocity, of the particle at P. Consequently each point Q, of phase space, corresponds to a recognizably distinct state, or condition, of the system, i.e. of the particle in the one-dimensional box.

† In (3), of course, p stands for a quantum number and is not, directly, the linear momentum of the particle.

Now classically, by equation (2), all those points Q corresponding to states in which the particle has energy E lie on one or other of the two straight lines

$$p_x = \pm \sqrt{(2mE)}$$

and therefore the classical condition $E_1 \leqslant E \leqslant E_2$ means that Q lies in one or other of the two shaded areas shown in Fig. 6 (b). According to quantum mechanics, however, the allowed energies of the particle (pertaining to stationary states) are given by equation (3), so that we can write

$$E_1 = \frac{h^2}{8m} \frac{p_1^2}{a^2}, \qquad E_2 = \frac{h^2}{8m} \frac{p_2^2}{a^2},$$

where p_1 and p_2 are positive integers. The portion of phase space corresponding to the classical condition $E_1 \leqslant E \leqslant E_2$ (shown shaded in Fig. 6 (b)) is then of area

$$2a\{\sqrt{(2mE_2)} - \sqrt{(2mE_1)}\} = 2a \frac{h}{2a} (p_2 - p_1) = h(p_2 - p_1)$$

which $= h$ if $p_2 = p_1 + 1$,

i.e. if E_1 and E_2 are successive quantal energy levels.

Now only the discrete energy levels ($p = 1, 2, 3,...$) have any meaning in quantum mechanics; we can therefore express our result by saying (pictorially) that quantization, i.e. the transition from classical mechanics to quantal mechanics, subdivides phase space into units of h ($= 6.62 . 10^{-27}$ erg. sec.). This is dimensionally correct, since 1 erg. sec. = 1 dyne cm. sec. = 1 cm. (dyne sec.) = 1 cm. (momentum).

The result which we have found in this simple example is a particular case of a general theorem of fundamental importance, and a direct consequence of the Heisenberg uncertainty principle. A proof of the general theorem is without the province of this book, but the theorem itself may be stated as follows:†

The classical energy surfaces in phase space (total energy = constant) which correspond to the energies which are allowed by quantum theory subdivide phase space into units of h^n where n is the number of spacial coordinates.

† In general, the theorem as here stated is true only for sufficiently large quantum numbers (energies)—see more detailed discussion in Fowler, R. H., *Statistical Mechanics*, C.U.P. (1936), pp. 18 ff. But the naïve statement above is not seriously misleading, and conveys the correct idea.

3. This principle provides a link between quantal and classical mechanics sufficient to enable us to pass from the statistical theory formulated in terms of discrete (quantal) energy levels, which we have developed hitherto, to the corresponding formulae of statistical mechanics based on classical dynamics. For classical and quantal theories will be equally appropriate only if the quantal energy levels are very close together (compared with kT): and when this is so we can write, on account of the above theorem (and of the meaning of integration)

$$h^n \sum_i e^{-\epsilon_i/kT} = \int e^{-\epsilon/kT}\, dA, \qquad (4)$$

where ϵ is the classical energy,† and dA stands for an element of 'area' of phase space. In other words

$$\sum_{\substack{\text{(summed over} \\ \text{allowed energies)}}} e^{-\epsilon_i/kT} \quad \text{and} \quad \frac{1}{h^n}\int \dots \int e^{-\epsilon(x,y\dots p_x,p_y\dots)/kT}\, dx\, dy\dots dp_x\, dp_y\dots$$

become indistinguishable when quantal conditions can be ignored.

Equation (4) is true even if the quantal energy levels are degenerate. Again we cannot prove this here, but, roughly speaking, the alternative wave-functions belonging to a degenerate energy level correspond to different regions of phase space. Thus, quite generally, the 'classical' formula for the partition function, $\sum_i \omega_i e^{-\epsilon_i/kT}$, is

$$(\text{p.f.}) = \frac{1}{h^n} \int \dots \int_{\text{(over phase space)}} e^{-\epsilon/kT}\, dx\, dy\dots dp_x\, dp_y\dots \qquad (5)$$

where n is the number of spacial coordinates required to describe a system, or $2n$ is the dimensionality of the phase space concerned.

Before we employ equation (5) to calculate the classical analogues of the partition functions already determined quantally, for the translational motion of a structureless particle and for the vibrational motion of an harmonic-oscillator, there are three comments concerning equation (5) which must be made.

The first comment is that equation (5), combined with the

† We return to our normal use of ϵ for the energy of a system. E was employed above as possibly more familiar, but we wish, in general, to reserve capital letters for properties of the whole assembly.

meaning of a partition function (which we discussed in paragraph 5 of Chapter II, and see also Chapter V), implies that any system with the energy ϵ is equally likely to be anywhere in the region of phase space corresponding to this particular energy.[†] For the classical justification of this basic principle of pre-quantal statistical mechanics, and its connexion with the famous Liouville theorem of classical dynamics, the reader is referred to the important standard work of Tolman (see bibliography). The basic principle is certainly no immediate consequence of Liouville's theorem applied to any one system, as is sometimes supposed. For it must be borne in mind that any particular system is constantly changing its energy due to collisions—or whatever other mechanism is maintaining statistical equilibrium in the assembly. Our attitude in this book is to regard as basic the fundamental hypothesis stated at the beginning of Chapter II (assumption (a) or (b)) and to consider 'classical' statistical mechanics as a particular limiting case of 'quantal' statistical mechanics. Apart from some further discussion in the final chapter, any deeper treatment is outside our chosen domain.

The second point calling for attention is the presence of the factor $1/h^n$ on the r.h.s. of (5). Obviously such a factor cannot belong to an entirely pre-quantal treatment. Nevertheless we shall retain it, and any terms deriving from it, in all our so-called 'classical' formulae. Historically, of course, classical statistical mechanics was based on the *phase integral*, i.e. the r.h.s. of (5) without this extraneous factor. For many purposes the presence or otherwise of the numerical factor $1/h^n$ is completely irrelevant: the reader will, for instance, verify without difficulty that it does not affect any expression we may calculate for E or P, and consequently C_v or C_p, as functions of temperature and volume. It is only formulae for the entropy, S, the free energy, F, and the chemical potential, μ, which are affected by the presence or otherwise of the numerical factor $1/h^n$ in the partition function (p.f.). For example, the term in the expression for S due to this particular factor in (p.f.) is $-Nkn \ln h$. But this is a constant, independent

[†] A more accurate statement would say 'with energy between ϵ and $\epsilon + \delta\epsilon$, where $\delta\epsilon$ is small, etc'.

of T and V, and so for many purposes (e.g. in estimating the entropy change in a gas reaction, when all such terms cancel out) quite irrelevant. It is only in attempts to calculate anything that may be called the *absolute* value of the entropy (or absolute entropy values) that this term involving h is important. We shall discuss the meaning to be attached to absolute entropy values in Chapter IX, and show then that pre-quantal statistical mechanics was incapable of predicting such quantities. Similar considerations apply to the terms involving h in expressions for F or μ. For the present this factor $1/h^n$ in (p.f.) should be regarded as a *normalization* factor, ensuring a correct transition between classical and quantal expressions for the partition function.

Finally, we remark that although equation (5) has been derived as a limiting case of the corresponding quantal formula, we are assigning to it a classical status of its own. By this we mean that we shall use it to show what classical dynamics would predict outside its own proper range of validity. When classical dynamics is strictly appropriate, the quantal and classical treatments will give identical results. But this will not be so if we use the classical formulae, implying a continuous range of permissible energies for any system, to describe an assembly in a thermodynamic state depending intrinsically on the discrete quantal nature of these energies. Thus comparison between classical and quantal formulae, when these lead to different expressions for the thermodynamic properties of an assembly, exposes those macroscopically observable effects which have their origin in specifically quantal behaviour.

4. As a first example on the evaluation of the classical phase integral we shall take the problem solved quantally in paragraph 2 of Chapter III. That is, we shall deal with an assembly of N independent non-localized structureless particles, supposing now that the energy (translational) of any system is given by the Newtonian expression

$$\epsilon = \tfrac{1}{2}m(\dot{x}^2 + \dot{y}^2 + \dot{z}^2)$$

which
$$= \frac{1}{2m}(p_x^2 + p_y^2 + p_z^2)$$

since for rectangular Cartesian coordinates $p_x = m\dot{x}$, $p_y = m\dot{y}$, and $p_z = m\dot{z}$. The partition function that we have to evaluate is then given by equation (5) above, i.e.

$$(\text{p.f.}) = \frac{1}{h^3} \int\limits_{-\infty}^{\infty} \int\limits_{-\infty}^{\infty} \int\limits_{-\infty}^{\infty} \int\limits_{0}^{c} \int\limits_{0}^{b} \int\limits_{0}^{a} e^{-(p_x^2+p_y^2+p_z^2)/2mkT}\, dx\,dy\,dz\,dp_x\,dp_y\,dp_z,$$

involving a 6-fold integration over phase space.† Three of these integrations, viz. those over the ranges of x, y, and z, are immediate, since x, y, and z do not themselves occur in ϵ, i.e. in the integrand. Consequently,

$$(\text{p.f.}) = \frac{abc}{h^3} \int\limits_{-\infty}^{\infty} \int\limits_{-\infty}^{\infty} \int\limits_{-\infty}^{\infty} e^{-(p_x^2+p_y^2+p_z^2)/2mkT}\, dp_x\,dp_y\,dp_z$$

$$= \frac{V}{h^3} \int\limits_{-\infty}^{\infty} \int\limits_{-\infty}^{\infty} \int\limits_{-\infty}^{\infty} e^{-(p_x^2+p_y^2+p_z^2)/2mkT}\, dp_x\,dp_y\,dp_z. \qquad (6)$$

We may pause here to observe that (6) is quite independent of the rectangular shape of the box, which we assumed in the quantal treatment of Chapter III and have carried over into the above equations. Since the spacial coordinates do not enter into the integrand, integration over these coordinates is bound to yield just the volume, V, of the container within which each and every system of the gaseous assembly is confined.

Returning to (6), we can factorize the triple integral (in just the same way as we factorized the triple sum in the quantal treatment) to obtain

$$(\text{p.f.}) = \frac{V}{h^3} \int\limits_{-\infty}^{\infty} e^{-p_x^2/2mkT}\, dp_x \int\limits_{-\infty}^{\infty} e^{-p_y^2/2mkT}\, dp_y \int\limits_{-\infty}^{\infty} e^{-p_z^2/2mkT}\, dp_z.$$

But each of these integrals is simply related to the standard integral, equation (7) of Chapter III. For we have

$$\int\limits_{-\infty}^{\infty} e^{-p_x^2/2mkT}\, dp_x = 2 \int\limits_{0}^{\infty} e^{-p_x^2/2mkT}\, dp_x$$

$$= 2\frac{\sqrt{\pi}\sqrt{(2mkT)}}{2} = \sqrt{(2\pi mkT)}.$$

† $\int\limits_{0}^{a}$ refers to dx, $\int\limits_{0}^{b}$ refers to dy, etc., working outwards from the integrand.

Therefore equation (6) gives

$$(\text{p.f.}) = \frac{V}{h^3}\sqrt{(2\pi m \boldsymbol{k} T)}\sqrt{(2\pi m k T)}\sqrt{(2\pi m \boldsymbol{k} T)}$$

$$= V\left(\frac{2\pi m \boldsymbol{k} T}{h^2}\right)^{\frac{3}{2}} \tag{7}$$

which is precisely the result that we obtained quantally.

Thus, as far as the partition function for free translational motion is concerned, classical dynamics and quantum mechanics both lead to the same expression, provided that the classical phase integral is 'normalized' (by the inclusion of the factor $1/h^3$) and provided also that the quantal treatment is based on classical statistics (as distinct from Fermi–Dirac or Einstein–Bose statistics). This is because the quantal energy levels are so close together, for atomic masses, that on any scale in which the yardstick of thermal energy, $\boldsymbol{k} T$, is appreciable these quantal energy levels are indistinguishable from the classical continuum. Since we have already deduced, from this expression for the translational partition function, both the Sackur–Tetrode entropy equation and a formula for the translational contribution to the chemical potential (Chapter III, (17) and (19)), we shall not discuss the expression further here, but proceed to a second example, and one for which classical and quantal treatments lead to markedly different results.

5. In Chapter II we considered the Einstein theory of the specific heat of an atomic crystal, and showed that this depended on evaluating the partition function for a simple-harmonic-oscillator. Accepting that, for a [1]-oscillator, the quantal energy levels are given by

$$\epsilon = (n+\tfrac{1}{2})h\nu \quad (n = 0, 1, 2,...)$$

with $\omega = 1$

we found that the partition function for a single oscillator was given by

$$(\text{p.f.}) = \frac{e^{-\frac{1}{2}h\nu/\boldsymbol{k} T}}{1-e^{-h\nu/\boldsymbol{k} T}}. \tag{8}$$

We shall now evaluate the phase integral, or classical form for the partition function, for a [1]-oscillator governed by classical dynamics, and shall find that we obtain a very different expression.

According to classical dynamics a [1]-oscillator having frequency ν is governed by the equation (Newton's law of motion for a particle in a parabolic potential field)

$$\ddot{x} + (2\pi\nu)^2 x = 0$$

whence

$$x = A\cos(2\pi\nu t + \delta)$$

where A is the amplitude of the oscillation and δ is an arbitrary phase, depending on the instant from which we start to measure the time t. The kinetic energy of the particle, at any time, is given by

$$\text{K.E.} = \tfrac{1}{2}m\dot{x}^2 = \tfrac{1}{2}m(2\pi\nu)^2 A^2 \sin^2(2\pi\nu t + \delta)$$

while its potential energy is given by

$$\text{P.E.} = \tfrac{1}{2}m(2\pi\nu)^2 x^2 = \tfrac{1}{2}m(2\pi\nu)^2 A^2 \cos^2(2\pi\nu t + \delta).$$

Consequently the total energy of the oscillator, the sum of both kinetic and potential energy, is a constant of the motion given by

$$\epsilon = \tfrac{1}{2}m(2\pi\nu)^2 A^2$$

and can have any value, between zero and infinity, depending on the amplitude, A, of the oscillation.

To form the phase integral we require ϵ as a function of x and p_x, the spacial coordinate and corresponding momentum of the particle. This is easily obtained, since $p_x = m\dot{x}$, and

$$\epsilon = \tfrac{1}{2}m\dot{x}^2 + \tfrac{1}{2}m(2\pi\nu)^2 x^2$$
$$= \frac{1}{2m}p_x^2 + \tfrac{1}{2}m(2\pi\nu)^2 x^2.$$

Thus the classical expression for the partition function, equation (5) above, reads

$$\text{(p.f.)} = \frac{1}{h}\int_{-\infty}^{\infty}\int_{-\infty}^{\infty} e^{-\{(1/2m)p_x^2 + \frac{1}{2}m(2\pi\nu)^2 x^2\}/kT}\,dx\,dp_x. \qquad (9)$$

In this case x, as well as p_x, can run from $-\infty$ to $+\infty$, there being no artificial restriction on the magnitude of x. But, of course, the contribution to (9) from large values of x (or p_x) is very small, since large x (or p_x) means large ϵ and so a very small value of the integrand.

As before, the phase integral factorizes and we have

$$\text{(p.f.)} = \frac{1}{h} \int_{-\infty}^{\infty} e^{-p_x^2/2mkT}\, dp_x \int_{-\infty}^{\infty} e^{-m(2\pi\nu)^2 x^2/2kT}\, dx$$

$$= \frac{1}{h}\sqrt{(2\pi mkT)}\frac{\sqrt{(2\pi kT)}}{\sqrt{m}(2\pi\nu)} \quad \begin{array}{l}\text{by equation (7) of}\\ \text{Chapter III,}\end{array}$$

i.e. $$\text{(p.f.)} = \frac{kT}{h\nu}. \tag{10}$$

Equation (10) is certainly very different from equation (8), and therefore the thermodynamic properties of an assembly of $3N$ identical, localized, [1]-oscillators (Einstein solid) calculated from (10) are necessarily different from those previously calculated on the basis of equation (8). A hypothetical assembly of $3N$ classical [1]-oscillators will not have the same thermodynamic, macroscopic, properties as an assembly of $3N$ quantal [1]-oscillators.

The easiest route to thermodynamics is still provided by the equation for the Helmholtz free energy (equation (22) of Chapter II) which for $3N$ localized systems reads

$$F = -3NkT \ln(\text{p.f.})$$

and on the basis of (10) becomes

$$F = -3NkT \ln\frac{kT}{h\nu}. \tag{11}$$

From (11) and the Gibbs–Helmholtz equation

$$E = F - T\left(\frac{\partial F}{\partial T}\right)_V,$$

we deduce

$$E = kT^2 \frac{\partial}{\partial T}\left(3N \ln\frac{kT}{h\nu}\right)$$

$$= 3NkT. \tag{12}$$

Consequently $$C_v = \left(\frac{\partial E}{\partial T}\right)_V = 3Nk,$$

i.e. the specific heat has the value $3R$ per mole, at all temperatures.

Thus classical mechanics would lead us to expect an assembly of $3N$ localized [1]-oscillators to have a specific heat independent of the temperature and given by the Dulong–Petit law. We have already seen that according to quantal mechanics such an assembly will have a specific heat equal to $3Nk$ only at high temperatures: at lower temperatures the specific heat will fall below this limiting, classical, value and, indeed, will tend to zero at very low temperatures. Since the latter behaviour is in general agreement with experimental data on the specific heats of solids, we are led to refer to the falling off of the specific heats of solids, at low temperatures, as an observable macroscopic consequence of microscopic quantal behaviour.

Two final comments. First, the equivalence of the classical and quantal expressions at high temperatures is not accidental. We have here merely another illustration of the law that when the yardstick of thermal energy, kT, is large compared with the spacing of the quantal energy levels (in the region of appreciably occupied levels) then the assembly will exhibit classical behaviour —as if the energy of its systems were not subject to quantization. We cannot prove this law in its complete generality here, but shall find other illustrations of it in later chapters. Secondly, the classical value of the energy, $3NkT$, or kT per [1]-oscillator, itself illustrates the general *classical principle that each 'squared' term in the exponent of the integrand of the phase integral contributes $\frac{1}{2}kT$ to the internal energy of the assembly*. In this particular case there were two such squared terms $(1/2m)p_x^2$ and $\frac{1}{2}m(2\pi\nu)^2x^2$, and the reader will easily verify that each of them leads to $\frac{1}{2}kT$ in the expression for E. The general rule is itself easily proved, and is also left as an exercise for the reader.

6. Having now evaluated the classical phase integral for those particular assemblies for which we had previously evaluated the quantal form of the partition function, we have almost brought the classical and quantal treatments to the same stage in our development of statistical theory. There remain, however, two gaps in the classical formulism which have still to be filled. We have shown that the classical analogue of

$$\sum_i \omega_i e^{-\epsilon_i/kT}$$

is

$$\frac{1}{h^n} \int \dots \int_{\text{(phase space)}} e^{-\epsilon(x\dots p_x\dots)/kT}\, dx\dots dp_x\dots,$$

but we have not yet given the classical version of the 'quantal' formulae

$$S = k \ln \Omega, \tag{13}$$

and

$$n_i^* = N \frac{\omega_i e^{-\epsilon_i/kT}}{\sum_i \omega_i e^{-\epsilon_i/kT}}. \tag{14}$$

In the quantal treatment we found (see equation (18′) of Chapter II, or (21) of Chapter III) that

$$\Omega = \left(\sum_i e^{-\epsilon_i/kT} \right)^N e^{E/kT} \tag{15}$$

or

$$= \frac{\left(\sum_i e^{-\epsilon_i/kT} \right)^N e^{E/kT}}{N!} \tag{15'}$$

according to whether the systems of the assembly were localized or non-localized. Evidently the classical forms of (15) and (15′) are

$$\Omega = \left(\frac{1}{h^n} \int \dots \int e^{-\epsilon(x\dots p_x\dots)/kT} \, dx \dots dp_x \dots \right)^N e^{E/kT} \tag{16}$$

and

$$= \frac{1}{N!} \left(\frac{1}{h^n} \int \dots \int e^{-\epsilon(x\dots p_x\dots)/kT} \, dx \dots dp_x \dots \right)^N e^{E/kT} \tag{16'}$$

respectively.

There is no need to discuss (16) and (16′) separately, for the factor $1/N!$ required for non-localized systems is easily interpreted. Confining attention, therefore, to (16) we observe that

$$\left(\frac{1}{h^n} \int \dots \int e^{-\epsilon(x\dots p_x\dots)/kT} \, dx \dots dp_x \dots \right)^N$$

$$= \left(\frac{1}{h^n} \int \dots \int e^{-\epsilon(x_1\dots p_{x_1}\dots)/kT} \, dx_1 \dots dp_{x_1} \dots \right) \times$$

$$\times \left(\frac{1}{h^n} \int \dots \int e^{-\epsilon(x_2\dots p_{x_2}\dots)/kT} \, dx_2 \dots dp_{x_2} \dots \right) \times$$

$$\times (\dots) \left(\frac{1}{h^n} \int \dots \int e^{-\epsilon(x_N\dots p_{x_N}\dots)/kT} \, dx_N \dots dp_{x_N} \dots \right), \tag{17}$$

since the addition of suffixes to 'dummy' variables—i.e. variables over all values of which we integrate, and so which do not appear in the final result—makes no difference. Also (17) can be written as

$$\left(\frac{1}{h^n}\right)^N \int \ldots \int e^{-[\epsilon(x_1\ldots p_{x_1}\ldots)+\epsilon(x_2\ldots p_{x_2}\ldots)+\ldots+\epsilon(x_N\ldots p_{x_N}\ldots)]/kT} \times$$
$$\times dx_1 \ldots dx_2 \ldots \ldots dx_N \ldots dp_{x_1} \ldots dp_{x_2} \ldots \ldots dp_{x_N} \ldots \quad (18)$$

by the inverse of the process of factorization of a multiple integral. Now we may regard $x_1\ldots$ and $p_{x_1}\ldots$ as the coordinates and corresponding momenta specifying system number one, $x_2\ldots$ and $p_{x_2}\ldots$ as the coordinates and corresponding momenta specifying system number two, and so on, for all the N independent systems of the assembly. Then, since these *are* independent systems,

$$\epsilon(x_1\ldots p_{x_1}\ldots)+\epsilon(x_2\ldots p_{x_2}\ldots)+\ldots+\epsilon(x_N\ldots p_{x_N}\ldots) = E,$$

the total energy of the assembly, and, further, $x_1\ldots x_2\ldots x_N\ldots$ serve as a complete (and non-superfluous) set of coordinates defining the spacial arrangement of the whole assembly, while $p_{x_1}\ldots p_{x_2}\ldots \ldots p_{x_N}\ldots$ are still the conjugate momentum variables: in other words, $x_1\ldots x_2\ldots \ldots x_N\ldots p_{x_1}\ldots p_{x_2}\ldots \ldots p_{x_N}\ldots$ define the position of *the representative point for the whole assembly in the 2nN-dimensional*† *phase space for the whole assembly.* Consequently (18) may be written

$$\left(\frac{1}{h^n}\right)^N \underset{\substack{\text{(the phase space for} \\ \text{the whole assembly)}}}{\int \ldots \int} e^{-E(q\ldots p\ldots)/kT} \, dq\ldots dp\ldots \quad (19)$$

where $q\ldots$ and $p\ldots$ stand simply for sufficient spacial coordinates, and corresponding momenta, completely to specify the state of all N systems of the assembly. Equation (16) then reads

$$\Omega = \left(\frac{1}{h^n}\right)^N e^{E/kT} \underset{\substack{\text{(the phase space for} \\ \text{the whole assembly)}}}{\int \ldots \int} e^{-E(q\ldots p\ldots)/kT} \, dq\ldots dp\ldots . \quad (20)$$

Now quantally we started with the postulate that E, the total energy of the assembly, was given. If we preserve this postulate when dealing with the assembly classically, then

$$e^{-E(q\ldots p\ldots)/kT} = e^{-E/kT}$$

† Each *system* has n coordinates $x\ldots$ and n coordinates $p_x\ldots$, and there are N systems.

and it is tempting to write (20) as

$$\Omega = \left(\frac{1}{h^n}\right)^N \int \dots \int dq\dots dp\dots, \qquad (21)$$

$$\{E(q\dots p\dots) = E\},$$

where $\{E(q\dots p\dots) = E\}$ denotes that part of phase space in which the assembly has energy E. A little thought, however, reveals that the r.h.s. of (21) is meaningless: the process that we are apparently trying to perform is akin to trying to integrate elements of area along a straight line, or elements of volume within an area. The best we can do with (20) is to restrict $E(q\dots p\dots)$ to the small range

$$E \leqslant E(q\dots p\dots) \leqslant E+\Delta E$$

when, to all intents and purposes, ΔE being sufficiently small, (20) becomes

$$\Omega = \left(\frac{1}{h^n}\right)^N \int \dots \int dq\dots dp\dots, \qquad (22)$$

$$\{E \leqslant E(q\dots p\dots) \leqslant E+\Delta E\},$$

which is dimensionally correct, i.e. a pure number. Moreover, by what we have said already in paragraph 2 above, applied now not to the stationary states of a single system but to those of *the whole assembly*, the r.h.s. of (22) goes over into the quantum-mechanical degeneracy (number of independent, distinguishable, stationary states pertaining to the energy E) when E and $E+\Delta E$ refer to adjacent allowed energy levels for the whole assembly.

Thus $S = k\ln\Omega$, with Ω given by equation (22), is the classical form of $S = k\ln\Omega$, with Ω given, on a quantum-mechanical basis, by (a) or (b) of Chapter II. For many purposes the normalizing factor, involving h, and the precise value of ΔE, are not essential: it is only when we require a correct transition between the classical and quantal formulisms that these become significant. The really important feature of (22) is the classical result that entropy is proportional to the logarithm of a certain extension ($[2nN]$-volume) in phase space, namely that extension of phase space defined by the narrow region $E \leqslant E(q\dots p\dots) \leqslant E+\Delta E$.

From this result it is possible to return to the formulae (equation (5) etc.) from which we derived it, in very much the same way as we derived the corresponding quantal formulae from the basic quantal postulate, (*b*) of Chapter II. Indeed, historically that is the logical sequence. But having chosen in this book to base our statistical theory on the quantal formulism, it is unnecessary to re-derive all the analogous classical equations classically, and sufficient for the present purpose to have shown how the classical basis fits into the general scheme. Having done this we shall not, in the sequel, make any direct use of equation (22).

Finally, we require the classical analogue of (14). It is immediately evident that this is simply

$$n^*(x..., p_x...) = \frac{N e^{-\epsilon(x..., p_x...)/kT}}{\int ... \int\limits_{\text{(phase space)}} e^{-\epsilon(x..., p_x...)/kT} dx...dp_x...} \qquad (23)$$

(where the phase space concerned is that of a single system; which is, of course, the only phase space related to the partition function (p.f.)). Moreover the functions $n^*(x..., p_x...)$ are such that

$$\int ... \int\limits_{\text{(phase space)}} n^*(x...p_x...) dx...dp_x... = N \qquad (24)$$

and

$$\int ... \int\limits_{\text{(phase space)}} \epsilon(x...p_x...)n^*(x...p_x...) dx...dp_x... = E \qquad (25)$$

(cf. equations (5′) and (6′) of Chapter II). So far we have not made much use of these equations giving the important values of the distribution parameters, and we proceed to discuss them in greater detail in the next chapter.

EXAMPLES

1. Prove that if the classical expression for the energy of a system can be written

$$\epsilon(q_1,..., q_n, p_1,..., p_n) = \sum_{i=1}^{n} a_i q_i^2 + \sum_{i=1}^{n} b_i p_i^2,$$

where none of the a's or b's are zero, then the classical value of the internal energy of the assembly is nkT, per system. If only l of the a's and m of the b's are different from zero, show that the classical value of the internal energy of the assembly is $\frac{1}{2}(l+m)kT$, per system.

2. Prove that for a [1]-harmonic oscillator, of classical frequency ν, the area of phase space which corresponds to classical motion with energy less than or equal to ϵ is given by ϵ/ν. Hence show that the quantally allowed energies subdivide phase space into regions of area h.

3. In terms of spherical polar coordinates (Fig. 5, p. 56), the kinetic energy of a particle of mass m is given by

$$\epsilon(r, \theta, \phi, p_r, p_\theta, p_\phi) = \frac{1}{2m}\left(p_r^2 + \frac{1}{r^2}p_\theta^2 + \frac{1}{r^2\sin^2\theta}p_\phi^2\right).$$

Evaluate the phase integral, and show that the classical expression for the partition function of such a system confined to a spherical box of radius a is given by

$$\left(\frac{2\pi mkT}{h^2}\right)^{\frac{3}{2}}V \quad \text{where} \quad V = \frac{4\pi}{3}a^3.$$

INTERNAL DISTRIBUTION FUNCTIONS

1. In the main, we have so far been content with evaluating, for any particular assembly, $\Omega(E, V, N)$, from which we have deduced $S(E, V, N)$ and thence calculated such other macroscopically measurable quantities as C_v or P.

> That in practice we have more often merely constructed the partition function, (p.f.), and thence found $F(T, V, N)$, does not invalidate this statement. For T was originally a complicated function of E, V, and N, which we identified with the temperature on account of the thermodynamic properties of S. Proceeding straight to the partition function is simply a practical short cut by which we can avoid working through the full details of the general theory in any particular case.

Now if we examine either the quantal or the classical formulation carefully (and we revert to quantal terminology for the general discussion) we shall find that we have really made no use at all of that part of our fundamental assumption—(a) or (b) of Chapter II—which said that all distinguishable stationary quantal states, corresponding to given values of E, V, and N, were to be treated as *a priori equally probable*. In doing what we have done so far we might equally well have just considered $\Omega(E, V, N)$—as a certain number or, more strictly, as a function of E, V, and N— and, by investigating the properties of $S(E, V, N)$ on the assumption that $S = k \ln \Omega$, we should have been led to the pragmatic belief that this provided the proper link between the microscopic and the macroscopic properties of the assembly. Why then, in framing our fundamental quantal assumption in Chapter II (and in discussing the classical analogue of this in Chapter IV) did we include the hypothesis that any two distinguishable microscopic states of the assembly were *a priori* equally probable?

Anything like the full answer to this must be reserved till we are in a better position to appreciate what is involved: see the final chapter. But an important partial answer can be given at once and has, indeed, already been indicated in paragraph 3 of Chapter III. And it is to the fuller elaboration of the discussion there given, with some applications to particular problems, that we must now proceed.

We have obtained the equations

$$n_i^* = N \frac{\omega_i e^{-\epsilon_i/kT}}{\sum_i \omega_i e^{-\epsilon_i/kT}} \quad (i = 1, 2, ...) \tag{1}$$

for the important values of the distribution numbers, n_1, n_2,..., n_i,.... Since the distribution numbers satisfy the restrictive conditions

$$\sum_i n_i = N,$$

$$\sum_i n_i \epsilon_i = E$$

this is true also of their important values, n_1^*, n_2^*,..., n_i^*,..., i.e. we have

$$\sum_i n_i^* = N, \tag{2}$$

$$\sum_i n_i^* \epsilon_i = E. \tag{3}$$

Indeed it was from equations (1) and (3) that we first calculated E, as a function of T, V, and N, for an actual assembly.

Now, as we discussed in paragraph 3 of Chapter II, the important values of the distribution numbers, n_1^*, n_2^*,..., n_i^*,..., are, by definition, such that there are overwhelmingly more distinct microscopic states of the assembly corresponding to this particular set† of distribution numbers than there are for all other possible sets of distribution numbers put together. Therefore, *if* all distinct microscopic states of the assembly are *a priori* equally probable, it is overwhelmingly more likely that the assembly (when it is in the condition of thermodynamical equilibrium at temperature T) is in a state specified by the distribution numbers n_1^*, n_2^*,..., n_i^*,... than that it is in a state specified by any other set of distribution numbers. And this has given a *real*, rather than a purely *mathematical*, meaning to the numbers n_1^*, n_2^*,..., n_i^*,....

In fact if we could *measure* the number of systems in the assembly with energy ϵ_i we should, if the argument above is correct, expect to find the value n_i^*. For states in which the distribution numbers are n_1^*, n_2^*,..., n_i^*,... are, on this argument, overwhelmingly the most probable. Actually, of course, no physical

† Or only negligible deviations from it.

observation is completely instantaneous, and what we should really measure is some kind of time average of n_i: but this only strengthens the importance of the numbers n_i^* as far as physical measurements are concerned. For during the small but finite time of an experiment we shall expect the assembly to be overwhelmingly most often in states corresponding to $n_i = n_i^*$ even if instantaneously we might hit on one of the very unlikely microscopic states for which n_i has a value other than n_i^*.

Consequently the statistical mechanics based on the fundamental assumptions we have made not only enables us to predict the macroscopic thermodynamic properties of the assembly but also to predict all measurable *internal distribution functions* determined by the equilibrium distribution numbers, $n_1^*, n_2^*,..., n_i^*,...$. In the sequel we shall frequently have occasion to refer to such internal distribution functions, and we shall now illustrate the use thus made of equation (1) by considering two of the most important of such applications. Once again we must, for the present, regard agreement between prediction and observation as providing an *a posteriori* justification of the validity of our basic assumptions.

2. The first problem we shall consider concerns the equilibrium distribution of energy among the systems of an assembly of N [1]-oscillators. It does not matter whether the oscillators are localized or not; in either case we have

$$n_i^* = N \frac{e^{-(n+\frac{1}{2})h\nu/kT}}{\sum\limits_{n=0}^{\infty} e^{-(n+\frac{1}{2})h\nu/kT}} \quad \text{(see equation (29) of} \\ \text{Chapter II).}$$

The suffix i, which numbers the energy levels 1, 2, 3,...., is, of course, equal to $n+1$, n being the quantum number which runs from 0, 1,... up to ∞.

On simplification, this becomes

$$n_i^* = N \frac{e^{-nh\nu/kT}}{\sum\limits_{n=0}^{\infty} e^{-nh\nu/kT}}$$

$$= N \frac{e^{-nh\nu/kT}}{(1-e^{-h\nu/kT})^{-1}},$$

or $\qquad n_{\epsilon=(n+\frac{1}{2})h\nu}^* = N[e^{-nh\nu/kT} - e^{-(n+1)h\nu/kT}].$ $\qquad$ (4)

From (4) we find

$$n_i^* + n_{i+1}^* + n_{i+2}^* + \dots = N[e^{-nh\nu/kT} - e^{-(n+1)h\nu/kT} + e^{-(n+1)h\nu/kT} -$$
$$- e^{-(n+2)h\nu/kT} + e^{-(n+2)h\nu/kT} - \dots]$$
$$= Ne^{-nh\nu/kT}.$$

In other words, the number of oscillators *with energy greater than or equal to* $(n+\tfrac{1}{2})h\nu$ is given by

$$N_{\epsilon \geqslant (n+\frac{1}{2})h\nu}^* = Ne^{-nh\nu/kT}. \qquad (5)$$

Fig. 7 shows the graph of equation (5). It is evident from equation (4) that a plot of $n_{\epsilon = (n+\frac{1}{2})h\nu}^*$ has precisely the same form, every ordinate being then reduced by multiplication by the extra, uniform, factor

$$(1 - e^{-h\nu/kT}).$$

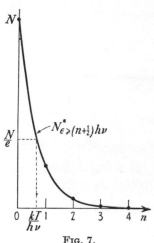

FIG. 7.

The corresponding classical analogues of equations (4) and (5) are likewise easily determined. Starting now with equations (23) and (10) of Chapter IV we have

$$n^*(x, p_x) = \frac{Ne^{-\epsilon(x,p_x)/kT}}{\underset{\text{(phase space)}}{\iint} e^{-\epsilon(x,p_x)/kT} \, dx dp_x}$$
$$= \frac{\nu}{kT} Ne^{-\epsilon(x,p_x)/kT}.$$

But the classical interpretation of $n^*(x, p_x)$ is simply that $n^*(x, p_x)\delta x \delta p_x$ is the equilibrium number of systems whose representative points lie in the small regions $(x, x+\delta x; \ p_x, p_x+\delta p_x)$ of their respective phase spaces (thinking of a separate phase space for each system). Consequently if we ask, What is the number of systems with energy between ϵ and $\epsilon+\delta\epsilon$, the answer is given by

$$\frac{\nu}{kT} Ne^{-\epsilon/kT} \delta A,$$

where $\delta A =$ area of phase space corresponding to energy between ϵ and $\epsilon + \delta\epsilon$.

It is convenient to denote this number by $n^*(\epsilon)\,\delta\epsilon$, and so we have

$$n^*(\epsilon)\,\delta\epsilon = \frac{\nu}{kT}Ne^{-\epsilon/kT}\,\delta A.$$

It can, however, be shown without difficulty (by considering the ellipses in phase space which correspond to constant energy) that†

$$\delta A = \frac{\delta\epsilon}{\nu}.$$

Therefore
$$n^*(\epsilon)\,\delta\epsilon = \frac{\nu}{kT}Ne^{-\epsilon/kT}\frac{\delta\epsilon}{\nu},$$

i.e.
$$n^*(\epsilon) = \frac{N}{kT}e^{-\epsilon/kT}. \tag{6}$$

Equation (6) is the classical analogue of (4). The classical analogue of (5) is immediately deduced from it. For if $N^*(\epsilon)$ denotes the equilibrium number of systems *with energy greater than or equal to ϵ*, we have

$$N^*(\epsilon) = \int\limits_{\epsilon}^{\infty} n^*(\epsilon)\,d\epsilon$$

$$= \frac{N}{kT}[-kTe^{-\epsilon/kT}]_{\epsilon}^{\infty},$$

i.e.
$$N^*(\epsilon) = Ne^{-\epsilon/kT}. \tag{7}$$

Comparison of (5) and (7) (or of (4) and (6)) shows that the sole differences between the quantal and classical formulae are those arising from

(i) the quantal zero-point energy,

(ii) the fact that quantally the energy is defined only for integer values of n.

It is just these novel quantal features, of course, and in particular (ii) above, which produce the marked differences in the quantal and classical formulae for E and C_v as functions of temperature—as we have already seen.

The above equations, (4)–(7), for the internal distributive properties describing the equilibrium condition of an assembly of

---

† A rather sophisticated proof is as follows: Quantally $\delta\epsilon = h\nu\,\delta n$, where δn is the number of quantal levels in the energy range $\delta\epsilon$. Also, by our theorem in Chapter IV, $\delta A = h\,\delta n$. Therefore $\delta A = \delta\epsilon/\nu$.

N [1]-oscillators have an important place in certain theories of reaction kinetics. It is necessary that the reader should recognize (despite the functional simplicity of equation (7)) that they apply only to an assembly of simple harmonic oscillators.

3. As the second illustration of the use of equation (1), or its classical analogue, to determine the internal distributive properties of an assembly, we shall derive Maxwell's famous law for the distribution of velocities among the systems of a perfect gas (proposed by Maxwell, 1859; proved by Boltzmann, 1896).

According to equation (23) of Chapter IV, and the work in paragraph 4 of that chapter, we have at once

$$n^*(x,y,z,p_x,p_y,p_z) = N\frac{e^{-(p_x^2+p_y^2+p_z^2)/2mkT}}{V(2\pi mkT)^{\frac{3}{2}}}.$$

This shows, as is physically self-evident, that $n^*(x,y,z,p_x,p_y,p_z)$ is independent of x, y, and z. There is no tendency for the systems to prefer any particular position in the assembly to any other position in the assembly. Consequently if

$$n^*(p_x,p_y,p_z)\,\delta p_x\delta p_y\delta p_z$$

denotes the number of systems having momenta in the ranges $(p_x,p_x+\delta p_x)$, $(p_y,p_y+\delta p_y)$, $(p_z,\,p_z+\delta p_z)$, we have

$$n^*(p_x,p_y,p_z) = \iiint n^*(x,y,z,p_x,p_y,p_z)\,dxdydz$$

$$= N\frac{e^{-(p_x^2+p_y^2+p_z^2)/2mkT}}{(2\pi mkT)^{\frac{3}{2}}}. \tag{8}$$

Now the r.h.s. of (8) depends only on $p^2 \equiv p_x^2+p_y^2+p_z^2$, i.e. on the total momentum p (= mv, where v is the actual, resultant, velocity of a system). But if $n^*(p)\,\delta p$ is the number of systems with momentum between p and $p+\delta p$, and $n^*(p_x,p_y,p_z)$ depends only on p, then

$$n^*(p)\,\delta p = 4\pi p^2 n^*(p_x,p_y,p_z)\,\delta p$$

[for, in polar coordinates,

$$\delta p_x\delta p_y\delta p_z = p^2\sin\theta\,\,\delta\theta\delta\phi\delta p$$

and θ and ϕ can have any values between 0 and π, and 0 and 2π, respectively]. Therefore

$$n^*(p) = N\frac{4\pi p^2 e^{-p^2/2mkT}}{(2\pi mkT)^{\frac{3}{2}}}.$$

Moreover,

$n^*(p)\,\delta p = $ number of systems with momentum between p and $p+\delta p$,

$=$ number of systems with velocity between v and $v+\delta v$,

which we denote by $n^*(v)\,\delta v$.

Therefore,

$$n^*(v)\,\delta v = N\frac{4\pi p^2 e^{-p^2/2mkT}}{(2\pi mkT)^{\frac{3}{2}}}\,\delta p$$

$$= N\frac{4\pi m^2 v^2 e^{-mv^2/2kT}}{(2\pi mkT)^{\frac{3}{2}}}\,m\,\delta v$$

$$= N\frac{4m^{\frac{3}{2}}}{\pi^{\frac{1}{2}}(2kT)^{\frac{3}{2}}}e^{-mv^2/2kT}\,v^2\,\delta v$$

or
$$n^*(v) = N\frac{4m^{\frac{3}{2}}v^2}{\pi^{\frac{1}{2}}(2kT)^{\frac{3}{2}}}e^{-mv^2/2kT}, \tag{9}$$

which is the Maxwell–Boltzmann law.

Like the formulae of the last paragraph, equation (9) plays an important part in the kinetic theory of reaction rates: but such applications to non-equilibrium assemblies are outside the scope of this book.

4. In so far as it provides an experimental check on such calculations of internal distribution functions, a brief account of the theory of the broadening of spectral lines by the well-known Doppler effect may, perhaps, suitably be inserted here.

According to the general properties of wave-motion, an atom (or other system) emitting light of wave-length λ_0 will, if it be moving with velocity v_x away from the observer, appear to be emitting light of wave-length

$$\lambda = \lambda_0\left(1+\frac{v_x}{c}\right) \tag{10}$$

where c is the velocity of light. The effect is known as the Doppler effect, and has application to all types of wave motion. Doppler was himself concerned with the apparent colour of receding stars.

If, then, we observe the spectrum of a glowing gas in the way shown diagrammatically in Fig. 8, we shall expect to receive light of wave-length given by equation (10) from each atom whose x-velocity is v_x. Now, if the gas is in thermodynamic equilibrium

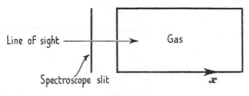

Line of sight

Gas

Spectroscope slit

x

FIG. 8.

at temperature T, the number of atoms for which the x-velocity lies between v_x and $v_x + \delta v_x$, is found from equation (8) above to be

$$n^*(v_x)\,\delta v_x = n^*(p_x)\,\delta p_x = \int_{-\infty}^{\infty}\int_{-\infty}^{\infty} n^*(p_x,p_y,p_z)\,dp_y\,dp_z\,\delta p_x$$

$$= \frac{Ne^{-p_x^2/2mkT}}{\sqrt{(2\pi mkT)}}\,\delta p_x$$

$$= \frac{mNe^{-mv_x^2/2kT}}{\sqrt{(2\pi mkT)}}\,\delta v_x,$$

i.e.
$$n^*(v_x) = n^*(0)e^{-mv_x^2/2kT} \tag{11}$$

where $n^*(0)$ is the value of $n^*(v_x)$ for $v_x = 0$.

But, from equation (10), v_x is given by

$$v_x = c\frac{(\lambda-\lambda_0)}{\lambda_0}$$

and therefore (11) may be written

$$n^*(\lambda) = n^*(\lambda_0)e^{-mc^2(\lambda-\lambda_0)^2/2\lambda_0^2 kT} \tag{12}$$

where replacing $n^*(v_x)$ by $n^*(\lambda)$ reminds us that every atom with x-velocity v_x appears to be emitting light of wave-length λ. Consequently, in terms of the intensity of light received by the spectroscope,

$$I(\lambda) = I(\lambda_0)e^{-mc^2(\lambda-\lambda_0)^2/2\lambda_0^2 kT}. \tag{12'}$$

Therefore, in so far as the width of the spectral line is due to the Doppler effect, the 'shape' of the spectral line will be that of Fig. 9; and a plot of $\ln I$ against $(\lambda - \lambda_0)^2$ will yield a straight line of slope $-mc^2/2\lambda_0^2 kT$.

In practice, of course, the shape of a spectral line depends on other factors besides Doppler broadening; but it has proved pos-

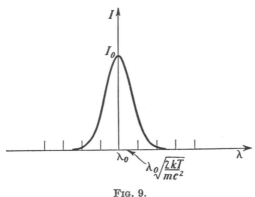

Fig. 9.

sible in some cases to disentangle the specific Doppler effect, and thus to obtain a very nice verification of the underlying statistical distribution formulae.

5. Before leaving this discussion of internal distribution functions and proceeding to further thermodynamic applications of our basic statistical formulae, there is one general theorem concerned with internal distribution functions which we must next prove. Its proof depends on the important *factorization property* of partition functions, to which we have not yet referred. Suppose that an assembly consists of N independent systems, each of which is capable of possessing quanta (classically: amounts) of different types of energy. For instance, in a gas of systems each of which is a simple harmonic oscillator each system can possess independent amounts of translational and vibrational energy.† We can express this quite generally by writing, for the energy of any system

$$\epsilon = \epsilon' + \epsilon'' + \epsilon''' + \dots.$$

† And also rotational energy, but we shall not be concerned with this till the next chapter.

If the various types of energy, denoted by ϵ', ϵ'', ϵ''',..., are quantized, then

$$\epsilon' \text{ can have values } \epsilon_1', \epsilon_2', ..., \epsilon_i', ...$$
$$\epsilon'' \text{ can have values } \epsilon_1'', \epsilon_2'', ..., \epsilon_i'', ...$$
$$\epsilon''' \text{ can have values } \epsilon_1''', \epsilon_2''', ..., \epsilon_i''', ...$$

and so on; and the permissible values of ϵ are given by

$$\epsilon_{i,j,k,...} = \epsilon_i' + \epsilon_j'' + \epsilon_k''' + ...$$

To simplify the discussion we shall suppose that all the degeneracy factors are unity.† Then

$$\begin{aligned}
\text{(p.f.)} &= \sum_{i,j,k,...} e^{-\epsilon_{i,j,k,...}/kT} = \sum_{i,j,k,...} e^{-(\epsilon_i' + \epsilon_j'' + \epsilon_k''' + ...)/kT} \\
&= \sum_i e^{-\epsilon_i'/kT} \sum_j e^{-\epsilon_j''/kT} \sum_k e^{-\epsilon_k'''/kT} ... \\
&= \text{(p.f.)}' \, \text{(p.f.)}'' \, \text{(p.f.)}''' ...,
\end{aligned} \tag{13}$$

i.e. the partition function for any one system is simply the *product* of partition functions for each separate kind of independent energy. This is the important factorization property of partition functions which we have just mentioned.

In considering the bearing of this factorization property on the general theory of internal distribution functions we may, for definiteness and without loss of generality, suppose that each system is capable of just three kinds of energy, denoted by ϵ', ϵ'', and ϵ'''. Then, by equation (1),

$$n_{i,j,k}^* = N \frac{e^{-\epsilon_{i,j,k}/kT}}{\sum\limits_{i,j,k} e^{-\epsilon_{i,j,k}/kT}} = N \frac{e^{-(\epsilon_i' + \epsilon_j'' + \epsilon_k''')/kT}}{\text{(p.f.)}} \tag{14}$$

and, of course, $n_{i,j,k}^*$ is the equilibrium number of systems for which the energy of type ϵ' has the value ϵ_i', the energy of type ϵ'' has the value ϵ_j'', and the energy of type ϵ''' has the value ϵ_k'''.

From equations (13) and (14) we deduce

$$\begin{aligned}
n_{i,j,.}^* &\equiv \sum_k n_{i,j,k}^* = N \frac{e^{-(\epsilon_i' + \epsilon_j'')/kT} \sum\limits_k e^{-\epsilon_k'''/kT}}{\text{(p.f.)}' \, \text{(p.f.)}'' \, \text{(p.f.)}'''} \\
&= N \frac{e^{-(\epsilon_i' + \epsilon_j'')/kT}}{\text{(p.f.)}' \, \text{(p.f.)}''},
\end{aligned} \tag{15}$$

where, of course, $n_{i,j,.}^*$ has the physical meaning that it gives the

---

† Their inclusion, however, does not affect the result in any way.

equilibrium number of systems for which ϵ' has the value ϵ_i', ϵ'' has the value ϵ_j'', while ϵ''' has any value of which it is capable.

In the same way,

$$n_{i,.,.}^* \equiv \sum_j n_{i,j,.}^* = N\frac{e^{-\epsilon_i'/kT}\sum_j e^{-\epsilon_j''/kT}}{(\text{p.f.})'\,(\text{p.f.})''}$$

$$= N\frac{e^{-\epsilon_i'/kT}}{(\text{p.f.})'}, \tag{16}$$

$n_{i,.,.}^*$ having the physical meaning that it gives the equilibrium number of systems for which ϵ' has the value ϵ_i', ϵ'' and ϵ''' having any values of which they are capable.

The quantities $n_{i,.,k}^*$, $n_{.,j,k}^*$, $n_{.,j,.}^*$ and $n_{.,.,k}^*$ can be defined and calculated in precisely the same way. In particular we find

$$n_{.,j,.}^* = N\frac{e^{-\epsilon_j''/kT}}{(\text{p.f.})''}. \tag{17}$$

From these results two important conclusions follow.

First, if we are interested in the internal distribution of any particular type of energy, say ϵ', we can omit all reference to the other and independent energies ϵ'' and ϵ'''. Equation (16) shows that the equation for $n_{i,.,.}^*$ is of the form of the equation for n_i^* in an assembly each system of which is capable simply of having the energies ϵ_1', ϵ_2', ϵ_3',..., ϵ_i',.... It is, of course, for this reason that in discussing the distribution of energy among an assembly of harmonic oscillators we were able to say that it was immaterial whether the systems were localized or non-localized. If they are non-localized they must, of course, be capable of translational as well as vibrational energy: but in discussing the equilibrium distribution of vibrational energy we can omit all reference to the simultaneous distribution of translational energy.

Secondly, comparison of (15), (16) and (17) shows that

$$\frac{n_{i,j,.}^*}{N} = \frac{n_{i,.,.}^*}{N}\frac{n_{.,j,.}^*}{N}. \tag{18}$$

Now $n_{i,j,.}^*/N$ may be regarded as the probability that any particular system has an amount ϵ_i' of energy of type ϵ' together with an amount ϵ_j'' of energy of type ϵ''—its energy of type ϵ''' being quite unspecified. For $n_{i,j,.}^*$ is the equilibrium number of such systems, and N is the total number of systems, in any state whatever, in the assembly. Similarly $n^*_{i,\ldots}/N$ may be regarded as the probability that any particular system has an amount ϵ'_i of energy of type ϵ'—there being no specification of its energies of types ϵ'' and ϵ'''. Thus equation (18) is capable of the verbal interpretation: *the probability that a given system has, simultaneously, specified values of two independent characteristics is the product of the probabilities that it has the given values of those two characteristics treated separately*. Evidently a complete proof of this would require the inclusion of the degeneracy, or weight, factors, ω. The argument is then slightly more elaborate, but its sequence and the final result are essentially unchanged.

Moreover, since
$$\frac{n^*_i}{n^*_j} = \frac{\omega_i\, e^{-\epsilon_i/kT}}{\omega_j\, e^{-\epsilon_j/kT}}$$

(returning for the moment to a less detailed notation) we may likewise say that, for any system, *the various terms of a partition function are proportional to the probabilities of the various states to which they refer*. And for the same reason any one such term, i.e. $\omega_i\, e^{-\epsilon_i/kT}$, is sometimes rather loosely referred to as the *relative probability* of the state, or set of states, to which it relates.

EXAMPLES

1. Show that, in the notation of §2 above, for an assembly of N [2]-oscillators (see example 5 of Chapter II)
$$N^*_{\epsilon \geqslant (n+1)h\nu} = N[(n+1)e^{-nh\nu/kT} - ne^{-(n+1)h\nu/kT}].$$

2. Similarly, for an assembly of N [3]-oscillators (see §7, Chapter II) show that
$$N^*_{\epsilon \geqslant (n+\frac{3}{2})h\nu} = N[\tfrac{1}{2}(n+1)(n+2)e^{-nh\nu/kT} - n(n+2)e^{-(n+1)h\nu/kT} +$$
$$+ \tfrac{1}{2}n(n+1)e^{-(n+2)h\nu/kT}].$$

3. Starting with the quantal formulae, prove that when $h\nu/kT$ is small
$$n^*(\epsilon) = \frac{N}{kT}\left(\frac{\epsilon}{kT}\right)e^{-\epsilon/kT}, \qquad \text{for a [2]-oscillator,}$$

and
$$n^*(\epsilon) = \frac{N}{2kT}\left(\frac{\epsilon}{kT}\right)^2 e^{-\epsilon/kT} \qquad \text{for a [3]-oscillator.}$$

(These classical formulae are the direct analogues of equation (6).)

4. Use equation (9) to prove that the average kinetic energy of a system within a perfect gas of structureless particles is given by $\tfrac{3}{2}kT$.

5. Use equation (9) to prove that the greatest value of $n^*(v)$ occurs when $\tfrac{1}{2}mv^2 = kT$.

THE SPECIFIC HEAT OF A DIATOMIC GAS

1. The foregoing chapters have been concerned much more with developing the tools of statistical mechanics than with using them. It is, indeed, the main purpose of this book to deal in an introductory way with the methods and techniques of statistical mechanics rather than to provide a summary of all of even the simplest results which follow when these techniques are applied to specific assemblies. But certain of these specific results of statistical theory are so fundamentally important in theoretical chemistry that it is essential, if we are to appreciate the part played by statistical mechanics in the interpretation of experimental data, that we should examine some of them more particularly. So far we have dealt in detail with the thermodynamic properties of only an idealized (Einstein) crystal and an ideal monatomic gas. This and the immediately following chapters, up to Chapter XI, will be primarily concerned with further applications to other, chiefly gaseous, assemblies. They will add little or nothing to the corpus of general statistical theory so far derived, but will emphasize and illustrate the practical importance of the preceding formulae.

The theory of the specific heat, and other thermodynamic properties, of a diatomic, or polyatomic, gas makes use of the factorization property of partition functions demonstrated at the end of Chapter V. We shall confine attention here to diatomic gases and shall, of course, consider both classical and quantal theories of their thermodynamic properties, contrasting their respective predictions. This time, however, we shall consider the predictions of classical dynamics first and then, secondly, give the corresponding quantal formulae.

A diatomic molecule, AB, may be thought of as two atomic centres, A and B, so bound together, by covalent or ionic binding, that they are at a distance r_0 apart. The atomic centre A differs from the corresponding atom A in its electronic distribution (due to the presence of B), and vice versa, but essentially the atomic centres A and B have the masses, m_A and m_B, of the corresponding atoms. Moreover, of course, the interatomic distance, r, is not rigidly fixed at the value r_0. The atoms move in a mutual potential field $V(r)$, Fig. 10, and r_0 is just that separation of A and B which corresponds to minimum potential energy. Any other value of r corresponds to a positive potential energy of distortion, $V(r)$.

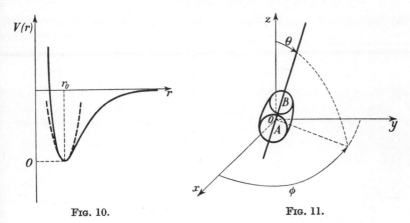

FIG. 10.   FIG. 11.

Relative to fixed Cartesian axes through their common mass-centre, O, the positions of A and B are completely determined by r (the distance AB) and the polar angles θ and ϕ, Fig. 11. And, according to general dynamical theory, the kinetic energy of the whole, diatomic, system is simply the sum of

(i) the kinetic energy of the whole mass, $m_A + m_B$, moving with the velocity of the centre of mass, O, and

(ii) the kinetic energy of the motion relative to the centre of mass.

Now the potential energy, $V(r)$, depends only on the 'internal' coordinate, r; consequently, and quite generally, for any system

$$\epsilon = \epsilon_{\text{trans}} + \epsilon_{\text{int}} \tag{1}$$

where ϵ_{trans} = kinetic energy of translational motion (of the mass of the whole system concentrated at its mass-centre)

and ϵ_{int} = energy of the internal motion of a system, relative to its mass-centre.

Moreover, as we see from Fig. 11, the internal configuration of the molecule, i.e. its configuration relative to fixed axes through its mass-centre, is specified by

> (i) the orientation of AB in space (given by the angles θ and ϕ)

and   (ii) the length of AB (given by r).

If, dynamically, these vary independently, we call the first motion, i.e. that concerned with changes in the orientation of AB, *rotational*, and the second motion, i.e. that concerned with changes in the length of AB, we call *vibrational*. In order that these two motions may be regarded as independent it is necessary that the centrifugal force due to rotation should not have an appreciable effect on the vibrations and, conversely, that vibrational fluctuations in r should not appreciably affect the moment of inertia of the 'rotating' system. This is generally true, or very approximately true, for diatomic molecules, and we shall proceed on this assumption. Then, for independent rotation and vibration,

$$\epsilon_{int} = \epsilon_{rot} + \epsilon_{vib}$$

and, therefore, $\epsilon = \epsilon_{trans} + \epsilon_{rot} + \epsilon_{vib}.$ (2)

Consequently, for such a diatomic system, by the theorem at the end of Chapter V,

$$(p.f.) = (p.f.)_{trans}(p.f.)_{rot}(p.f.)_{vib}.$$ (3)

Now we have already, effectively, evaluated $(p.f.)_{trans}$, for this is simply the partition function for the translational motion of a system of mass $m_A + m_B$ confined to a volume V, i.e.

$$(p.f.)_{trans} = \left(\frac{2\pi(m_A + m_B)kT}{h^2}\right)^{\frac{3}{2}}V.$$ (4)

Also, for the vibrational partition function, $(p.f.)_{vib}$, we may use the expression already obtained for a simple harmonic oscillator (provided that the vibrations of the diatomic molecule are sufficiently small). This is equivalent, of course, to replacing the curve $V(r)$ by a parabola, see Fig. 10, and rules out, for instance, the possibility of thermal decomposition. But generally if it is permissible to separate out $(p.f.)_{rot}$ and $(p.f.)_{vib}$ it is permissible also to suppose that the vibrations occur only at the bottom of the curve $V(r)$ and may be treated as simple harmonic vibrations. Consequently, according to classical dynamics,

$$(\text{p.f.})_{\text{vib}} = \frac{kT}{h\nu},\tag{5}$$

where ν is the vibration frequency.

The only part† of the partition function for a diatomic molecule which has yet to be evaluated is the rotational part, $(\text{p.f.})_{\text{rot}}$, and to the evaluation of this on the basis of classical dynamics we now turn.

2. In calculating $(\text{p.f.})_{\text{rot}}$ we shall have to take the dynamics on trust, but if p_θ and p_ϕ are the momenta conjugate to θ and ϕ, it is not difficult to show that the classical rotational energy is given by

$$\epsilon = \frac{1}{2A}\left(p_\theta^2 + \frac{1}{\sin^2\theta}p_\phi^2\right),\tag{6}$$

where A is the moment of inertia of the molecule about an axis perpendicular to its length and through its centre of mass. In terms of m_A, m_B, and r_0, in fact,

$$A = \frac{m_A m_B}{m_A + m_B}\,r_0^2,$$

but we shall continue to use the less explicit symbol, A, for this moment of inertia.

Consequently, according to the general theory,

$$(\text{p.f.})_{\text{rot}} = \frac{1}{h^2}\int_0^{2\pi}\int_0^{\pi}\int_{-\infty}^{\infty}\int_{-\infty}^{\infty}\exp\left\{-\left(p_\theta^2 + \frac{1}{\sin^2\theta}p_\phi^2\right)\Big/2AkT\right\}dp_\theta\,dp_\phi\,d\theta d\phi,\tag{7}$$

for the momenta, p_θ and p_ϕ, can take any values between $-\infty$ and $+\infty$ while all spacial configurations of AB are covered if θ runs from 0 to π while ϕ runs from 0 to 2π (the reader should convince himself of this).

Now there is a slight difficulty in the general use of equation (7): for though the r.h.s. of (7) is perfectly correct for an unsymmetrical AB molecule like HCl, when the two ends of the molecule

---

† The possibility of an 'electronic' contribution is discussed briefly in paragraph 6 below.

are indentical, as for H_2 say, the spacial configurations corresponding to $0 \leqslant \theta \leqslant \frac{1}{2}\pi$ are indistinguishable from (i.e. identical with) the spacial configurations which correspond to $\frac{1}{2}\pi \leqslant \theta \leqslant \pi$. Therefore, since it is a general rule that only distinguishable configurations are enumerated, in the case of AA molecules we have either to restrict the range of θ to $0 \leqslant \theta \leqslant \frac{1}{2}\pi$ or to divide the r.h.s. of (7) by 2. It is customary, in order to preserve complete generality in equation (7) to write

$$(\text{p.f.})_{\text{rot}} = \frac{1}{h^2\sigma} \int\limits_0^{2\pi}\int\limits_0^{\pi} \int\limits_{-\infty}^{\infty} \int\limits_{-\infty}^{\infty} \exp\left\{-\left(p_\theta^2 + \frac{1}{\sin^2\theta}p_\phi^2\right)\middle/ 2AkT\right\} dp_\theta\, dp_\phi\, d\theta d\phi,$$

$$(7')$$

where σ is called a *symmetry factor*. σ has the value 1 when the ends of the diatomic molecule are unlike (e.g. HCl) and the value 2 when the ends of the molecule are alike (e.g. H_2). Equation (7') thus formally embraces both possibilities. A symmetry factor such as σ, however, being temperature-independent, does not enter into the expression derived from the partition function for the specific heat of the assembly.

The phase integral is easily evaluated by mathematics with which we are already familiar: the ϕ-integration can be performed at once to give

$$(\text{p.f.})_{\text{rot}} = \frac{2\pi}{h^2\sigma} \int\limits_0^{\pi} \int\limits_{-\infty}^{\infty} \int\limits_{-\infty}^{\infty} \exp\left\{-\left(p_\theta^2 + \frac{1}{\sin^2\theta}p_\phi^2\right)\middle/ 2AkT\right\} dp_\theta\, dp_\phi\, d\theta,$$

and now, integrating successively w.r.t. p_θ, p_ϕ, and θ, we obtain

$$(\text{p.f.})_{\text{rot}} = \frac{2\pi}{h^2\sigma}\sqrt{(2\pi AkT)} \int\limits_0^{\pi} \int\limits_{-\infty}^{\infty} e^{-p_\phi^2/2AkT\sin^2\theta}\, dp_\phi\, d\theta$$

$$= \frac{2\pi}{h^2\sigma}\sqrt{(2\pi AkT)}\sqrt{(2\pi AkT)} \int\limits_0^{\pi} \sin\theta\, d\theta,$$

i.e. $$(\text{p.f.})_{\text{rot}} = \frac{8\pi^2 AkT}{h^2\sigma}. \qquad (8)$$

Equation (8) gives us then the classical expression for the rotational partition function for a diatomic molecule.

3. Grouping together equations (4), (5), and (8) we have, for a diatomic molecule according to classical dynamics,

$$
\left.
\begin{aligned}
(\text{p.f.})_{\text{trans}} &= \left(\frac{2\pi(m_A+m_B)kT}{h^2}\right)^{\frac{3}{2}}V \\[2mm]
(\text{p.f.})_{\text{vib}} &= \frac{kT}{h\nu} \\[2mm]
(\text{p.f.})_{\text{rot}} &= \frac{8\pi^2 AkT}{h^2\sigma}
\end{aligned}
\right\}
\tag{C}
$$

and from these expressions we can immediately derive the specific heat or any other thermodynamic property of the gaseous assembly that we may require. We shall confine attention to the specific heat.

Since

$$ E = -T^2\frac{\partial}{\partial T}\left(\frac{F}{T}\right)_V \quad \text{(Gibbs–Helmholtz)} $$

and $F = -kT\ln[(\text{p.f.})^N/N!]$ (gaseous assembly),

we have

$$ E = NkT^2\frac{\partial}{\partial T}\ln(\text{p.f.}) $$

$$ = NkT^2\frac{\partial}{\partial T}[\ln(\text{p.f.})_{\text{trans}}+\ln(\text{p.f.})_{\text{vib}}+\ln(\text{p.f.})_{\text{rot}}] $$

$$ = E_{\text{trans}}+E_{\text{vib}}+E_{\text{rot}}, $$

where

$$ E_{\text{trans}} = NkT^2\frac{\partial}{\partial T}\ln\left[\left(\frac{2\pi(m_A+m_B)kT}{h^2}\right)^{\frac{3}{2}}V\right] = \tfrac{3}{2}NkT, $$

$$ E_{\text{vib}} = NkT^2\frac{\partial}{\partial T}\ln\frac{kT}{h\nu} = NkT, $$

and $E_{\text{rot}} = NkT^2\dfrac{\partial}{\partial T}\ln\dfrac{8\pi^2 AkT}{h^2\sigma} = NkT.$

Consequently $E = \tfrac{7}{2}NkT$

and $C_v = \left(\dfrac{\partial E}{\partial T}\right)_V = \tfrac{7}{2}Nk$ or $\tfrac{7}{2}R$, per mole.   (9)

Also, since $C_p = C_v + R$, per mole   (thermodynamically),

we have $C_p = \tfrac{9}{2}R$, per mole   (10)

and $\gamma = C_p/C_v = \tfrac{9}{7} = 1\cdot286.$ (11)

Such then is the classical theory of the specific heat of a diatomic gas. We notice, first, that the general classical theorem that a contribution of $\frac{1}{2}kT$ to E derives from each 'squared' term in the expression for the energy of the assembly is again exemplified. Secondly, however, we must observe that the result, equation (9), (10), or (11) is *not* in good agreement with experiment. Fig. 12

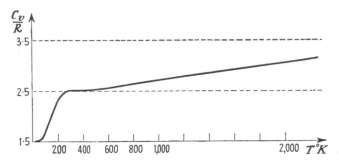

FIG. 12. Specific heat of H_2, per mole.

shows the experimentally determined value of C_v for diatomic hydrogen over a fairly extensive range of temperature. In general shape (i.e. with an appropriate distortion of the temperature scale) the curve is typical of that observed for all diatomic gases except that

(i) the drop from 2·5 to 1·5 has been observed only for H_2, D_2, and HD (though there is every reason to believe that it will always occur at a sufficiently low temperature) and

(ii) the drop from 3·5 to 2·5 is generally sharper than for H_2 (the reason being that for H_2 the fundamental vibration frequency is very high: also for H_2 the rotational and vibrational energies are not strictly separable).

We see that we have, just as in the former case of a simple crystalline solid, a temperature-dependent C_v which is not explicable on the basis of classical dynamics: though the 'high-temperature' specific heat is again given correctly by the classical theory. This suggests that a statistical theory based on quantum mechanics is again required, and to the development of this we now turn.

4. Assuming, as in the classical treatment, that the translational, vibrational, and rotational motions may be treated separately, the only new result that we require is the quantal expression for the rotational partition function. The quantal analogues of equations (4) and (5), i.e. of the translational and vibrational factors in the partition function, have been given already when dealing with structureless particles and harmonic oscillators respectively. We shall summarize these results again below, but must first obtain the quantal form of (p.f.)$_{\text{rot}}$—for which the classical expression was obtained in paragraph 2.

According to quantum mechanics, the energies corresponding to the stationary states of a rigid linear rotator having moment of inertia A (about a line perpendicular to its axis and through its centre of mass) are given by

$$\epsilon_j = \frac{h^2}{8\pi^2 A} j(j+1) \quad (j = 0, 1, 2, ...)$$

and the corresponding degeneracies (weights) are given by

$$\omega_j = 2j+1.$$

Consequently we have

$$(\text{p.f.})_{\text{rot}} = \sum_{j=0}^{\infty} (2j+1)e^{-j(j+1)h^2/8\pi^2 AkT} \tag{12}$$

$$= 1 + 3e^{-2\Theta_r/T} + 5e^{-6\Theta_r/T} + ...$$

where

$$\Theta_r \equiv h^2/8\pi^2 Ak. \tag{13}$$

Unfortunately the r.h.s. of (12) cannot be summed explicitly. Several approximate closed expressions have been derived, by Mulholland and others, by which the sum can be replaced in detailed numerical work, but these need not concern us. It is sufficient to notice here that if Θ_r/T is sufficiently small then the r.h.s. of (12) can be replaced by an integral, i.e. on putting $j(j+1) = x$, we can write

$$\sum_{j=0}^{\infty} (2j+1)e^{-j(j+1)\Theta_r/T} = \int_0^{\infty} e^{-x\Theta_r/T}\, dx$$

$$= -\frac{T}{\Theta_r}\left[e^{-x\Theta_r/T}\right]_0^{\infty} = \frac{T}{\Theta_r} = \frac{8\pi^2 AkT}{h^2}, \tag{14}$$

which is precisely the classical expression for (p.f.)$_{\text{rot}}$. Thus, as we should expect, the quantal and classical expressions for (p.f.)$_{rot}$ coincide at sufficiently high temperatures.

At lower temperatures, when Θ_r/T is not so small that the sum can be replaced by an integral, we must resort either to direct numerical computation of the partition function or to use of one of the approximate expressions mentioned, but not particularized,

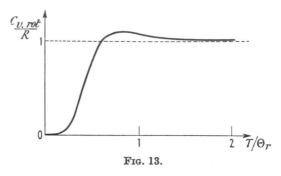

FIG. 13.

above. From (p.f.)$_{rot}$ the rotational contribution to C_v, which we suitably denote by $C_{v,rot}$, is found by means of the formula

$$C_{v,\text{rot}} = \frac{\partial}{\partial T}\left[NkT^2\frac{\partial}{\partial T}\ln(\text{p.f.})_{\text{rot}}\right]. \qquad (15)$$

Now (p.f.)$_{rot}$ depends on T only through the reduced temperature $\tau \equiv T/\Theta_r$. Moreover (15) may be written also in the form

$$C_{v,\text{rot}} = \frac{\partial}{\partial \tau}\left[Nk\tau^2\frac{\partial}{\partial \tau}\ln(\text{p.f.})_{\text{rot}}\right]. \qquad (15')$$

Consequently $C_{v,rot}$ itself depends on T only through the reduced temperature τ, and, furthermore, depends on A, the one relevant characteristic of the diatomic molecule concerned, again only through the reduced temperature. From a graph of $C_{v,rot}$ as a function of τ we can, therefore, read off the rotational contribution to C_v for any molecule at any temperature. We have only first to estimate the corresponding value of τ ($\equiv T/\Theta_r = 8\pi^2AkT/h^2$) and take, from the graph, the value of C_v corresponding to this reduced temperature. The graph itself, calculated from equation (12), is shown in Fig. 13. Apart from the curious maximum, which will concern us later, the most important feature of Fig. 13 is that $C_{v,rot} \sim 0$ when $T \ll \Theta_r$ while $C_{v,rot} \sim R$, per mole, when $T \gg \Theta_r$.

5. We are now in a position to synthesize the various quantal contributions to the specific heat of a diatomic gas. In place of the classical factors in the partition function, (C) above, we have now

$$\left.\begin{aligned}
\text{(p.f.)}_{\text{trans}} &= \left(\frac{2\pi(m_A+m_B)\boldsymbol{k}T}{h^2}\right)^{\frac{3}{2}}V \\
\text{(p.f.)}_{\text{vib}} &= \frac{e^{-\frac{1}{2}\Theta_v/T}}{1-e^{-\Theta_v/T}}, \quad \text{where} \quad \Theta_v = \frac{h\nu}{\boldsymbol{k}} \\
\text{(p.f.)}_{\text{rot}} &= \sum_{j=0}^{\infty}(2j+1)e^{-j(j+1)\Theta_r/T}, \quad \text{where} \quad \Theta_r = \frac{h^2}{8\pi^2 A\boldsymbol{k}}.
\end{aligned}\right\} \quad (Q)$$

We have not previously employed the abbreviation Θ_v for $h\nu/\boldsymbol{k}$ but, from the Einstein theory of the specific heat of a simple solid in Chapter II, it is evident that $C_{v,\text{vib}}$ depends only on T/Θ_v just as $C_{v,\text{rot}}$ depends only on T/Θ_r. (A plot of $C_{v,\text{vib}}$—actually three times $C_{v,\text{vib}}$—was given in Fig. 1.) Indeed just as

$$C_{v,\text{rot}} \sim 0 \text{ when } T \ll \Theta_r \quad \text{and} \quad C_{v,\text{rot}} \sim R \text{ when } T \gg \Theta_r$$

so also

$$C_{v,\text{vib}} \sim 0 \text{ when } T \ll \Theta_v \quad \text{and} \quad C_{v,\text{vib}} \sim R \text{ when } T \gg \Theta_v.$$

Θ_v and Θ_r are consequently known as *characteristic temperatures* for the vibrational and rotational motions respectively. The former depends only on the vibrational frequency of the diatomic molecule concerned, and the latter only on (the reciprocal of) its moment of inertia. At any temperature considerably below the relevant characteristic temperature the vibrational or rotational motion concerned is 'frozen out' and so makes no contribution to the specific heat: at temperatures considerably above the characteristic temperature quantal and classical differences disappear and $C_{v,\text{rot}}$ or $C_{v,\text{vib}}$ has its classical value of R per mole. Finally, of course, we still have $C_{v,\text{trans}} = \frac{3}{2}R$, per mole, independent of the temperature.

It follows that, for a diatomic gas, we shall expect

$C_v = \frac{3}{2}R$, per mole, at sufficiently low temperatures, and

$C_v = \frac{3}{2}R+R+R = \frac{7}{2}R$, per mole (the classical value), at
         sufficiently high temperatures.

The behaviour at intermediate temperatures clearly depends on the relative values of Θ_v and Θ_r.

Now Θ_v and Θ_r, i.e. ν and A, the characteristic properties of the diatomic molecule concerned, can be determined spectroscopically (see Chapter VIII). And we find that Θ_r is always very much smaller than Θ_v. Consequently the specific heat of a diatomic gas

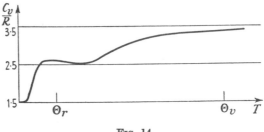

Fig. 14.

as predicted on the basis of quantum mechanics depends on the temperature as shown diagrammatically in Fig. 14.

But, as we see from Table II, in which Θ_r and Θ_v are listed for a number of diatomic molecules, Θ_r is usually so small as to be virtually inaccessible to experimental measurement, and for such

TABLE II

Gas	Θ_{rot}†	$\Theta_{vib}/1000$
H_2	85·4	6·10
N_2	2·86	3·34
O_2	2·07	2·23
CO	2·77	3·07
NO	2·42	2·69
HCl	15·2	4·14
HBr	12·1	3·7
HI	9·0	3·2

gases C_v will appear to increase with temperature from $2·5R$ to $3·5R$, per mole, $C_{v,rot}$ having its full, classical, value at all the temperatures of measurement. For these gases theory, when based on quantum mechanics, is entirely in accordance with observation. The lower fall, from $2·5R$ to $1·5R$, preceded by a rise in C_v, has been observed for the diatomic molecule HD, again in good agreement

† Θ_{rot} is sometimes so defined as to have a value equal to *twice* that here listed.

with the theory. For H_2, or D_2, however, the fall from $2 \cdot 5R$ to $1 \cdot 5R$, although observed, does not follow the curve of Fig. 13: the explanation of this, for H_2, will be given in the next chapter.

6. There are two points which may conveniently be made here.

The first might, perhaps, be better left till the fuller discussion of the rotational specific heat of H_2, but is introduced here since it may already have occurred to the reader. What, he may ask, has happened, in the quantal treatment, to the classical symmetry number, σ? Equation (14) is identical with (8) only if $\sigma = 1$, i.e. only for heteronuclear diatomic molecules. Now this, of course, is really why it is only for the heteronuclear molecule HD that we have agreement between observation and the theory of $C_{v,\mathrm{rot}}$ as given above. As we shall see in Chapter VII, for a homonuclear molecule the rotational partition function is given quantally by

$$(\mathrm{p.f.})_{\mathrm{rot}} = \sum (2j+1)e^{-j(j+1)\Theta_r/T},$$

where the sum is taken over *either even or odd values of j but not both*. And it is possible to show that, when Θ_r/T is sufficiently small,

$$\sum_{j=0,2,4\ldots} (2j+1)e^{-j(j+1)\Theta_r/T} = \sum_{j=1,3,5\ldots} (2j+1)e^{-j(j+1)\Theta_r/T} = \frac{8\pi^2 AkT}{2h^2}.$$

$$(16)$$

Thus at high temperatures, whether we are summing over j even or j odd, we recover the classical partition function, *with the symmetry factor, $\sigma = 2$, included*. This answers the immediate question, and a fuller discussion of the behaviour, at lower temperatures, of $C_{v,\mathrm{rot}}$ for homonuclear diatomic molecules may be left till later, when we shall deal in detail with the case of H_2 only.

The second point is of an entirely different kind. It is that for a few particular diatomic molecules, notably O_2 and NO, there is a fourth contribution to the specific heat other than that due to the translational, rotational, or vibrational motion of the molecule. This is an *electronic* contribution due to the presence of two separate electronic energy-levels lying very close together.

For atomic systems the electronic energy-levels, corresponding to stationary states, are such that the gap between the lowest, or ground, state and the first excited state is always† far too big for thermal excitation to be appreciable at experimental temperatures. But with molecular species it does sometimes happen that the two lowest electronic levels are sufficiently close together for thermal excitation from the ground state to the first excited state to be appreciable under fairly ordinary conditions. In particular, this is the case for the two diatomic molecules NO and O_2—though for rather different reasons in the two instances. For NO the ground state is part of a multiplet of which the lowest energy gap is about 0·015 e.v., while for O_2 we have two distinct electronic energy-levels separated by only 0·97 e.v.‡

Now if we denote the lowest energy level by ϵ_1 and the first excited level by ϵ_2, the corresponding degeneracies being ω_1 and ω_2, then the partition function for these two states is

$$\omega_1 e^{-\epsilon_1/kT} + \omega_2 e^{-\epsilon_2/kT} \tag{17}$$

or, denoting $\epsilon_2 - \epsilon_1$ by ϵ, and measuring the energy of the system from its ground state, we have

$$(\text{p.f.})_{\text{el}} = \omega_1 + \omega_2 e^{-\epsilon/kT} \tag{17'}$$

(we shall assume that further terms are entirely negligible).

From equation (17'), the corresponding electronic specific heat is easily deduced, and is found to be given by

$$C_{v,\text{el}} = Nk\left(\frac{\epsilon}{kT}\right)^2 \frac{\omega e^{-\epsilon/kT}}{(1+\omega e^{-\epsilon/kT})^2} \quad \text{where} \quad \omega = \frac{\omega_2}{\omega_1}. \tag{18}$$

As a function of kT/ϵ this is shown diagrammatically in Fig. 15. The peak occurs at $kT/\epsilon \sim 1/2$, and its height, which depends strongly on ω, is about 0·44R, per mole, when $\omega = 1$, and about 0·76R when $\omega = 2$.

We shall not attempt fully to justify the fourfold factorization of (p.f.) when there is a choice of electronic energy-levels, but comment here only that for NO and O_2 the peaks, as calculated

† There is a possible exception in atomic thallium, for which the lowest energy state is a multiplet.

‡ For atomic species $\Delta\epsilon$ is usually of the order of 10 e.v. The definition of an electron-volt is given in Chapter VIII.

from (18), occur at about 74° K. and 5,000° K. respectively, at which temperatures the rotational contributions to the specific heats are fully classical.

Finally we would observe that a specific heat of the form shown in Fig. 15 will result from any assembly whose systems are capable

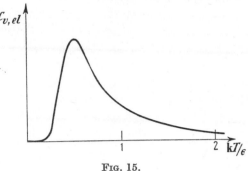

FIG. 15.

of making a single energy jump (or energy step) whose height is comparable with the measure, kT, of the thermal energy. The reader should contrast the shapes of the specific heat curves of Figs. 1, 13, and 15.

EXAMPLES

1. Confirm that equation (18) follows from the expression for $(p.f.)_{el}$ given in (17').

2. Show that $(p.f.)_{vib}$ leads to the formula

$$C_{v,vib} = Nk\left(\frac{\Theta_v}{T}\right)^2 \frac{e^{\Theta_v/T}}{(e^{\Theta_v/T}-1)^2} \quad \text{(see Chapter II)},$$

and thence plot $C_{v,vib}$ accurately against T/Θ_v. Use the curve so obtained, and the data of Table II, to determine the vibrational specific heat of the gases there listed at

(a) 500° K.,   (b) 1,500° K.

3. Prove that the classical expression for the vibrational entropy contribution is given by

$$S_{vib} = Nk\left[\ln\frac{T}{\Theta_{vib}}+1\right].$$

(This expression for S_{vib} is of little practical importance, since we seldom have to deal with temperatures at which the classical expression is valid.)

4. Similarly, prove that the classical expression for the rotational entropy contribution is given by

$$S_{\text{rot}} = Nk\left[\ln\frac{T}{\sigma\Theta_{\text{rot}}} + 1\right],$$

where σ is the symmetry factor for the diatomic molecule concerned. Use this formula to calculate S_{rot} at 300° K. for the gases listed in Table II.

5. Show that equation (17') leads to

$$E_{\text{el}} = N\frac{\omega_2\,\epsilon e^{-\epsilon/kT}}{\omega_1 + \omega_2\,e^{-\epsilon/kT}} \quad\text{and}\quad F_{\text{el}} = -NkT\ln(\omega_1 + \omega_2\,e^{-\epsilon/kT}).$$

Plot E_{el} and F_{el} against kT/ϵ in the case $\omega_1 = \omega_2 = 1$.

ORTHO- AND PARA-HYDROGEN: METASTABLE EQUILIBRIUM

1. WE have already observed that the experimental low temperature specific heat of diatomic hydrogen does not follow the rotational specific heat curve at first expected on the basis of quantum theory. The solution of this problem was given by Dennison in 1928, and provides a good illustration of the importance of statistical theory in the analysis of experimental data: leading in this instance to the discrimination in H_2 of two distinct chemical species, ortho-hydrogen and para-hydrogen. A discussion, along semi-historical lines, of this particular problem will serve, however, not only so to illustrate the value of statistical theory but also to introduce two or three concepts with which we have not hitherto dealt and which are of importance in many other practical applications of statistical mechanics.

At 300° K., or room-temperature, the specific heat, C_v, of diatomic hydrogen, H_2, is effectively $\frac{5}{2}R$, per mole, in complete accordance with the classical theory of the specific heat of a diatomic gas possessing translational and rotational, but no vibrational, energy. At 50° K., and lower temperatures, C_v is only $\frac{3}{2}R$, per mole: the specific heat of a monatomic gas. This fall in C_v is qualitatively in accord with the quantal freezing out of rotational energy at sufficiently low temperatures—due to the finite energy gaps between the ground state and the excited rotational energy states (of a diatomic molecule). Moreover the position, on the temperature scale, of this transition in C_v is certainly, at any rate approximately, in agreement with the characteristic temperature for rotations, Θ_r, as calculated from the moment of inertia of H_2 (see (Q) of Chapter VI). Thus even prior to 1928 the temperature dependence of C_v for H_2 below 300° K. was assigned to the freezing out of rotational energy demanded by quantum theory. Quantitative agreement between theory and experiment could not, however, be obtained since the experimental data, Fig. 12, failed to show the maximum, or peak, in C_v which follows, Fig. 13, from the rotational partition function

$$(\text{p.f.})_{\text{rot}} = \sum_{j=0}^{\infty} (2j+1)e^{-j(j+1)\Theta_r/T}. \tag{1}$$

At that date there were, of course, no data for the heteronuclear isomeric molecule HD to suggest at once that the discrepancy was due to equation (1) having omitted to take account of the homonuclear nature of H_2: this conclusion was reached, as we shall see, through a proper quantum-mechanical interpretation of the far ultra-violet band spectrum of H_2.

2. It is, of course, of the essence of quantum mechanics that the energy levels corresponding to the stationary states of a system are directly related to the positions of the spectral lines in the absorption or emission spectrum of the system concerned. The relationship
$$h\nu_{ik} = \epsilon_i - \epsilon_k, \tag{2}$$
where h is Planck's constant, gives the frequency, ν_{ik}, of light corresponding to a transition between the ith and kth stationary states of a system. We shall discuss this relationship more fully in the next chapter: sufficient to state here that the rotational energy levels for H_2 given, at any rate approximately, by the formula
$$\epsilon_j = \frac{h^2}{8\pi^2 A} j(j+1) \tag{3}$$
are reflected, together with their degeneracies, in the ultra-violet band spectrum of H_2. Moreover, we must emphasize that not every transition between two energy levels is allowed, quantum mechanically: certain *selection rules*, prescribing the allowed changes in quantum numbers, determine the permissible transitions, which are reflected in the ensuing spectrum.

The first important steps towards an understanding of the rotational specific heat of H_2 were made, in 1927, by Hund and Hori, at Copenhagen. Hund, extending previous work by Heisenberg on the symmetry of the wave-functions for helium (1926), showed that the wave-functions for diatomic hydrogen (including translational, electronic, vibrational, and rotational factors) can be divided into two categories—those which are symmetrical with respect to reflection in the mid-plane of the molecule and those which are anti-symmetrical (i.e. change sign) with respect to such a reflection (of both nuclei and electrons). In either case, of course, $|\psi|^2$, the physically significant quantity, is symmetrical: as it must be for a homonuclear molecule. Further, transitions between symmetrical and anti-symmetrical states are impossible *in the absence of nuclear spin.*† If the nuclei do possess spin, so that each is capable of ρ distinct spin states, then there are $\frac{1}{2}\rho(\rho-1)$ anti-symmetrical nuclear spin factors and $\frac{1}{2}\rho(\rho+1)$ symmetrical spin factors (to be combined with the previous molecular wave-functions). And in this case transitions between the above symmetrical and anti-symmetrical wave-states (in which the nuclear spin factors were excluded) are possible, though the transition probability is very small.

Now Hori, examining the far ultra-violet band spectrum‡ of H_2, found that

(i) there were no lines visible corresponding to transitions between symmetrical and anti-symmetrical wave states, and

(ii) the lines corresponding to transitions between anti-symmetrical wave-functions were three times as intense as those corresponding to transitions between symmetrical wave-functions; or, as Hori expressed it, H_2 behaved as if it contained three times as many molecules in anti-symmetrical wave-states as in symmetrical wave-states. (This alternation of intensities had been previously observed by Mecke in 1924.)

The second of these results is intelligible, on the basis of the Heisenberg–Hund classification of wave-states, if we assume

(*a*) that each hydrogen nucleus has spin $\frac{1}{2}$, in units of $h/2\pi$ (like an electron),

(*b*) that only wave states which are *completely anti-symmetrical when the nuclear spin factors are included* occur at all.

For a nucleus with spin $\frac{1}{2}$ has spin degeneracy $\rho = 2$ (i.e. there are two independent directions for the spin).§ There are, therefore,

---

† Angular momentum possessed by the nuclei themselves, as distinct from the whole molecule.

‡ See footnote on page 116 (Chapter VIII).

§ Compare the weight factor $2j+1$ for the degeneracy of a rotational state with quantum number j.

by the formulae quoted above, three alternative symmetrical nuclear spin factors and only one possible anti-symmetrical nuclear spin factor. Then, if (b) is satisfied, a symmetrical wave function never occurs with a symmetrical spin factor, and an anti-symmetrical wave-function never occurs with the anti-symmetrical spin factor. Consequently the anti-symmetrical wave-states possess an extra weight factor, or degeneracy, of three compared with the symmetrical wave-states: which explains (ii) above.

This implies, of course, that when account is taken of nuclear spin degeneracy extra weight factors, of numerical value 3, have to be included in certain terms of the complete partition function for H_2. A complete discussion would be cumbersome, but is very considerably simplified if we observe that at ordinary temperatures (say room temperature) H_2 is in its ground state as far as electronic and vibrational levels are concerned (see Table II). Now the lowest electronic and vibrational states possess symmetrical wave-functions; and wave-functions for translation are always symmetrical in the present sense. Consequently the symmetry of the wave-states for H_2 at ordinary temperatures is simply that of the rotational part of the wave-function. Therefore, since

rotational states for $j = 0, 2, 4,...$ have symmetrical wave-functions,

while

rotational states for $j = 1, 3, 5,...$ have anti-symmetrical wave-functions,

we should expect that the rotational partition function, including nuclear spin degeneracy, for diatomic hydrogen unexcited vibrationally, would be given by

$$(\text{p.f.})_{\text{rot}} = \sum_{j=0,2,4,...} (2j+1)e^{-j(j+1)\Theta_r/T} + 3 \sum_{j=1,3,5,...} (2j+1)e^{-j(j+1)\Theta_r/T}.$$
(4)

Now Hori's spectral measurements enabled the moment of inertia, A, of H_2, i.e. Θ_r, to be determined accurately (see Table II), and we can therefore use equation (4) to predict, numerically, the low-temperature specific heat of hydrogen. This was actually first done by Dennison, and the result is shown in Fig. 16. The disagreement between theory and experiment is even more marked than it was before.

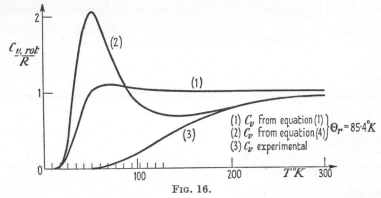

FIG. 16.

3. Despite this apparent failure to account for the observed rotational specific heat of hydrogen by taking proper account of the nuclear spin degeneracies and their coupling with the symmetry properties of the molecular wave-functions, the correct solution was now not far off and, as we have remarked, was given by Dennison in 1928. Before proceeding to it, however, it is convenient to distinguish verbally between those hydrogen molecules with anti-symmetrical nuclear spin states and those with symmetrical nuclear spin states. By convention, the former are called *para*-hydrogen molecules, and the latter *ortho*-hydrogen molecules. Then the partition function (4) tells us that at ordinary temperatures (when electronic and vibrational excitation may be ignored) the *equilibrium ratio* of the number of ortho-hydrogen molecules to para-hydrogen molecules, being determined by the ratio of the sums of the corresponding terms in the partition function, is given by

$$\frac{o\text{-}H_2}{p\text{-}H_2} = \frac{3 \sum\limits_{j=1,3,5,\ldots} (2j+1)e^{-j(j+1)\Theta_r/T}}{\sum\limits_{j=0,2,4,\ldots} (2j+1)e^{-j(j+1)\Theta_r/T}} \tag{5}$$

which is shown graphically, as a function of T, in Fig. 17. We see that at room temperature the equilibrium ratio is 3:1—in agreement with Hori's second result, (ii) above and with equation (16) of Chapter VI.

Now Dennison saw that it would be in keeping with Hori's first observation, (i) above, to suppose that even though molecular hydrogen was formed in the equilibrium ratio $o\text{-}H_2/p\text{-}H_2 = 3/1$, transitions between ortho- and para- states might be so infrequent,

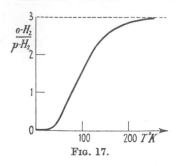

FIG. 17.

particularly at the temperatures of the specific heat measurements, as to be virtually negligible. In this case ordinary hydrogen (technically known as normal hydrogen, $n\text{-}H_2$) should be regarded as a mixture of ortho-hydrogen and para-hydrogen not in mutual thermal equilibrium but in the fixed proportions of $3:1$ (the equilibrium ratio at much higher

temperatures, akin to the temperature at which the hydrogen was formed).

On this assumption, moreover, the specific heat, per mole, of normal hydrogen will be given by

$$C_{v,n\text{-}H_2} = \tfrac{3}{4}C_{v,o\text{-}H_2} + \tfrac{1}{4}C_{v,p\text{-}H_2} \qquad (6)$$

—since $n\text{-}H_2$ is a simple mixture of the two gases $o\text{-}H_2$ and $p\text{-}H_2$ in the ratio $3:1$. The rotational specific heat of $o\text{-}H_2$ will derive from the partition function

$$(\text{p.f.})_{\text{rot},o\text{-}H_2} = 3 \sum_{j=1,3,5,\ldots} (2j+1)e^{-j(j+1)\Theta_r/T}, \qquad (7)$$

while that of $p\text{-}H_2$ will similarly derive from the partition function

$$(\text{p.f.})_{\text{rot},p\text{-}H_2} = \sum_{j=0,2,4,\ldots} (2j+1)e^{-j(j+1)\Theta_r/T}, \qquad (8)$$

there being nothing to prevent true thermal equilibrium between the different states accessible to ortho-hydrogen or, similarly, between the different states accessible to para-hydrogen.

In Fig. 18 we show the specific heats of $o\text{-}H_2$ and $p\text{-}H_2$ calculated, as functions of the temperature, from equations (7) and (8), respectively, together with the specific heat of $n\text{-}H_2$ as then found from equation (6). For the sake of comparison, the specific heat curve for *equilibrium hydrogen*, $e\text{-}H_2$, derived from equation (4), is also given (broken curve). Although experimental points

are not shown in Fig. 18, the agreement between the theoretical
curve for n-H$_2$ and the experimental results for ordinary hydrogen,
in the temperature range concerned, is all that could be desired.

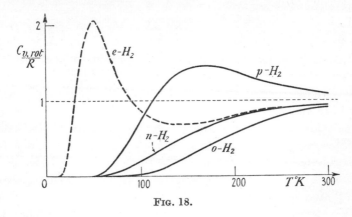

FIG. 18.

4. Dennison's success in thus accounting for the observed
specific heat of diatomic hydrogen at temperatures below 300° K.,
being based on the assumption that at these temperatures ordinary
hydrogen is a mixture of o-H$_2$ and p-H$_2$ in the fixed 'high-
temperature' proportion of 3:1, depends for its theoretical validity
on the extreme slowness of ortho-para conversion. Now it has
since been shown theoretically that, at N.T.P., the half-lifetime
of transition between ortho- and para- states, due either to radiation or collision processes, is certainly not less than some three
years. Therefore, during an ordinary specific-heat experiment, the
ratio of o-H$_2$ to p-H$_2$ will certainly not have time to adjust itself
to the equilibrium value, given by equation (5), and Dennison's
supposition is entirely justified, theoretically as well as empirically.

Additional striking confirmation of Dennison's theory was
provided by the experimental results of Bonhoeffer and Harteck
who showed, in 1929, that active charcoal acts as a catalyst for
ortho-para-hydrogen conversion. It is thus possible to prepare an
equilibrium mixture of ortho- and para-hydrogen in the proportions, $x:1-x$ say, corresponding to any given temperature (see
Fig. 17). If now such a mixture is removed from the presence of
the catalyst, then the ratio of o-H$_2$ to p-H$_2$ remains $x/(1-x)$ during

specific-heat measurements over the temperature range 20° K. to 300° K.—as is shown by the fact that the specific heat is predicted accurately by the equation

$$C_v = xC_{v,o\text{-}H_2} + (1-x)C_{v,p\text{-}H_2}.$$

In the absence of the catalyst ortho-para conversion is entirely negligible. The specific-heat measurements were first made by Eucken, Clusius, and Hiller.

By taking normal hydrogen down to 20° K. in the presence of active charcoal it has been possible to prepare almost pure para-hydrogen (99·7 per cent.). Although only in metastable equilibrium, this remains as pure para-hydrogen at higher temperatures (away from the catalyst) for a very long time. As we see from Fig. 17, it is not possible to prepare pure ortho-hydrogen in any analogous way.

Since the discovery of *heavy* hydrogen, in 1931, it has been possible to apply entirely analogous considerations to the rotational specific heat of heavy molecular hydrogen, D_2, and again to obtain complete agreement between theory and experiment on the assumption that, in the absence of a catalyst, para-states are not sensibly accessible to ortho-molecules (and vice versa) at the relatively low temperatures at which the temperature dependence of the rotational specific heat is manifested. The details of the theory, however, are different from those relating to H_2 molecules since the spin quantum number for a D nucleus is 1, and not $\frac{1}{2}$. Moreover, and as a consequence of this, only totally symmetrical quantum states occur, and not the totally anti-symmetrical states possessed by H_2. Otherwise the theory proceeds along entirely analogous lines (and the reader should have no difficulty in reconstructing it if he so wishes).

For heteronuclear diatomic hydrogen, HD, transitions between symmetrical and anti-symmetrical molecular wave states are not prohibited, even in the absence of nuclear spin: consequently there is no discrimination between ortho- and para- states and, as we have already seen, the original simple theory of rotational specific heat is in excellent agreement with experimental measurements. It is only for molecules with two or more identical nuclei that nuclear spin symmetry considerations become relevant. Gases of all such molecules should, theoretically, behave as mixtures of two or more modifications (distinguished by their nuclear spin symmetries) at sufficiently low temperatures; but in every case, with the single exceptions of H_2 and D_2, the assembly will have liquefied, i.e. ceased to be gaseous, before the temperatures are reached at which such metastable equilibrium would become apparent in specific-heat measurements. Indeed the rotational specific heat of gaseous assemblies other than H_2, HD, and D_2 can always be taken to have its full classical value (see Chapter IX).

5. In this chapter we have encountered two new concepts of importance in statistical mechanics: first, nuclear spin degeneracy and, secondly, the possibility of metastable equilibrium rather than true, thermodynamic, equilibrium. Before proceeding to further applications of our previous formulae it will be well to say a final word about each of these two matters.

Nuclear spin provides merely one other molecular or atomic property† which can vary among the systems of an assembly and which must, therefore, be taken into account in any proper enumeration of the total number of possible distinguishable configurations of the assembly. Actually, however, it is generally permissible to forget all about the nuclear spin weight factors: the following discussion, based on the case of diatomic molecules, will sufficiently indicate why this is so.

Consider first an assembly of diatomic heteronuclear molecules. Let the spin degeneracies of the two nuclei be ρ_1 and ρ_2 (so that the spin of a nucleus of type 1 can be in any one of ρ_1 'directions', etc.). Then, whether the partition function for any given system be evaluated classically or quantally, corresponding to every state of any system when nuclear spin is ignored there are $\rho_1 \rho_2$ states distinguished by the 'directions' of the spins of the two nuclei. In other words,

$$(\text{p.f.})_{\text{including nuclear spin}} = \rho_1 \rho_2 (\text{p.f.})_{\text{excluding nuclear spin}}. \qquad (9)$$

Secondly, consider an assembly of diatomic homonuclear mole-

† i.e. the 'direction' of the spin.

cules, each nucleus having spin degeneracy ρ. Then *classically* we again have

$$(\text{p.f.})_{\text{including nuclear spin}} = \rho^2(\text{p.f.})_{\text{excluding nuclear spin}} \qquad (10)$$

(the identity of the two ends of the molecule having already been recognized by the inclusion of a factor $\frac{1}{2}$ in the rotational part of the partition function: see (C), Chapter VI). Quantally, however, we now have for the rotational part of the partition function, either

$$\tfrac{1}{2}\rho(\rho-1)\sum_{j=0,2,4,\ldots}(2j+1)e^{-j(j+1)\Theta_r/T}+$$
$$+\tfrac{1}{2}\rho(\rho+1)\sum_{j=1,3,5,\ldots}(2j+1)e^{-j(j+1)\Theta_r/T}$$

or

$$\tfrac{1}{2}\rho(\rho+1)\sum_{j=0,2,4,\ldots}(2j+1)e^{-j(j+1)\Theta_r/T}+$$
$$+\tfrac{1}{2}\rho(\rho-1)\sum_{j=1,3,5,\ldots}(2j+1)e^{-j(j+1)\Theta_r/T}$$

according as either only totally anti-symmetrical or only totally symmetrical quantal states occur. (We are supposing, for simplicity, that the system is unexcited vibrationally in the temperature range in which the rotational partition function is non-classical.) But we have already said (equation (16) of the more elementary discussion in Chapter VI) that each of the two sums occurring here, over j even or j odd, can be replaced by $8\pi^2 AkT/2h^2$ when $T \gg \Theta_r$ (actually $T \sim 5\Theta_r$ is sufficient). Consequently for $T \geqslant 5\Theta_r$ the rotational part of the partition function in either case is simply

$$[\tfrac{1}{2}\rho(\rho-1)+\tfrac{1}{2}\rho(\rho+1)]\frac{8\pi^2 AkT}{2h^2}, \quad \text{i.e.} \quad \rho^2\frac{8\pi^2 AkT}{2h^2},$$

which is the classical expression including the nuclear spin weight factors. It follows, therefore, that equation (10) is equally true quantally, provided only that the temperature is such that the rotational specific heat has its classical value, i.e. for all gases excepting only H_2 and D_2 at temperatures below room-temperature.

Now the important point about equations (9) and (10) is that the spin weight factors for the various nuclei concerned appear only as constants multiplying the partition function (as calculated ignoring nuclear spin). This being so, the only effect of these

new factors on the thermodynamic properties of the assembly is
in the introduction of new terms

$$-NkT \ln \rho_1 - NkT \ln \rho_2 - \ldots \tag{11}$$

(one for each atomic nucleus within a system) into the expression†
for the Helmholtz free energy, F. There are, correspondingly,
new terms
$$Nk \ln \rho_1 + Nk \ln \rho_2 + \ldots \tag{12}$$

in the expression for the entropy, S; but E and P are unaffected.

Apart, therefore, from the exceptional cases (H_2 and D_2) already
noted, nuclear spin degeneracies produce no effect on either the
specific heat or the equation of state of a gaseous assembly. They
enter only into expressions for the absolute values of the entropy
or free energy: and even here their presence is comparatively
unimportant. For in practice we are concerned with *changes* in
entropy or free energy, rather than with absolute values: and
since atomic nuclei carry their spins about with them, the spin
weight factors necessarily cancel out in any such change. Nuclear
spin can, consequently, generally be omitted from further consideration (see Chapter IX). In the detailed interpretation of
atomic and molecular spectra, however, and in certain fundamental statistical problems outside the scope of this book, nuclear
spin assumes a very important role.

Chemistry in the ordinary sense is concerned only with atoms
whose nuclei are in their lowest, or ground, states. It is now
known, of course, that nuclei do also possess excited states: but
these are appreciably occupied only at enormous temperatures,
such as those existing inside stars.

6. The second new concept, which we have described as metastable equilibrium, is of considerable practical importance in
physical chemistry. An assembly is said to be in a condition of
metastable equilibrium if thermodynamic equilibrium exists only
among a certain class or group of states open to its systems, rather
than among the whole corpus of states theoretically available.

† Given by $F = -kT \ln\left[\dfrac{(\text{p.f.})^N}{N!}\right]$ for a gaseous assembly.

In this it is to be distinguished from true thermodynamic equilibrium (in which all the theoretically available states are occupied in their correct proportions).

The deciding factor between metastable equilibrium and true equilibrium is generally the time factor. As an example other than that afforded by the equilibrium of ortho- and para-hydrogen, we may consider the condition of a binary metallic alloy which has been quenched, i.e. suddenly cooled from a high temperature. It is possible that true equilibrium at the lower temperature would correspond to a state of order among the two atomic species in the alloy—each atom of one kind being, perhaps, surrounded by atoms of the other kind, and vice versa: nevertheless, on sudden cooling the alloy may be frozen in a more random state (more appropriate to the higher temperature) and remain in this random state indefinitely because at the lower temperature the atoms are not sufficiently mobile to migrate into their positions of true thermodynamic equilibrium. Even then, however, there will still be thermodynamic equilibrium between, say, the various vibrational states of the low temperature, disordered, alloy.

Since we are primarily concerned with statistical methods and not with the details of practical applications, we shall not embark on the further discussion of particular instances. It is sufficient to draw attention here to the need for care in deciding upon the alternative and distinguishable states available, *a priori*, to an assembly. It is not a matter of deciding whether certain states are, *a posteriori*, probable or improbable, but whether, during the time available to the assembly, any one conceivable state can be reached from any other. Usually this is so: but, as we have seen, there are important exceptional cases in which only a metastable equilibrium is possible, certain otherwise available states being virtually inaccessible in the time allowed.

EXAMPLES

1. Show that for D_2 (spin 1) the equilibrium rotational partition function is given by

$$(\text{p.f.})_{\text{rot}} = 6 \sum_{j=0,2,4,\dots} (2j+1)e^{-j(j+1)\Theta_r/T} + 3 \sum_{j=1,3,5,\dots} (2j+1)e^{-j(j+1)\Theta_r/T}$$

(sufficient information has been given in §§ 2, 4, and 5 above).

2. Deduce that the high-temperature value of the ratio of o-D_2 to p-D_2 is equal to 2.

3. Show that at low temperatures true equilibrium corresponds to almost pure ortho-deuterium.

4. Since H and D atoms are chemically similar, whilst D has twice the mass of H, show that the rotational characteristic temperature, Θ_r, for D_2 is approximately 43° K.

NOTES ON ROTATIONAL AND VIBRATIONAL
SPECTRA AND CONVERSION FACTORS

1. AT the beginning of Chapter VI we said that we were turning, temporarily, from a systematic development of the theoretical scheme of statistical mechanics (as the body of theory which bridges the gap between mechanics, whether quantal or classical, and thermodynamics) to a brief discussion of some of the more fundamental results of applying statistical formulae so far obtained to certain definite problems presented by physical chemistry. To this end we have considered the theory of the interpretation of the specific heats of diatomic gases, including ortho- and para-hydrogen. As we emphasized then, our purpose in making these applications is primarily the general one of illustrating the usefulness of statistical mechanics as a theoretical tool in the interpretation of experimental data rather than the narrowly practical one of interpreting, in terms of a particular model, any particular set of observational measurements. In the working practice of theoretical chemistry the latter task is often our immediate aim. But before embarking on such calculations (which are embraced by the scope of this book only incidentally: as in the last chapter and the next) it is necessary not simply to appreciate the qualitative aspects of certain basic statistical formulae but also to have some understanding of the *magnitudes* of the entities involved therein. The last two chapters have paid particular attention to qualitative behaviour: the present chapter and the next will deal principally with the more quantitative aspects of formulae with which we are already familiar.

Most of our formulae have involved quantal energy levels. In particular we have derived expressions for the vibrational and rotational partition functions of diatomic molecules. Let us start then by considering in rather more detail than hitherto, the quantitative aspects of rotational and vibrational energy levels and the spectral lines associated with quantum jumps, up or down, between these levels. We shall assume that it is legitimate to separate the energy, other than translational or electronic energy, of a diatomic molecule into distinct vibrational and rotational contributions. For mechanical reasons this is always permissible to a first approximation: usually the approximation is valid to a fairly high degree of accuracy.

We are already acquainted with the formulae for the quantally permissible energies of a simple harmonic oscillator of classical frequency ν and a rigid linear rotator having moment of inertia A. The equations are (see § 7 of Chapter II and § 4 of Chapter VI)

$$\epsilon_{\text{vib}} = (n+\tfrac{1}{2})h\nu \qquad (n = 0, 1, 2,...) \tag{1}$$

and

$$\epsilon_{\text{rot}} = \frac{h^2}{8\pi^2 A} j(j+1) \quad (j = 0, 1, 2,...), \tag{2}$$

h, in each formula, standing for Planck's constant, of magnitude $6 \cdot 62 . 10^{-27}$ erg sec.

We know too that if light is emitted by a system as its energy falls from ϵ_2 to ϵ_1, then the frequency of the radiation is given by

$$\nu = \frac{\epsilon_2 - \epsilon_1}{h}; \tag{3}$$

and conversely, that when in the state with energy ϵ_1 the system is capable of absorbing light of frequency ν, given by (3), and is then excited to the state of higher energy ϵ_2. Thus with any set of energy levels there are associated the spectral lines of both emission and absorption spectra.

But, as we saw in the last chapter, not all direct transitions between energy levels can occur. The allowed transitions are governed by certain *selection rules*: selection rules which impose a restriction on the corresponding changes in the quantum numbers concerned. For instance (and here we must again quote quantum-mechanical formulae without proof), for transitions between two vibrational levels from the set (1) we require

$$\Delta n = \pm 1 \tag{4}$$

(where Δn denotes the change in n between the initial and final states of the system), while for transitions between two rotational levels from the set (2) we need

$$\Delta j = \pm 1. \tag{5}$$

I

Combining (1) and (4), we see that the emission or absorption spectrum of a simple harmonic oscillator consists of a single line with frequency ν, the classical frequency of the oscillator. Similarly, from (3) and (5), the spectrum of a rigid linear rotator is given by

$$\nu = \frac{h}{8\pi^2 A}[j(j+1)-(j-1)j],$$

i.e.
$$\nu = \frac{h}{8\pi^2 A} 2j. \tag{6}$$

Here we have supposed that the higher level has rotational quantum number j, and therefore, in (6), j takes the values 1,2, 3,.... Consequently, whilst the vibrational spectrum of a simple harmonic oscillator comprises only a single line at the frequency ν, the rotation spectrum of a rigid linear rotator consists of a series, or *band*, of lines with frequencies given by equation (6). And, as we see from this equation, these lines will be equally spaced, at intervals of $h/4\pi^2 A$, on the frequency scale.

Before discussing the bearing of statistical mechanics on these results of quantum theory we must first consider, very briefly, some of the ways in which the rotational and vibrational spectra of actual diatomic molecules may, and do, differ significantly from those of the hypothetical rigid linear rotator and simple harmonic oscillator. For on the basis of the above simple theory we would be led to suppose that for a diatomic molecule the sum of the rotational and vibrational energies is given by

$$\epsilon = (n+\tfrac{1}{2})h\nu + \frac{h^2}{8\pi^2 A} j(j+1), \tag{7}$$

so that, by (4) and (5), the spectrum would be

$$\nu = \nu \pm \frac{h}{8\pi^2 A} 2j \quad (j = 1, 2, 3,...),$$

which is shown schematically in Fig. 19.

And although Fig. 19 does often represent very closely *part* of the complete spectrum, the whole spectrum is always much more complex.

There are two main causes of this greater complexity. First, the diatomic molecule is capable of electronic excitation, so that to the rotational and vibrational energies already calculated we have to add any one of the allowed electronic energy-levels: this means that we should expect a spectrum as in Fig. 19 to be associated with each line of the spectrum produced by purely electronic transitions. Secondly, there is the important fact that

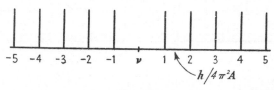

FIG. 19.

the vibrations of a diatomic molecule are only approximately those of a simple harmonic oscillator. For a simple harmonic oscillator the potential function giving the energy of displacement (of the two atoms of the molecule from their equilibrium distance apart) is represented by a parabola: the broken curve in Fig. 10. But for an actual diatomic molecule the potential energy function must (i) become very large, due to mutual repulsions, when the atoms are pressed close together and (ii) tend to a constant value (determined by the dissociation energy) when the atoms are pulled apart. Consequently the actual potential energy function must resemble that represented by the full line in Fig. 10. This has two consequences as far as the vibrational spectrum is concerned:

(i) the lowest quantum energy-levels are now given by

$$\epsilon = h\nu[(n+\tfrac{1}{2}) - k(n+\tfrac{1}{2})^2 + ...]$$

where k is small, i.e. they are no longer quite equidistantly spaced; further the higher quantum levels crowd together as ϵ approaches the dissociation energy of the molecule, and

(ii) the selection rule $\Delta n = \pm 1$ is relaxed, and becomes

$$\Delta n = 0, \pm 1, \pm 2,...$$

(which means that all vibrational transitions are allowed).

It is evident that (i) and (ii) are both effective in adding considerably to the complexity of the resulting molecular spectrum.

In the absence of electronic jumps, the selection rule for j given above is not subject to modification. Since vibrational motion is necessarily symmetrical in the nuclei, it is clear that $\Delta j = \pm 1$ is not compatible with the requirement (Chapter VII) that for *homonuclear* diatomic molecules transitions from symmetrical to antisymmetrical states (in the nuclei) are prohibited. Therefore homonuclear diatomic molecules can show no such rotational-vibrational spectrum. This is in agreement with experiment. On the other hand rotational-vibrational spectra for homonuclear molecules are possible when associated with electronic jumps.†

After these quantum-mechanical preliminaries, we must now turn to examine the bearing on these results of our previous statistical formulae.

2. The quantum-mechanical results presented in the above paragraph would, as they stand, suggest that the molecular spectrum produced by diatomic molecules is quite impossibly complicated. For we must imagine great numbers of spectra, each like that depicted in Fig. 19, superposed, with different origins, one on top of another and each stretching across the whole length of the frequency scale. It would then be almost impossible to make any sense of the resulting composite spectrum. Actually molecular spectra are decidedly complex, but for diatomic molecules they can certainly be unravelled without too great difficulty. The reason, of course, is that not all the lines so far envisaged are equally *intense*; indeed most of them are far too faint to be observed at all even with the most powerful techniques available. It is only the particularly bright, or intense, lines that we can observe, or photograph; and this limitation gives an order, or simplicity, to the resulting spectrum which it would otherwise lack.

Now statistical mechanics enables us to decide which, of all the above spectral lines, will be the most intense. For the intensity of a given spectral line depends (to a first approximation) on two factors: a transition probability, and the number of systems in the given initial state. And, at any given temperature, the number of systems in any particular state (and therefore, the number in any particular initial state, if we assume that radiative transitions

† It was such a spectrum which was observed by Hori for H_2. Alternatively Raman spectra can be examined, since the selection rule is then $\Delta j = 0, \pm 2$. This was done for H_2 by Rasetti (1929).

help to maintain, but do not upset, the statistical equilibrium) is directly determinable by our previous statistical theory.

We shall illustrate this important application of statistical mechanics to the theory of spectra by considering simply the relative intensities of the lines represented in Fig. 19. Here the various lines of the spectrum are produced by systems jumping out of initial states which differ in their rotational quantum number j. So we must investigate the internal distribution of systems among their various possible rotational-energy states.

According to the arguments of Chapter V, the equilibrium number, n_j^*, of systems having rotational quantum number j, is given by

$$n_j^* = N \frac{\omega_j e^{-\epsilon_j/kT}}{(\text{p.f.})_{\text{rot}}}, \tag{8}$$

where N is the total number of systems in the assembly. But

$$\epsilon_j = \frac{h^2}{8\pi^2 A} j(j+1)$$

and

$$\omega_j = 2j+1$$

and, therefore, equation (8) becomes

$$n_j^* = N \frac{(2j+1)e^{-j(j+1)h^2/8\pi^2 AkT}}{(\text{p.f.})_{\text{rot}}}. \tag{8'}$$

The only part of the r.h.s. of (8') which depends on j is the numerator. If, as hitherto, we write for simplicity Θ_r in place of $h^2/8\pi^2 Ak$, and now regard j as a continuous variable, then the reader will easily verify that this numerator has a maximum at a value of j given by

$$2j+1 = \sqrt{\frac{2T}{\Theta_r}}. \tag{9}$$

Assuming, provisionally, that $T \gg \Theta_r$, equation (8') may be written

$$n_j^* = N \frac{\Theta_r}{T} (2j+1) e^{-j(j+1)\Theta_r/T} \tag{8''}$$

and is shown schematically, as a function of j, in Fig. 20. We observe that, at least for $T \gg \Theta_r$, the most occupied state is *not* the ground state. This is in marked distinction to the case (see Chapter V) of the distribution of systems among the vibrational energy levels of a simple harmonic oscillator and is, of course, entirely due to the influence, in the present case of rotational energy levels, of the degeneracy factor, ω.

If now we assume, as is in fact the case, that the dominant factor determining the intensity of a spectral line produced by systems leaving any state is simply the factor n^* for that state,

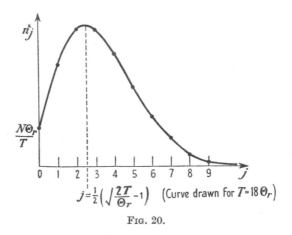

$$j = \tfrac{1}{2}\left(\sqrt{\tfrac{2T}{\Theta_r}} - 1\right) \quad \text{(Curve drawn for } T = 18\,\Theta_r)$$

Fig. 20.

then the bearing of equation (8″) on the lines of Fig. 19 is immediate. For consider an absorption spectrum and suppose that, by good fortune, the two sets of energy levels concerned do not overlap. Then when the coordinate numbering the lines in Fig. 19 is negative, i.e. when the frequency of the lines is less than ν, the absolute value of this coordinate gives j, while when this coordinate is positive, i.e. when the frequency of the line is greater than ν, this coordinate measures $j+1$; j, in each case, being the quantum number of the initial state of the system. Consequently, the relative intensities of the lines may be expected to be somewhat as in Fig. 21.

Such characteristically butterfly-shaped bands, i.e. with two intensity maxima, are indeed observed in molecular spectra. Usually there are more lines than are shown in Fig. 21 and the lines lie very close together so that they are only separated by spectrometers with high resolving power. In fact Fig. 21 represents the intensity distribution of the fine-structure of a band spectrum.

Moreover, this intensity distribution is markedly different from that which we should expect to be found among the different lines, or bands, due to various jumps in the vibrational quantum number, n. For, again considering an absorption spectrum, if the distribution number is again the dominant factor determining the intensity of a spectral line, we should expect a series of lines (or

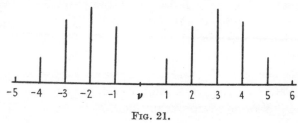

FIG. 21.

bands) more or less equally spaced (but slowly converging as the dissociation energy is approached) arising from systems initially in the ground state, a fainter series arising from those initially in the first excited vibrational state, and so on. Actually, if the temperature of the gas is not too high, these latter lines are not visible and we accordingly have a simplification of the spectrum. Such intensity considerations, *inter alia*, enable us to disentangle the spectra (emission or absorption) of diatomic molecules fairly completely, for we do find series of such lines approximately equally spaced and each exhibiting the rotational fine-structure discussed above. Having correctly identified the lines, measurements of their spacings gives us knowledge of the characteristic properties, A, ν, etc., of the diatomic molecule concerned.

3. The previous paragraph has indicated how temperature-dependent statistical factors help to determine the intensities of the lines of a molecular spectrum, and thereby effect a great simplification in the observed spectrum compared with that which we might otherwise expect on purely, and too naïvely, quantum-mechanical grounds. In the unravelling of a spectrum both the spacings and the intensities of the lines must be taken into account. And it is found that the rotational energy-levels superpose a fine-structure on the lines of a hypothetical purely vibrational spectrum: i.e. that each line of the vibrational spectrum

gives place to a fine band of lines with relative intensities and spacings much as in Fig. 21. It is not our purpose to go into the theory of molecular spectra in greater detail. But we propose now to summarize, rather crudely, the orders of magnitude of some of the quantities determined by such spectral analysis.

The basic quantities, for any particular diatomic molecule, are the magnitude of $h\nu$, which, to a first approximation, determines the spacings of the vibrational levels, and the magnitude of $h^2/8\pi^2 A$, the quantity which enters into the formula for the rotational energy-levels. Both these quantities, $h\nu$ and $h^2/8\pi^2 A$, have the dimensions of energy and are, therefore, necessarily expressed in energy units. The natural unit of energy to use is the electron volt (e.v.).† Now, in the main, we find that for diatomic molecules:

$$h\nu \text{ is of the order of } \tfrac{1}{10} \text{ e.v.}$$

while $h^2/8\pi^2 A$ is of the order of $\tfrac{1}{10000}$ e.v.

Both quantities, of course, have a fairly wide range of magnitudes, and their values for any particular molecule may differ from those here given by as much as a factor of 10, either way; but these are, perhaps, the best we can give for the sake of obtaining a rough idea of orders of magnitude.

With the same qualification, we may say that, roughly, the dissociation energy of a diatomic molecule (into neutral, unexcited, atoms) is of the order of 5 e.v., while electronic excitation energies for diatomic molecules are of roughly the same order. More precisely, for single-bonded diatomic molecules, dissociation energies range from 1 to 6 e.v., approximately, whilst for diatomic molecules with double or triple bonds the dissociation energies range from 5 to 10 e.v. Electronic excitation energies are usually 5 e.v. or greater.

Thus the energy-level diagram for a typical diatomic molecule (rather over-simplified, and not to scale) will somewhat resemble Fig. 22. It is useful to bear such a picture in mind, crude though it is, when considering the correlation between energetic and thermal units to which we proceed in the next section. A thorough,

† The energy acquired by an electronic charge moving through a potential difference of 1 volt.

and quantitative, grasp of this correlation is of immense importance in acquiring an intuitive appreciation of the bearing of statistical theory on practical problems of physical chemistry.

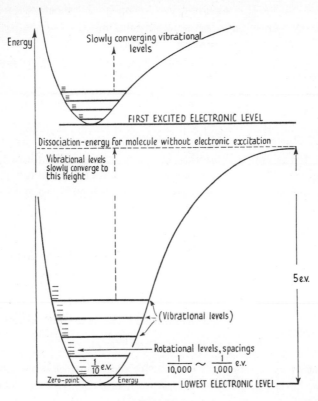

FIG. 22.

4. The rough magnitudes given above express, in electron volts, certain energy differences, i.e. intervals between energy levels, for diatomic molecules. Thus $h\nu$ is, to a first approximation, the difference between two successive vibrational energy-levels, and we have said that it is commonly of the order of 0·1 e.v. We obtained, in principle, this energy difference, $\Delta\epsilon$, by measuring a frequency, ν, associated with $\Delta\epsilon$ by the fundamental equation

$$\nu = \frac{\Delta\epsilon}{h} \tag{3'}$$

where h is Planck's constant. Thus knowledge of a frequency is equivalent to knowledge of an energy difference and, conversely, instead of specifying $\Delta\epsilon$ in electron volts we could equally well describe $\Delta\epsilon$ by the number ν. Actually, in spectroscopy, it is customary to work not in terms of ν but in terms of the reciprocal wave-length (or wave-number), λ^{-1}, given by

$$\lambda^{-1} = \frac{\nu}{c} \tag{10}$$

where c is the velocity of light. λ^{-1} is measured in terms of reciprocal centimetres, or cm.$^{-1}$ It is indeed quite customary to talk of measuring a frequency in terms of cm.$^{-1}$: the measure, of course, being the corresponding value of λ^{-1}. It follows that we can, conventionally, express energy differences in terms of cm.$^{-1}$, for an energy $\Delta\epsilon$ corresponds, by (3') and (10), to a reciprocal wave-length,

$$\lambda^{-1} = \frac{\Delta\epsilon}{hc}. \tag{11}$$

We therefore ask, How many cm.$^{-1}$ correspond to $\Delta\epsilon = 1$ e.v. ? Now (see Appendix VI for a table of fundamental magnitudes)

$$h = 6 \cdot 624 . 10^{-27} \text{ erg sec.},$$

$$c = 2 \cdot 998 . 10^{10} \text{ cm. sec.}^{-1},$$

and $\qquad 1 \text{ e.v.} = 1 \cdot 602 \cdot 10^{-12} \text{ ergs},$ $\qquad\qquad$ (12)

the last equation depending on the definition of a volt and the magnitude of the electronic charge. Consequently, by (11),

$$\lambda^{-1} = \frac{1 \cdot 602 . 10^{-12}}{6 \cdot 624 . 10^{-27} . 2 \cdot 998 . 10^{10}} \text{ cm.}^{-1}$$

$$= 8{,}067 \text{ cm.}^{-1},$$

so that an energy difference of 1 e.v. corresponds to a spectral line of 'frequency' 8,067 cm.$^{-1}$

In the course of this calculation we expressed an electron volt in terms of ergs, or fundamental centimetre-gram-second energy-units. Now, as we can see from (12), chemically the erg is not a very useful unit of energy: it is far too big. On the other hand we often find it convenient to consider not just one molecule, or system, but a *mole* of systems, i.e. N_0 systems where N_0 is Avogadro's number. Then the energy required to change the energy of every system in the mole by one electron volt is simply N_0 e.v., and since

$$N_0 = 6 \cdot 023 \cdot 10^{23}$$

this energy is, by (12),

$$6 \cdot 023 \cdot 10^{23} \cdot 1 \cdot 602 \cdot 10^{-12} \text{ ergs,}$$

i.e. $9 \cdot 649 \cdot 10^{11}$ ergs.

Thus, while the erg is too big a unit for convenient use on the molecular scale, it is too small a unit for convenience when dealing with the corresponding molar quantities. However, it is well known that we can transform from energy units to heat units by means of the *mechanical equivalent of heat*

$$J = 4 \cdot 186 \cdot 10^7 \text{ ergs per calorie.}$$

Thus to raise the energy of every system of a mole by 1 e.v. we have to give

$$\frac{9 \cdot 649 \cdot 10^{11}}{4 \cdot 186 \cdot 10^7} = 2 \cdot 305 \cdot 10^4 \text{ calories}$$

$$= 23 \cdot 05 \text{ k.cal.}$$

of heat energy to the assembly.

We can summarize these results by writing, formally,

$$1 \text{ e.v.} = 1 \cdot 602 \cdot 10^{-12} \text{ ergs}$$

$$= 8{,}067 \text{ cm.}^{-1}$$

$$= 23 \cdot 05 \text{ k.cal. per mole,}$$

the equals sign being interpreted as the phrase 'corresponds to'. Better still, we can construct a table giving any one of these units of energy in terms of any other. The result of so doing (but omitting the unit of ergs, on account of its relative unimportance) is Table III, as the reader will easily confirm:

TABLE III

	e.v.	*cm.*$^{-1}$	*k.cal.*
1 e.v. =	1	8,067	23·05
1 cm.$^{-1}$ =	$1 \cdot 240 \cdot 10^{-4}$	1	$2 \cdot 859 \cdot 10^{-3}$
1 k.cal. =	$4 \cdot 337 \cdot 10^{-2}$	349·9	1

It must be remembered that the rows and columns refer, in order, to

(1) the energy change in a single system,
(2) the reciprocal wave-length of the corresponding radiation,
(3) the corresponding energy change (in heat units) for a mole of systems.

For most purposes it is sufficient to bear in mind that (approximately)

350 cm.$^{-1}$ corresponds to 1 k.cal. which corresponds to $\frac{1}{23}$ e.v.

5. The statements in the last line of §4 depend essentially for their validity and meaning on the first law of thermodynamics and the fundamental quantum-mechanical law expressed in equation (3). In evaluating the numbers concerned we have used the experimental values of J, the mechanical equivalent of heat, and h, Planck's constant. We have nowhere, however, made use of Boltzmann's constant, k.

Now the reader will recall that in Chapter VI we defined characteristic temperatures, Θ_v and Θ_r, by the equations

$$\Theta_v = \frac{h\nu}{k}$$

and

$$\Theta_r = \frac{h^2}{8\pi^2 A k}$$

where in each case, of course,

$$k\Theta = \text{energy}.$$

It so happens that these temperatures, Θ_v and Θ_r, are of importance calorimetrically in that they fix (see Fig. 14) the temperatures at which vibrational and rotational specific heats are, respectively, frozen out on account of the quantum-mechanical characteristics of the underlying statistical theory. But in any case, whether the result has a phenomenological importance or not, an energy divided by Boltzmann's constant gives a temperature on the absolute scale.

Boltzmann's constant is, as we have seen, numerically equal to the gas constant divided by Avogadro's number, i.e.

$$k = R/N_0.$$

But $R = 1 \cdot 987$ cal. deg.$^{-1}$ (per mole),

so that $k = (1 \cdot 987 . 10^{-3})(4 \cdot 337 . 10^{-2})$ (see Table III)

                $= 8 \cdot 618 . 10^{-5}$ e.v. deg.$^{-1}$ (per system)

(i.e. k is roughly 1/10,000 e.v. per deg.), whence also

            $k = (8 \cdot 618 . 10^{-5})(1 \cdot 602 . 10^{-12})$

            $= 1 \cdot 3805 . 10^{-16}$ erg deg.$^{-1}$

(which is the value usually given in tables of physical constants).

The reciprocal of k enables us to state at once the temperature corresponding to a given increment of energy according to the relationship

$$\Theta = \frac{\Delta \epsilon}{k}.$$

Thus $R^{-1} = 0 \cdot 5033$ deg. per calorie

and $k^{-1} = 1 \cdot 160 . 10^4$ deg. per e.v.

But (Table III) 1 e.v. corresponds to 8,067 cm.$^{-1}$; therefore the temperature corresponding to a reciprocal wave-length of 1 cm.$^{-1}$ is

$$\frac{1 \cdot 160 . 10^4}{8,067} = 1 \cdot 438 \text{ deg.},$$

and we can write, conventionally

            $\Theta = 503 \cdot 3$ deg. per k.cal.

            $= 1 \cdot 160 . 10^4$ deg. per e.v.

            $= 1 \cdot 438$ deg. per cm.$^{-1}$,

the equal sign having the same interpretation as before.

These conversion factors are of great importance in telling us at what temperature the yardstick of thermal energy, kT, is comparable with a given energy interval. For instance, we see at once that if the spacing of rotational energy-levels is of the order of a few ten-thousandths (10^{-4}) of an electron volt then the rotational partition function will have its classical value at temperatures as low as a few degrees absolute; and, similarly, if the spacing of the vibrational levels of a diatomic molecule is of the order of a tenth of an electron volt then the characteristic temperature at which the vibrational specific heat starts to fall off, or freeze out, will be of the order of a thousand degrees absolute.

These observations show that the crude generalities of § 3 of this chapter are fairly well in agreement with the data of Table II in Chapter VI.

Finally, it is worth remembering that at 300° K. (approximately room-temperature) the commensurate energy step ($\Delta\epsilon = kT$) is roughly $\frac{1}{40}$ e.v. per system or 0·6 k.cal. per mole. An energy step of $\frac{1}{40}$ e.v. corresponds to a reciprocal wave-length of about 200 cm.$^{-1}$ The reader should confirm these figures.

EXAMPLES

1. Confirm, from the data in Table III and the values of k given in § 5, that

$$300° \text{ K.} \sim \tfrac{1}{40} \text{ e.v.} \sim 0\cdot6 \text{ k.cal.} \sim 200 \text{ cm.}^{-1}$$

2. Confirm that the wave-lengths of visible light, approximately 4,000 A to 8,000 A, correspond to energy changes ranging from approximately 3 e.v. to 1·5 e.v. or 70 k.cal. to 35 k.cal.

3. Using the data of Table II determine the fundamental vibration frequencies, in cm.$^{-1}$, for HCl, HBr, and HI. (Approx. 2,880, 2,470, and 2,230 cm.$^{-1}$)

POLYATOMIC MOLECULES, THE THIRD LAW OF THERMODYNAMICS, HINDERED ROTATION

1. THE partition function, (p.f.), for a single system of a monatomic gas is, as we have seen,

$$V\left(\frac{2\pi m kT}{h^2}\right)^{\frac{3}{2}}(\omega_1 e^{-\epsilon_1/kT}+\omega_2 e^{-\epsilon_2/kT}+...) \tag{1}$$

where the first factor is the partition function for translational energy and the second factor arises from the possibility of various electronic energy levels. For a monatomic gas, however, $\epsilon_2-\epsilon_1$ is always so large compared with kT that, for almost all purposes, we can ignore all terms in this sum except the first: and, if we choose to measure energy from the lowest electronic level as zero, (1) then becomes simply

$$V\left(\frac{2\pi m kT}{h^2}\right)^{\frac{3}{2}}\omega_1 \tag{1'}$$

where ω_1 is the degeneracy of the lowest electronic energy-level.

In the same way, for diatomic molecules we can usually write

$$(\text{p.f.}) = V\left(\frac{2\pi m kT}{h^2}\right)^{\frac{3}{2}}\omega_1(\text{p.f.})_{\text{vib}}(\text{p.f.})_{\text{rot}}. \tag{2}$$

Here m is the total mass of the molecule, and we have assumed

(i) that the higher electronic states are not appreciably excited, and

(ii) that the vibrational-rotational partition function separates into independent vibrational and rotational factors.

On these assumptions we have

$$(\text{p.f.})_{\text{vib}} = \frac{e^{-\frac{1}{2}h\nu/kT}}{(1-e^{-h\nu/kT})} \tag{3}$$

and

$$(\text{p.f.})_{\text{rot}} = \frac{8\pi^2 A kT}{\sigma h^2} \tag{4}$$

where the symmetry factor σ equals 1 for heteronuclear molecules and 2 for homonuclear molecules. The expression (4) is the classical form of $(p.f.)_{rot}$: we have already seen that specifically quantal effects arise, for rotational motion, only at very low temperatures.

The partition functions for polyatomic molecules can likewise be constructed without difficulty provided that the molecules are *rigid*. This restriction to rigid molecules does not, of course, exclude vibrational motion: the difficulties arise only when molecules are capable of relatively large internal motions such, for instance, as the bendings of a flexible long chain (saturated) hydrocarbon molecule or, on a less grand scale, the rotation of one sub-group independently of the whole molecule. In such cases the accurate evaluation of the partition function may present a mathematically formidable problem; and in many instances this has not yet been satisfactorily solved. But, fortunately, many polyatomic molecules (including most molecules comprising only three or four atoms) are essentially rigid; and for these we can construct the partition functions accurately—or, at least, as accurately as is usually necessary. The discussion of the next section is confined to the case of rigid polyatomic molecules.

2. If a polyatomic molecule consists of n atoms, then $3n$ spacial coordinates are required to specify the positions of these atoms in space. If the molecule is rigid, then it is useful to specify

  (i) the position of its mass-centre, and
  (ii) the orientation in space of the molecule as a whole.

For (i) we require 3 coordinates. For (ii) we shall, in general, require another 3 coordinates (see § 3 below), but in the case of a *linear* molecule (e.g. all diatomic molecules, N_2O etc.) only two such coordinates are needed, for rotation about the axis of the molecule does not give rise to new positions. Consequently we are left with either

$$3n - 6 \quad \text{(general case)}$$

or $\qquad\qquad 3n - 5 \quad$ (linear case)

internal† coordinates, and, mechanically, the molecule is then capable of $3n - 6$, or $3n - 5$, independent *normal modes of vibration*. The corresponding fundamental vibration frequencies of a

---

† A rather stricter use of 'internal' than in Chapter VI.

polyatomic molecule can be determined spectroscopically (and with the aid of mathematical group theory) if the molecule concerned is not too complicated. Then for each normal frequency ν we have a factor in the partition function

$$\frac{e^{-\frac{1}{2}h\nu/kT}}{(1-e^{-h\nu/kT})};$$

the product of $3n-6$ or $3n-5$ such factors making up $(p.f.)_{vib}$.

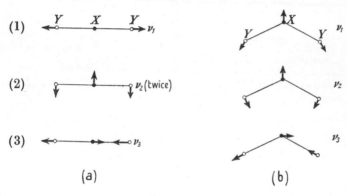

Fig. 23.

As an illustration we may consider the vibrational partition functions of symmetrical XY_2 molecules. Such molecules can be either linear or non-linear. Fig. 23 (a) shows, diagrammatically, the normal vibrations of a linear molecule of this type; Fig. 23 (b) represents the corresponding vibrations of a non-linear molecule. (Vibrations of the forms (1) and (2) are often known as 'breathing' and 'bending' modes, respectively.) We see at once the essential difference between the linear and non-linear cases: the motion represented by 2 (a) can take place in two independent planes (e.g. the plane of this page and perpendicular thereto), while that represented by 2 (b) is confined to the plane defined by the XY_2 molecule itself. For this reason the frequency ν_2 has to be counted *twice* in the linear case, and only once in the non-linear case. Table IV gives the values of the frequencies, ν_1, ν_2, and ν_3, measured in cm.$^{-1}$, for a small number of typical triatomic molecules (including non-symmetrical molecules).

TABLE IV

Molecule	Frequency in cm.$^{-1}$		
	ν_1	ν_2	ν_3
H_2O	3,652	1,592	3,756
H_2S	2,611	1,290	2,684
NO_2	1,320	648	1,621
CO_2 (*l*)	1,337	667 (2)	2,349
CS_2 (*l*)	657	397 (2)	1,523
N_2O (*l*)	1,285	587 (2)	2,224
HCN (*l*)	2,089	712 (2)	3,312
BrCN (*l*)	580	368 (2)	2,187

(*l*) stands for 'linear'.

(2) indicates that ν_2 is to be counted twice: i.e. that there are four factors in
(p.f.)$_{vib}$ corresponding to ν_1, ν_2, ν_2, ν_3.

So much for the vibrational part of the partition function. We
have still to calculate the rotational partition function, (p.f.)$_{rot}$.
When the molecule is linear the rotational partition function will
have precisely the same form as for a diatomic molecule, i.e.

$$(\text{p.f.})_{rot} = \frac{8\pi^2 A k T}{\sigma h^2},$$

A standing for the moment of inertia of the molecule about a line
perpendicular to the axis of the molecule (and through its mass-
centre). The symmetry factor, σ, has, of course, the value 2 or 1
according as the molecule is or is not symmetrical. When the
molecule is not linear it will, in general, be characterized by three
principal moments of inertia, A, B, and C, about certain mutually
perpendicular lines through its mass-centre. This, of course, is
true only provided that we are dealing with a rigid molecule.
In this case we find

$$(\text{p.f.})_{rot} = \frac{\sqrt{\pi}(8\pi^2 kT)^{\frac{3}{2}}(ABC)^{\frac{1}{2}}}{\sigma h^3},\tag{5}$$

where σ is again a symmetry number. We proceed, in the next
section, to derive this formula and to contrast it with equation (4).

3. As always we are concerned only with the statistical part of
the derivation of our formulae, and not with the mechanical preliminaries. But although the reader who is unacquainted with
the equations of classical mechanics must simply take these on

trust, it is nevertheless useful at least to visualize the coordinates by means of which the orientation of a general rigid molecule is most conveniently described.

The orientation of the molecule is fixed if the positions of its principal axes (products-of-inertia zero) through the mass-centre are given. We denote these axes by $O1$, $O2$, $O3$, chosen so as to form a right-handed system. It is then sufficient to describe the positions of $O1$ and $O3$. The position of $O3$ is determined (relative to axes Ox, Oy, Oz fixed in space) by the angles θ and ϕ with which we are already familiar (Fig. 11: $O3$ corresponds to the axis AB of the diatomic molecule). The position of $O1$ is now fixed if we assign the angle between the planes $zO3$ and $1O3$: we call this angle ψ (Fig. 24). The three angles

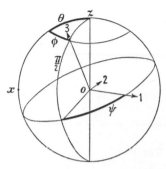

FIG. 24. (Oy is not shown; but Ox, Oy, and Oz form a right-handed system of axes; as do $O1$, $O2$, and $O3$.)

θ, ϕ, and ψ are known as Euler's angles and unambiguously describe the orientation of the molecule with respect to the fixed reference frame Ox, Oy, Oz.

If A, B, and C are the moments of inertia of the molecule about its principal axes $O1$, $O2$, and $O3$, respectively, then, according to classical mechanics, its rotational kinetic energy is given by

$$\epsilon = \tfrac{1}{2}A(\dot{\theta}\sin\psi - \dot{\phi}\sin\theta\cos\psi)^2 + \tfrac{1}{2}B(\dot{\theta}\cos\psi + \dot{\phi}\sin\theta\sin\psi)^2 + $$
$$+ \tfrac{1}{2}C(\dot{\psi} + \dot{\phi}\cos\theta)^2. \quad (6)$$

[Note: if $A = B$ and $C = 0$ we obtain
$$\epsilon = \tfrac{1}{2}A(\dot{\theta}^2 + \sin^2\theta.\dot{\phi}^2),$$
which leads to equation (6) of Chapter VI.]

In terms of θ, ϕ, ψ and the conjugate momenta, p_θ, p_ϕ, and p_ψ, (6) becomes

$$\epsilon = \frac{1}{2A}\left\{\sin\psi\, p_\theta - \frac{\cos\psi}{\sin\theta}(p_\phi - \cos\theta\, p_\psi)\right\}^2 + $$
$$+ \frac{1}{2B}\left\{\frac{\sin\psi}{\sin\theta}(p_\phi - \cos\theta\, p_\psi) + \cos\psi\, p_\theta\right\}^2 + \frac{1}{2C}p_\psi^2. \quad (7)$$

The evaluation of

$$(\text{p.f.}) = \frac{1}{h^3} \int \dots \int e^{-\epsilon/kT} \, dp_\theta \, dp_\phi \, dp_\psi \, d\theta d\phi d\psi$$

looks very unpleasant, but becomes tractable if we change from p_θ, p_ϕ, p_ψ to new variables, ξ, η, ζ, defined by

$$\xi = \sin\psi \, p_\theta - \frac{\cos\psi}{\sin\theta}(p_\phi - \cos\theta \, p_\psi),$$

$$\eta = \frac{\sin\psi}{\sin\theta}(p_\phi - \cos\theta \, p_\psi) + \cos\psi \, p_\theta,$$

$$\zeta = p_\psi.$$

For ϵ then reads,

$$\epsilon = \frac{1}{2A}\xi^2 + \frac{1}{2B}\eta^2 + \frac{1}{2C}\zeta^2$$

while $dp_\theta \, dp_\phi \, dp_\psi$ transforms into $d\xi d\eta d\zeta / J$, where

$$J \equiv \frac{\partial(\xi, \eta, \zeta)}{\partial(p_\theta, p_\phi, p_\psi)} = \begin{vmatrix} \sin\psi & \cos\psi & 0 \\ -\dfrac{\cos\psi}{\sin\theta} & \dfrac{\sin\psi}{\sin\theta} & 0 \\ \cdot & \cdot & 1 \end{vmatrix} = \frac{1}{\sin\theta}.$$

[The reader who is unfamiliar with the rules for change of variables in a multiple integral must accept this result, or refer to such a text-book as R. Courant's *Differential and Integral Calculus*, Vol. II; the process corresponds to replacing dx by $d\xi/(d\xi/dx)$ in a simple integral.]

The partition function becomes

$$(\text{p.f.}) = \frac{1}{h^3} \int \dots \int \exp\left\{ -\left(\frac{1}{2A}\xi^2 + \frac{1}{2B}\eta^2 + \frac{1}{2C}\zeta^2\right) \Big/ kT \right\}$$

$$d\xi d\eta d\zeta \sin\theta \, d\theta d\phi d\psi \quad (8)$$

and all the integrations can be performed without difficulty.

Each of the variables ξ, η, ζ (since they depend directly on the momenta p_θ, p_ϕ, p_ψ) can take all values between $-\infty$ and $+\infty$;

we therefore have

$$\text{(p.f.)} = \frac{1}{h^3} \int\limits_{-\infty}^{\infty} e^{-\xi^2/2AkT} d\xi \int\limits_{-\infty}^{\infty} e^{-\eta^2/2BkT} d\eta \times$$

$$\times \int\limits_{-\infty}^{\infty} e^{-\zeta^2/2CkT} d\zeta \int\int\int \sin\theta\, d\theta d\phi d\psi$$

$$= \frac{1}{h^3}(2\pi AkT)^{\frac{1}{2}}(2\pi BkT)^{\frac{1}{2}}(2\pi CkT)^{\frac{1}{2}}.2.2\pi.2\pi$$

$$= \frac{\sqrt{\pi}(8\pi^2 kT)^{\frac{3}{2}}(ABC)^{\frac{1}{2}}}{h^3}.$$

It remains only to correct this result in case the molecule has such symmetry that during the rotations defined by $0 \leqslant \theta < \pi$, $0 \leqslant \phi < 2\pi$, $0 \leqslant \psi < 2\pi$ the molecule returns into a configuration indistinguishable from that in which it started. If σ is the number of times the initial configuration is assumed during these rotations (equal to 1 if all the positions are distinct and, for instance, equal to 2 for H_2O—a non-linear, symmetrical molecule) then we must divide by σ in order to compensate for having counted every distinguishable configuration σ times. Finally, therefore, we have

$$\text{(p.f.)}_{\text{rot}} = \frac{\sqrt{\pi}(8\pi^2 kT)^{\frac{3}{2}}(ABC)^{\frac{1}{2}}}{\sigma h^3},$$

which is the formula, (5), quoted above. The derivation has been given in some detail for the sake of an important point which will arise in the next chapter.

We have now derived expressions for all the factors in the partition function of a rigid polyatomic molecule. But before we proceed to show how these expressions can be used to obtain knowledge of the structural properties of molecules, or molecular assemblies, there are two questions which the reader may raise at this point and to which an answer, though necessarily rather sketchy, must be given.

First, it is apparent from (5) that the rotational specific heat†

† Classical: but at ordinary temperatures quantum effects are negligible.

of a polyatomic molecule is $\frac{3}{2}R$ (per mole). The proof is immediate, and is left as an exercise. Now, combined with the discussion of the previous section, this means that the specific heat, C_v, of an assembly of independent, non-localized, rigid, *non-linear* poly-atomic molecules, each comprising n atoms, is (per mole) given by

$$C_v = C_{v,\text{trans}} + C_{v,\text{vib}} + C_{v,\text{rot}}$$
$$= \tfrac{3}{2}R + (3n-6)R + \tfrac{3}{2}R$$
$$= (3n-3)R, \tag{9}$$

provided that each vibrational factor gives the full classical, or high temperature, contribution. On the other hand, in the corresponding case of *linear* polyatomic molecules we have (using equation (4)),

$$C_v = \tfrac{3}{2}R + (3n-5)R + R$$
$$= (3n - \tfrac{5}{2})R. \tag{10}$$

And, at first sight, the difference between (9) and (10) is somewhat puzzling—for how does the molecule know whether it is strictly linear or not ?

To this rather subtle question, only an indication of the answer can be given here. But we can see, without difficulty, that the problem is more apparent than real. For any paradox there is depends essentially on our being able to separate the energy of the molecule into distinct (independent) rotational and vibrational contributions. Now at temperatures at which $C_{v,\text{vib}}$ has its full classical value it may well be that (speaking pictorially) transverse vibrations of the linear molecule are so pronounced as to make it illegitimate any longer to regard the molecule as linear at all. That is not to say that such will, necessarily, be the case. There may be temperature regions in which (9) and (10) are valid: but then the molecule does 'know whether it is linear or not' and no question arises.

The second possible perplexity comes from a comparison not of equations (9) and (10) but of equations (4) and (5). For if we put $A = B$ and $C = 0$ in (5) we do not recapture (4) although, physically, we appear to have passed smoothly from the case of a non-linear polyatomic molecule to that of a linear polyatomic molecule. Why is this?

No very simple explanation of this second paradox can be given in terms of classical mechanics. But we can answer the question at once in quantal terms. For as C becomes small, that part of the rotational energy which comes from rotation about $O3$ becomes rapidly quantized (i.e. the effects of quantization begin to show) and when C is very small indeed (as for a linear molecule) the step from the ground state to the first excited state, as far as this part of the energy is concerned, becomes so great that, to all intents and purposes, it is never made. Provided that the other part of the rotational partition function can be treated classically (as is the case) we have now no difficulty in understanding the apparently abrupt transition from (5) to (4).

4. From the expressions so far obtained for the factors contributing to the partition function of a rigid polyatomic molecule we can at once derive expressions for the corresponding thermodynamic functions. Thus if the assembly is a perfect one-component gas (i.e. comprises N identical, non-localized, independent systems in a volume V at temperature T) then, by equation (3′) of Chapter III, the Helmholtz free energy is given by

$$F = -kT \ln \frac{(\text{p.f.})^N}{N!},$$

and thence

$$S = -\left(\frac{\partial F}{\partial T}\right)_V$$

$$= k\frac{\partial}{\partial T}\left(T \ln \frac{(\text{p.f.})^N}{N!}\right)$$

$$= k\frac{\partial}{\partial T}\left[T \ln \frac{(\text{p.f.})^N_{\text{trans}}}{N!}(\text{p.f.})^N_{\text{el}}(\text{p.f.})^N_{\text{vib}}(\text{p.f.})^N_{\text{rot}}\right]$$

$$= k\frac{\partial}{\partial T}\left[T \ln \frac{(\text{p.f.})^N_{\text{trans}}}{N!}\right] + Nk\frac{\partial}{\partial T}[T \ln(\text{p.f.})_{\text{el}}] +$$

$$+ Nk\frac{\partial}{\partial T}[T \ln(\text{p.f.})_{\text{vib}}] + Nk\frac{\partial}{\partial T}[T \ln(\text{p.f.})_{\text{rot}}]. \quad (11)$$

The first term on the right-hand side of (11) represents the translational entropy of the gas and leads, as we have already seen (Chapter III, equation (17)), to the Sackur–Tetrode formula,

$$S_{\text{trans}} = \tfrac{5}{2}R + \tfrac{5}{2}R \ln T - R \ln P + R \ln \frac{(2\pi m)^{\frac{3}{2}} k^{\frac{5}{2}}}{h^3}, \text{ per mole.}$$

The second term on the r.h.s. of (11) is the contribution to the entropy due to uncertainty of the electronic state of any system, and, as we said in § 1 above, it is generally accurately represented by

$$S_{\text{el}} = R \ln \omega_1, \quad \text{per mole,}$$

where ω_1 is the degeneracy of the electronic ground-state.† The third and fourth terms give the vibrational and rotational contributions to the entropy, S_{vib} and S_{rot}, when we use the above expressions, (3), (4), and (5), for the vibrational and rotational partition functions.

In order to employ these formulae, in connexion with any particular perfect gas, we must know the values of the fundamental frequencies, ν_i, and the moments of inertia, A, B, C of the systems concerned. We have, however, already indicated, in the last chapter, how these quantities are, at least in principle, derivable spectroscopically.‡ Consequently, spectroscopic study of the light (radiation) emitted, or absorbed, by a gas provides data which, in conjunction with the above statistical formulae, enable us to derive a value for the entropy of the (gaseous) assembly. Indeed, we can deduce the entropy, per mole, at any temperature and pressure, provided only that we are really dealing with independent systems, i.e. provided that the perfect-gas law, $PV = NkT$, is satisfied.

In the same way we can, of course, calculate, from the partition function, values for all other thermodynamic properties of the assembly. We have singled out the entropy for special attention simply on account of its particular interest in connexion with Nernst's law, or the so-called third law of thermodynamics.

Since the basic equations expressing the first and second laws

---

† Most often $\omega_1 = 1$, so that $S_{\text{el}} = 0$.

‡ The assumption that the rotational and vibrational energies are separable can be avoided, when necessary: the composite rotatory-vibratory energy levels being deduced directly from the observed spectrum.

of thermodynamics relate, respectively, to small *changes* in the internal energy and entropy of an assembly, it is evident that only *differences* in these thermodynamic properties, between two conditions of an assembly, have any real meaning. Likewise, of course, we can only *measure* differences in these quantities, and not their absolute values.

The entropy change in an assembly in going from the thermo-dynamic state specified by (T_1, P, N) to that specified by (T_2, P, N) is given by

$$\Delta S = \int_{T_1}^{T_2} \frac{\delta Q}{T} = \int_{T_1}^{T_2} \frac{C_p \, dT}{T}, \tag{12}$$

where C_p is the specific heat at constant pressure. If, in going from T_1 to T_2, we pass through a temperature, T_m say, at which the assembly undergoes a phase change with latent heat Λ_m, then on the r.h.s. of (12) we have also a term Λ_m/T_m corresponding to the sudden change in the entropy of the assembly on passing through the temperature T_m. But, for brevity, we shall not include such a term explicitly in (12), leaving it to be understood that such a term is to be added, when necessary, at each phase change.

If, as appears always to be the case, the integral in (12) con-verges as T_1 tends to zero, the absolute zero of temperature on the Kelvin scale, then we can write

$$S(T) - S(0) = \int_0^T \frac{C_p}{T} dT$$

or

$$S(T) = \int_0^T \frac{C_p}{T} dT + S(0), \tag{13}$$

where we may call $S(0)$ the entropy of the assembly at absolute zero. And we see that if, in any way, we can fix $S(0)$ then, from sufficient *calorimetric* data (values of C_p, Λ_m, T_m) we can compute the value of S at any temperature.

With regard to $S(0)$, the integration constant in (13), Nernst suggested, on experimental grounds, the simple hypothesis,

$$\Delta S(0) = 0 \text{ for all chemical changes}, \tag{14}$$

whilst Planck later advanced the apparently stronger postulate†

$$S(0) = 0 \text{ for all assemblies.} \qquad (15)$$

The equalities (14) or (15) are variously regarded as expressing
the so-called third law of thermodynamics. The question we have
now (see paragraph 5, below) to answer is, Does statistical theory
provide any evidence for, or against, either of these hypotheses?

In order to do so intelligibly, we must first be quite clear about
two things. It is convenient, and customary, to denote the value
of S calculated, by means of the above statistical formulae, from
spectroscopic data, by S_{spec}; and likewise to denote the value
calculated from calorimetric data, using equation (13) and Planck's
postulate (15), by S_{calor}. And the first thing which has to be clearly
understood is the precise meaning of S_{spec}.

S_{spec}, calculated as already described, appears at first sight to
depend solely on properties of the gas phase. It is, for instance,
the sum of translational, vibrational, and rotational contributions
all of which have meaning only for the gaseous assembly.‡ We
must, therefore, ask, From what zero of entropy, or standard state
of the assembly, is this entropy estimated? The answer to this
is not to be found in the statistical formulae so far given in this
chapter. For these formulae are valid, in any real sense, only for
temperatures at which the assembly behaves as a perfect gas, and
certainly cannot be extrapolated to very low temperatures. But
the answer is revealed at once when we remember that all these
formulae derive from our fundamental hypothesis

$$S(E, V, N) = k \ln \Omega(E, V, N),$$

and express this hypothesis with exactitude provided that, at the
temperature concerned, the model used (in the present case that
of a perfect gas of rigid molecules) is applicable to the assembly
under consideration. Thus, *the zero of entropy which is implied in*

† Strictly, Planck maintained this only for chemically pure substances. The
chemical changes covered by Nernst's hypothesis included physical changes, such
as changes in pressure, and allotropic changes, as well as chemical reactions.

‡ It is true that molecular vibrations persist, almost unchanged, in a liquid
phase, but that is neither here nor there. Even if this were not so we should
still not be led to modify our calculated value of S_{spec}.

the calculation of S_{spec} is one which corresponds to a physical state of the assembly for which $\Omega(E, V, N) = 1$. In other words, S_{spec} gives the difference in entropy between the actual gaseous state of the assembly and a state of the assembly, real or hypothetical, in which there is absolutely no randomness, i.e. in which there is no choice of, nor ignorance about, the configuration of the systems.

It may, perhaps, be held that this answer to our question merely transfers attention from S to Ω without making the general situation much clearer. But this is far from true. For Ω is a perfectly definite mechanical concept, being the number of independent stationary states of the whole assembly corresponding to the energy E. Now theory suggests, and experiment confirms, that Ω increases with E. Consequently Ω *can* have the value unity only if the assembly is certainly in its lowest possible energy state and, therefore, only if the assembly is at the absolute zero of temperature. For complete generality, however, let us denote the degeneracy of the lowest energy state of the whole assembly by Ω_0. Then, if Ω is the number of complexions of the assembly in the gaseous state specified by (T, V, N), the gain in entropy between absolute zero and the temperature T is

$$k \ln \Omega - k \ln \Omega_0. \tag{16}$$

But, as we have seen, $k \ln \Omega$ is simply S_{spec}; and equation (13) with $S(0) = 0$ shows that this particular entropy change is the value we adopt for S_{calor}. Consequently

$$S_{\text{calor}} = S_{\text{spec}} - k \ln \Omega_0,$$

or

$$S_{\text{spec}} = S_{\text{calor}} + k \ln \Omega_0. \tag{17}$$

This brings us, however, to the second matter on which a clear understanding is essential: the nature of the extrapolation of the thermal data at very low temperatures.

In practice, measurement of the specific heat may be made, calorimetrically, at closely spaced temperatures down to, perhaps, $10°$ K., but thereafter measurements become impracticable. Fig. 25 shows, schematically, the low-temperature end of such a series of measurements, T_1 being the lowest temperature reached. At these very low temperatures molecular rotation is generally impossible, on account of intermolecular forces, and, in the absence of contrary evidence, it is natural to suppose that the only energy still to be frozen out is that due to low-frequency vibrations of the solid state. The final extrapolation to absolute zero is, therefore, usually made, graphically, on the basis of Debye's theory

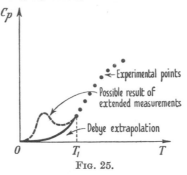

FIG. 25.

(see Chapter II) on which C_p is proportional† to T'^3 as T approaches zero.

There is still, however, the possibility that there exist energy levels of the assembly (other than these remaining vibrational levels) so low that they are small compared even with the yardstick of low-temperature thermal energy, kT_1. And if this is so we should expect such levels to produce a hump in the C_p curve (see Fig. 15, Chapter VI) which would be revealed by measurements at temperatures between T_1 and zero. In this case, then, extended calorimetric measurements, if practicable, would lead to a greater value for the calculated calorimetric entropy, S_{calor}. Consequently S_{calor} relates, in a certain sense, to the temperature T_1. We may forget about the low lying vibrational levels, for these are probably correctly accounted for by the Debye extrapolation. Then, apart from this vibrational extrapolation, S_{calor} effectively treats T_1 as absolute zero: so (17) ought, strictly, to read

$$S_{\text{spec}} = S_{\text{calor}} + k \ln \Omega_1, \qquad (18)$$

where Ω_1 is the number of complexions of the assembly corresponding not to absolute zero but to the temperature T_1 (omitting factors due to the low vibrational levels).

† For condensed phases, C_p and C_v are indistinguishable at very low temperatures.

It is, however, quite impossible in practice to distinguish between (17) and (18). Absolute zero cannot be actually attained. When comparison between S_{spec} and S_{calor} leads, on the basis of (17) or (18), to the conclusion that Ω_0 or Ω_1 is *not* unity then, so far, we must recognize two possibilities. Either the lowest energy level of the assembly is strictly degenerate (weight factor Ω_0) or there is a group of levels, corresponding to energy differences small compared with kT_1, which are still occupied randomly (weight factor Ω_1). Of these alternatives the second is probably the more likely: but there is a third possibility which is more likely than either of them. On cooling the assembly down to T_1 the systems may have become so clamped, by intermolecular forces, that they are not now free to move into positions which would, could they be realized, actually correspond to states of lower energy. The solid is then in a state of *metastable* equilibrium. In this case further cooling will not realize a hump in C_p as described above, but, even so, an equation analogous to (18) remains valid: we may write it as

$$S_{\text{spec}} - S_{\text{calor}} + k \ln \Omega_2, \qquad (19)$$

Ω_2 being the number of equally probable complexions in the metastable state.

The reader may here object that, since the metastable state is 'frozen in' the assembly is in a perfectly definite state and not free to choose among Ω_2 possible such states. This, however, is to misunderstand the

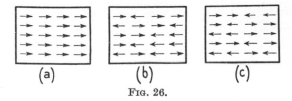

(a)   (b)   (c)

FIG. 26.

significance of Ω_2. By way of illustration we may consider, as the assembly, a crystal of heteronuclear diatomic molecules each of which we can represent by a short arrow. Let the 'ordered' arrangement of Fig. 26 (a) correspond to the true equilibrium state of the assembly at the low temperature T_1, and suppose that, on cooling, the systems get clamped in the random configuration of Fig. 26 (b).

Now assume that we have sample assemblies corresponding to both cases, (a) and (b), both at temperature T_1, and that we raise the temperature of both samples to a temperature T_2 at which the equilibrium state of the assembly corresponds, Fig. 26 (c), to a random arrangement, as in (b), but for which there is no longer any question of metastability. Then in case (i), (a) to (c), there is a gain of configurational entropy given by $k \ln 2^N$, since at T_2 each system has an arbitrary choice of two directions which it does not possess at T_1. And since the energy in (a) is less than that in (c) the specific heat curve between T_1 and T_2 will exhibit a hump accordingly. In case (ii), (b) to (c), however, no gain of configurational energy will be determined calorimetrically: the configurational entropy of (b) is simply the configurational entropy of (c) which has become 'frozen in' on lowering the temperature from T_2 to T_1. The sense in which we have referred to 'equally probable' complexions at T_1, at the end of the above paragraph, is justified since there is a one-to-one correspondence between configurations of (c) and configurations in which the metastable state (b) might be realized. It is for this reason, of course, that the symbol Ω_2, rather than Ω_1, has been used.

It is not possible to decide between the three possibilities represented by equations (17), (18), and (19) simply on the basis of a comparison between S_{spec} and S_{calor}. Which situation actually obtains must be decided on other, physical, grounds. But such a comparison does suffice to give us Ω^0 (Ω^0 standing for either Ω_0, Ω_1, or Ω_2) the number, apart from any vibrational factor, of alternative complexions persisting (or frozen in) at the lowest temperature reached in the calorimetric measurements: and thus contributes markedly to our knowledge of the microscopic properties of solids at very low temperatures.

After the above careful consideration of the precise meanings of S_{spec} and S_{calor} we are in a much better position from which to discuss the so-called third law. Our equation

$$S_{\text{spec}} = S_{\text{calor}} + k \ln \Omega^0, \tag{20}$$

or $$k \ln \Omega = S_{\text{calor}} + k \ln \Omega^0,$$

or $$S_{\text{calor}} = k \ln \Omega - k \ln \Omega^0 \tag{21}$$

shows plainly that S_{calor} is an entropy difference, and not an absolute entropy. Any suggestion that we have surreptitiously assumed the third law in evaluating S_{calor} is quite unfounded. The equation

$$S(T) = \int_0^T \frac{C_p}{T} dT + S(0), \quad \text{with} \quad S(0) = 0,$$

although introduced above in order to provide a basis for our discussion, does not really define S_{calor} at all. We see now that S_{calor} is simply *the best attempt we can make* to evaluate $\int_0^T C_p/T \,.\, dT$ from thermal data: and, apart from the vibrational extrapolation, would be more accurately written

$$\int_{T^0}^T \frac{C_p}{T} dT,$$

where T^0 is the temperature to which the degeneracy Ω^0 corresponds.

5. In statistical terms, Nernst's form of the third law of thermodynamics can be expressed simply as

$\Delta(\sum \ln \Omega^0) = 0$ *for all chemical changes provided T_1 is taken low enough,* (i)

while Planck's stronger postulate would assert that

Ω^0 *has, for all assemblies, the value unity.* (ii)

Neither of these hypotheses can be proved true; and, indeed, there is every reason to suppose that they are both false. After justifying this statement we shall proceed, very briefly, to indicate something of the true significance of Nernst's valuable concept.

We shall deal first with the stronger postulate, (ii) above. Clearly, from equation (21), S_{calor} is unchanged if we multiply both Ω and Ω^0 by the same quantity. Thus if we have omitted any factor from Ω, a comparison of S_{spec} and S_{calor} leads to a value of Ω^0 from which this factor is also omitted. Now, in the discussion above, factors have indeed been omitted from the evaluation of Ω: we have not, for instance, included a weight factor to take account of nuclear spin degeneracy (i.e. arbitrary directions of the spins of the atomic nuclei). The fact that, in many cases, comparison between S_{calor} and S_{spec} leads to the conclusion that $\Omega^0 = 1$ simply shows that even at the lowest temperatures reached (T_1 above) the nuclear spins are still as randomly directed in the solid as they are in the gaseous state of the molecules concerned. If, in such a case, we could reach lower temperatures we should expect the spins to become preferentially orientated; and then, if we *persist* in omitting the spin weight factor from Ω we must expect Ω^0 to have a fractional value less than unity (so that $\ln\Omega^0$ is negative). Thus, as indeed is obvious, the value we obtain for Ω^0 depends not only on the low temperature, T_1, but also on the value assigned to Ω.

In the same way, we have omitted from Ω any factor due to the presence of different *isotopes* of the species constituting the assembly. Once again if, as is often the case, having omitted this factor a comparison of S_{calor} and S_{spec} leads to $\Omega^0 = 1$ this simply shows that the isotopic statistical weight factor is the same at the low temperature, T_1, as at the high temperature, T: if we had included an isotopic weight factor in Ω then Ω^0 would have emerged equal to this new factor after a comparison of the values of S_{spec} and S_{calor}. There is, however, no evidence to show that isotopic separation will occur if the temperature T_1 is taken sufficiently low.† So, once again, the value of Ω^0 depends, somewhat arbitrarily, on the value we choose to adopt for Ω.

Now, in practice, we always do omit nuclear spin and isotopic weight factors from Ω. This is simply conventional (indeed, hydrogen is usually dealt with differently as far as nuclear spin is concerned): but it is a useful convention since it leads to $\Omega^0 = 1$ in many (but not all) cases at the low temperatures which are actually reached. Entropy values obtained, either thermally by extrapolation from temperatures at which nuclear spin orientation has not yet occurred or statistically, omitting nuclear spin and isotopic weight factors from Ω, are known as *practical* entropy values: and it is with these that we shall, in future, be concerned. It is, however, already evident that the hypothesis (ii) is quite meaningless. Any new knowledge about molecules which may lead us to distinguish between their states in such a way as to introduce a new factor into Ω will change the value of Ω^0 associated with any low temperature T_1 already reached.

† In this respect isotopic degeneracy differs from nuclear spin degeneracy. Although at fantastically low temperatures we might expect isotopic separation to be energetically favoured, it is even more certain that at such temperatures the solid would be frozen in a metastable state with the isotopic nuclei distributed randomly among the molecules.

Of the first postulate, (i) above, less need now be said. As it stands it lacks experimental validity. It is true that for many substances the practical values of S_{spec} and S_{calor} agree so well that we must conclude that $\Omega^0 = 1$ in each case: but there may well be compounds of these for which comparison of S_{spec} and S_{calor} leads to values of Ω^0 different from unity. And if, as is perhaps generally the case, the Ω^0 so obtained has the nature of Ω_2 in our discussion above, then there is no evidence that further cooling, even if possible, would resolve the metastability.

Having thus shown that two common, though crude, statements of Nernst's heat theorem are either false or meaningless and, at the same time, having indicated how a comparison of S_{calor} and S_{spec} can lead to valuable information about the behaviour of molecules in the solid state at very low temperatures we ought, before proceeding to an actual numerical illustration of such a comparison, to refer briefly to the present status of the third law. Applied to a single substance it has, as we have seen, no meaning.† But when formulated so as to deal only with entropy changes consequent upon isothermal reactions between chemical substances it can be made meaningful. Isotopic and nuclear spin weight factors always balance out in such reactions (and we may suppose that this is true likewise for any other, unknown, factors yet to be associated with the Ω's). Then a fairly unobjectionable statement of the third law is that, as the temperature T_1 tends to absolute zero the entropy change ΔS, occurring at the temperature T_1 consequent on the reaction, will also tend to zero *provided that metastable states of the assemblies are not involved*. This, however, is not the place to take the matter further, and the reader must be referred to the fuller discussions to be found in standard works (see Bibliography).

6. After the rather lengthy preamble of the last two sections we return now to our explicit statistical equations and give, by way of illustration, the results of using these formulae to calculate the practical spectroscopic entropy of water vapour at 25° C. and at a pressure of one atmosphere.

† We exclude from consideration here changes in the *environment* of the assembly, due, for instance, to changing an external magnetic field.

We have, of course, to specify the pressure as well as the temperature, since the pressure enters into the Sackur–Tetrode expression for the translational entropy.

We shall not give full details of the calculations, preferring to leave these as exercises for the reader: the molecular constants required are given in the examples at the end of the chapter. Here it is primarily important that we observe the relative magnitudes of the ensuing contributions to the spectroscopic entropy. Table V lists the values of S_{trans}, S_{rot}, and S_{vib} as calculated from equations (2), (5), and (3) respectively. For H_2O, $\omega_1 = 1$ while σ, the symmetry factor, has the value 2.

TABLE V

Contributions to the Spectroscopic Entropy of H_2O at 298·1° K. and 1 Atm. pressure

		Entropy cal./g. mol. deg.
S_{trans}	(Sackur–Tetrode equation)	34·61
S_{rot}	(Classical partition function)	10·48
S_{vib}	($\nu = 3,652,\ 1,592,\ 3,756$ cm.$^{-1}$)	0·00
		45·09

There are two things to notice about these values. First, that the dominant contribution is the entropy associated with translational motion. And secondly, that there is no contribution at all from the vibrational partition functions. This absence of any significant vibrational contribution is due, of course, to the fact that at 25° C. kT is equivalent to only about 200 cm.$^{-1}$ whilst all three vibrational frequencies for an H_2O molecule are very much larger than this.

We turn now to the details of the calorimetric entropy of H_2O at the same temperature and pressure. These are summarized in Table VI.

The last two items in this table do not particularly concern us here. They have to be included, of course, because the gas into which the water is evaporated at 25° C. is at a low pressure and must be compressed (hypothetically) to bring it to the standard state of one atmospheric pressure at which we have chosen to

TABLE VI

Contributions to the Calorimetric Entropy of H_2O at 298·1° K. and 1 Atm. pressure

	Entropy cal./g. mol. deg.
0–10° K.: Debye extrapolation	0·022
10–273·1° K.: C_p curve for ice	9·081
Melting at 273·1° K.: Λ/T	5·257
273·1–298·1° K.: C_p curve for water	1·580
Vaporization at 298·1° K.: Λ/T	35·220
Compression to 1 Atm.	−6·886
Correction for gas imperfection	0·002
	44·28 (±0·05)

compare the values of S_{spec} and S_{calor}. The correction for this pressure change is simply $R \ln P$, where P is the pressure, measured in atmospheres, of water vapour at 25° C.† The other correction, for gas imperfection, is due to the fact that even the low-pressure vapour into which the liquid is evaporated at 25° C. is not, on account of intermolecular forces, a completely perfect gas. In the spectroscopic calculation we assumed that the assembly concerned was a perfect gas. The final, small, correction then represents the difference in entropy between the actual gas produced on evaporating the water and a hypothetical perfect gas (of the same substance) at the same temperature and pressure. We would here observe further only that our standard state for comparison purposes is specified not simply by the temperature and pressure but also by the requirement that we refer to a (hypothetical) perfect gas of the substance concerned.

Next we notice that the calorimetric entropy for temperatures below 10° K., estimated on the basis of the Debye theory of crystalline specific heats, is very small—less indeed than the estimated uncertainty in the final result. This is not, of course, always the case: such contributions are frequently at least ten times as large as in the present instance.

Finally, we may remark that by far the largest contribution to the calorimetric entropy comes from the entropy of vaporization

---

† This may be proved either thermodynamically or from the Sackur–Tetrode equation.

of the liquid. This, of course, is entirely in accordance with what we should expect from the spectroscopic data of Table V. For the chief difference between a liquid and a gas lies in the possession by the systems of the gas of a large-scale translational motion of which they are not capable in the liquid phase.

Comparing the two results thus obtained, for S_{spec} and S_{calor} respectively, we find

$$S_{\text{spec}} - S_{\text{calor}} = 0.81,$$

i.e.
$$k \ln \Omega^0 = 0.81.$$

This difference is by no means negligible. Before attempting, however, to account for the discrepancy it will be well to give a short list, Table VII, of the results of similar calculations for other substances. The data are selected from the high-precision work of Giauque and his collaborators in America and relate, in every case, to the same standard state as was used in the comparison for water vapour given above. Fuller lists are available in many standard treatises on physical chemistry.

TABLE VII

Ideal gas (25° C. and 1 Atm.)	Practical entropy		$k \ln \Omega^0$
	S_{spec}	S_{calor}	
HCl	44·64	44·5	—
HBr	47·48	47·6	—
HI	49·4	49·5	—
O_2	49·03	49·1	—
Cl_2	53·31	53·32	—
CO	47·31	46·2	1·11
N_2O	52·58	51·44	1·14
H_2O	45·09	44·28	0·81
H_2S	49·10	49·15	—
C_2H_4	52·47	52·48	—
CH_3Cl	55·98	55·94	—

The general agreement between the values of S_{spec} and S_{calor} shown by the data of Table VII is most impressive and witnesses both to the experimental skill displayed in making the calorimetric measurements and to the accuracy of modern knowledge concerning the nature of simple molecules in the gas phase (on which the statistical calculations were based). It is with some confidence, therefore, that we can assign the outstanding discrepancies, listed to the right of Table VII, to a real departure, in these cases, of Ω^0 from the value unity. Now it is significant that CO and N_2O are both *linear, asymmetric* molecules; for after the discussion in paragraph 4 above we should not be surprised to find that, at very low temperatures, these molecules had become locked in metastable random arrangements (see Fig. 26). If this is so then we shall have, as was argued above,

$$k \ln \Omega^0 = k \ln 2^N = 1 \cdot 38 \text{ (per mole)},$$

which is certainly quite close to the observed discrepancy between S_{spec} and S_{calor} in these two cases. Indeed this is the generally accepted explanation of the value of Ω^0 for crystals of these molecules.

A somewhat similar explanation has been advanced to account for the result $k \ln \Omega^0 = 0 \cdot 81$ in the case of ice. Roughly speaking, it is suggested that even at temperatures approaching absolute zero there is a randomness (probably of the above metastable nature) in the mutual orientations of the water molecules. In detail, the theory gives $k \ln \Omega^0 = k \ln(\frac{3}{2})^N = 0 \cdot 81$ (per mole)—in quite remarkable accordance with the experimental value. Indeed, these eminently reasonable explanations of non-zero values of $k \ln \Omega^0$ furnish strong additional evidence of the accuracy of the thermal measurements and correctness of the statistical theory.

7. So far in this chapter we have dealt only with rigid polyatomic molecules: and these molecules have contained relatively few atoms. If similar comparisons, between S_{spec} and S_{calor}, are made for larger, more complex, molecules, again on the assumption that these have essentially rigid structures, then we are frequently led to rather large values for $k \ln \Omega^0$ which are not easily ascribed to properties of the solid state at absolute zero.

In such cases we must conclude that our evaluation of Ω, i.e. of the partition function for a single molecule in the gaseous phase, is incorrect, due to our having used an inappropriate model for the molecule concerned, and the model must be modified.

For instance, in the case of the dimethylacetylene molecule, C_4H_6, we have to assume that the two methyl groups are capable of free rotation about the axis of the C—C triple bond. On this assumption we obtain excellent agreement between the calorimetric entropy of dimethylacetylene and the spectroscopic, or statistical, entropy calculated from the partition function appropriate to such a system with two free-rotation groups. But the mathematical evaluation of the partition function for such a system is much more difficult technically than in the case of rigid structures, and the derivation of the appropriate formulae is certainly outside the scope of this book.

If, however, for the ethane molecule, C_2H_6, we assume free mutual rotation of the two methyl groups (about the C—C single bond) then we still find a significant difference between S_{spec} and S_{calor}. The same is true of propylene, dimethyl sulphide, propane, and other molecules involving methyl groups: neither the assumption of rigidity nor that of free rotation of the methyl groups leads to agreement between S_{spec} and S_{calor}. There are several reasons why these discrepancies cannot be ascribed to non-zero values of $k \ln \Omega^0$, but the simplest and most conclusive of these is the fact that the difference in magnitude between S_{spec} and S_{calor} depends, in each case, on the temperature, T, of the gas phase. This makes it quite certain that the discrepancies are due, at least primarily, to our using a wrongly temperature-dependent partition function to describe the gas molecules.

For this reason, it is now supposed that the methyl groups in these and other such molecules are neither rigidly attached to the general framework of the molecule nor capable of perfectly free rotation about the bonds attaching them thereto. It is, indeed, supposed that rotation of the methyl groups is opposed by the presence of potential barriers so that we have what is alternatively called *restricted* or *hindered rotation*. It is usually assumed that, for such a methyl group, these potential barriers are of the form

$$V = \tfrac{1}{2}V_0(1-\cos 3\psi), \tag{22}$$

where ψ measures the angular rotation of the group from some fixed position. The shape of this potential field is shown in Fig. 27: the field repeats itself three times in a complete rotation, corresponding to the fact that there are three equivalent positions of a methyl group when the rest of the molecule is fixed.

The statistical problem of calculating the partition functions of molecules possessing groups capable of such hindered rotation is decidedly complicated but has, nevertheless, been solved in many of the practically important cases. The corresponding values of the entropy, and other thermodynamic functions, have been tabulated (tables of Pitzer and Crawford): they depend, of course,

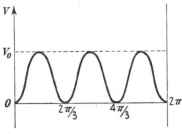

FIG. 27.

not only on the temperature, T, but also on V_0 and such other molecular parameters as the moment of inertia of the rotating group about its axis of rotation.

We have then, for the particular molecule concerned, to try to choose V_0 to produce agreement between the calorimetric and statistical entropy values at some one temperature: and the tables referred to above, once they have been constructed, allow us to do this without difficulty. The final test of the theory (unfortunately it is not always applied) is then to check that, with this particular value of V_0, the calorimetric and statistical entropies agree at other temperatures: when they do we then have strong evidence for the existence of potential barriers, restricting free rotation, of approximately the height V_0. Table VIII gives the values of V_0 at present associated with hindered rotation of the methyl groups in a number of organic molecules.

TABLE VIII

Molecule	V_0 in k.cal./g. mol.
Ethane	2·75
Propane	3·40
Isobutane	3·87
Propylene	2·12
Dimethyl sulphide	2·02

The origin of the restrictive potentials is uncertain. It is sometimes ascribed to repulsive forces between the hydrogen atoms
attached to the molecule: but this is still very much an open
question.

8. Restrictive potentials of the form represented by equation
(22) arise in other problems of physical chemistry besides the one
just instanced, and a qualitative understanding of their thermodynamic manifestations is very useful. Let us consider then the
kind of specific heat curve that we should expect to be shown by
an assembly of N independent 'restricted rotators' each governed
by a potential field of this kind. Each system is thus essentially
a small top with its point fixed and capable of rotating about a
fixed axis under the influence of a potential field of the type
depicted in Fig. 27.

At high temperatures, when $kT \gg V_0$, the restraining potential
will have negligible effect and each system will behave as a free
rotator. The partition function for such a free rotator, if its axial
moment of inertia is I, is easily shown to be given by

$$\text{(p.f.)} = \frac{2\pi}{\sigma h}(2\pi I kT)^{\frac{1}{2}}, \tag{23}$$

where σ is a symmetry number (equal to 3 for a methyl group).
From this we can at once deduce that the specific heat for free
rotation, i.e. the high-temperature specific heat of the assembly,
has the value $\frac{1}{2}Nk$, or $\frac{1}{2}R$ per mole of systems.

At low temperatures, when $kT \ll V_0$, the systems will be in
their lowest quantum energy levels which will be very much like
those of a simple harmonic oscillator: each system being effectively clamped in one of the hollows of the potential-energy curve.
Thus, at very low temperatures, the specific heat of the assembly
will resemble the specific heat of an assembly of harmonic oscillators at low temperatures, tending to zero as T tends to zero.

At intermediate temperatures, between these extremes, the
precise shape of the specific heat curve depends on the relative
magnitudes of I and V_0: a typical behaviour is illustrated schematically in Fig. 28. In some circumstances the maximum specific
heat may even exceed the value R appropriate to a simple

harmonic oscillator. To obtain the exact shape we must know
the magnitudes of I and V_0 and then refer to Pitzer's tables. But
it is sufficient here to observe the general form of the curve, and
the reader should contrast it with the other specific heat curves
for simple systems which have been given earlier in the book.

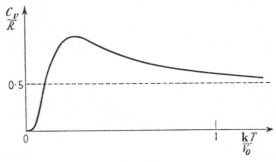

FIG. 28.

This brings us to the end of a rather long chapter mainly
concerned with the statistical evaluation of the thermodynamic
properties of single molecules: and with showing how a combination of statistical theory and calorimetric experiment can make
important contributions to our knowledge of the (microscopic)
mechanical properties of such systems. In the ensuing chapters
our principal concern will be with so developing the basic con-
concepts, or framework, of statistical mechanics that we are able
to deal with more general assemblies and not simply those comprising independent identical systems in one phase. First, however, we shall devote a single chapter to the problem of evaluating
the partition function for a system in an external field of force—
a problem on which we have already touched, though in a somewhat specialized way, in the present paragraph.

EXAMPLES

1. Show that equation (5) leads to a rotational specific heat, for a non-
linear rigid polyatomic molecule of $\frac{3}{2}R$, per mole.

2. Prove that the rotational entropy, per mole, of an assembly of non-
linear rigid polyatomic molecules is given by

$$S_{\text{rot}} = R[\ln(\text{p.f.})_{\text{rot}} + \tfrac{3}{2}],$$

where $(\text{p.f.})_{\text{rot}}$ is given by equation (5). (Cf. Example 4, Chapter VI.)

3. Using the numerical data of Chapter VIII, show that the Sackur-Tetrode formula may be written

$$S_{\text{trans}} = R(\tfrac{5}{2}\ln T + \tfrac{3}{2}\ln M - \ln P - 1\cdot164),$$

where M is the mass in grams of 1 mole of the substance concerned and P is measured in atmospheres. (Note: 1 atm. $= 1\cdot013 . 10^6$ c.g.s.u.)

4. Prove that for an assembly of non-linear rigid polyatomic molecules

$$S_{\text{rot}} = R(\tfrac{3}{2}\ln T + \tfrac{1}{2}\ln ABC - \ln\sigma - 3\cdot471),$$

where A, B, and C are in units of 10^{-40} g. cm.^{2}

5. Prove that for an assembly of linear rigid molecules

$$S_{\text{rot}} = R(\ln T + \ln A - \ln\sigma - 2\cdot695),$$

where A is in units of 10^{-40} g. cm.^{2}

6. For H_2O, $M = 18\cdot02$, $A = 1\cdot024 . 10^{-40}$, $B = 1\cdot921 . 10^{-40}$, and $C = 2\cdot947 . 10^{-40}$ c.g.s. units. Confirm the data of Table V.

7. Prove formula (23), giving the partition function for a rigid rotator having just one degree of freedom. $\left(\text{Hint: K.E.} = \tfrac{1}{2}I\dot\theta^2 = \dfrac{1}{2I}p_\theta^2.\right)$

POLAR AND NON-POLAR GASES IN EXTERNAL FIELDS

1. An electronic charge e situated in an electric field of strength F is acted upon by a force of magnitude eF, in the direction of the electric field.

Therefore, if we have two charges, $+e$ and $-e$, localized at the ends of a short rod PQ of length a, and both situated in the same external electric field F, then two forces, of magnitudes $+eF$

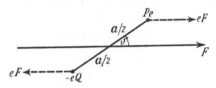

Fig. 29.

and $-eF$, will act on the rod at P and Q respectively. These constitute a couple tending to turn QP into the direction of the field F. If QP makes an angle ϑ with the direction of the field F (see Fig. 29), then the magnitude of the couple so exerted is $aeF\sin\vartheta$. Consequently the work done in turning the rod from the position in which it is parallel to F, $(\vartheta = 0)$, to one in which it makes an angle ϑ with F is given by

$$W = \int_0^\vartheta aeF\sin\vartheta \, d\vartheta = -aeF\cos\vartheta \Big]_0^\vartheta$$
$$= aeF - aeF\cos\vartheta.$$

This, then, is the potential energy of the charge system in virtue of its position, i.e. in virtue of its orientation in the external field.

The first term, aeF, is simply a constant and can be ignored: it is the same for all such systems whatever their orientation. We may, therefore, equally well write

$$W = -aeF\cos\vartheta,$$

provided we recognize that the zero of potential energy now corresponds to the position of the rod in which it is perpendicular to the field, $(\vartheta = \tfrac{1}{2}\pi)$.

Such a system of two equal and opposite charges is called an electric *dipole*. The product ae is known as the strength of the dipole, or electric dipole moment. It is usually denoted by the symbol μ. The potential energy of an electric dipole of strength μ situated in an electric field of strength F is thus given by

$$W = -\mu F \cos \vartheta, \tag{1}$$

where ϑ denotes the inclination of the dipole to the direction of the external field.

2. We may consider an assembly of N independent non-localized systems (a perfect gas) each of which carries an electric dipole of strength μ. Since we are assuming that the systems are independent, the gas must be at a low enough pressure for mutual interactions between the dipoles to be unimportant.† If this assembly is introduced into a uniform electric field, then each system will have a tendency (disturbed, of course, by its thermal motion) to turn so that its dipole points along the direction of the field. We can thus profitably ask the question, When statistical equilibrium is reached, how many systems are orientated so that their dipoles are inclined at a given angle, ϑ, to the external field? We shall treat this problem only on the basis of classical mechanics.

Naturally, since ϑ is a continuous variable, the answer to our question involves the determination of an angular distribution function, $n(\vartheta)$, given by an equation similar in type to equation (23) of Chapter IV and having the meaning that‡

$n(\vartheta)\,d\vartheta =$ equilibrium number of systems having their dipoles inclined at an angle between ϑ and $\vartheta+d\vartheta$ to the external field.

Moreover, since the expressions for the translational energy and the internal vibrational energy of a rigid molecule are quite independent of the orientation of the molecule in space (on the legitimate assumption that vibrational and rotational motions are effectively independent), we can at once make use of the general theory of Chapter V, § 5, and forthwith omit the translational and

---

† See § 7, below.

‡ At this point, where no confusion can arise, we drop the * from our former notation, writing $n(\vartheta)$ instead of $n^*(\vartheta)$.

vibrational motions of the systems from further consideration. The rotational motion of a system, however, is itself intimately associated with the angle ϑ (since the concepts of rotation and orientation are fundamentally inseparable). Consequently we cannot further factorize the partition function for a system into a rotational factor and an orientational factor: we are confronted simply with the statistical problem of systems which are able to rotate in an external field. For convenience, however, we shall denote the resulting partition function by (p.f.)$_\text{o-rot}$, the suffix o-rot. standing for 'orientational-rotational', and reserve the symbol (p.f.)$_\text{rot}$ to denote the corresponding partition function for free rotation, i.e. when $F = 0$. Our immediate problem, therefore, is to calculate the new partition function, (p.f.)$_\text{o-rot}$.

3. We have, essentially, already dealt with the purely mechanical problem which necessarily precedes the present statistical calculation. For when calculating the rotational partition function of a rigid polyatomic molecule (Chapter IX, § 3) we gave an expression for the rotational kinetic energy of such a molecule in terms of three Eulerian angles, θ, ϕ, and ψ, and the corresponding conjugate momentum variables, p_θ, p_ϕ, and p_ψ. The Eulerian angles concerned specified the orientation of the principal axes of the molecule $(O1, O2, O3)$ with respect to a set of axes fixed in space (Ox, Oy, Oz). Suppose now that we choose Oz to coincide with the direction of the external field, F; then, since the dipole of strength μ is supposed to be rigidly attached to the molecule, specification of the Eulerian angles θ, ϕ, and ψ will also, indirectly, specify the angle ϑ between the electric dipole and the external electric field.

Now the total energy of a system is the sum of its kinetic and potential energies. In the present case the kinetic energy is simply the kinetic energy of rotation, given by equation (7) of Chapter IX, while the potential energy is given by equation (1) of the present chapter. Introducing the new variables ξ, η, ζ, defined in paragraph 3 of Chapter IX, in place of p_θ, p_ϕ, and p_ψ, we thus have

$$\epsilon = \frac{1}{2A}\xi^2 + \frac{1}{2B}\eta^2 + \frac{1}{2C}\zeta^2 - \mu F \cos\vartheta, \qquad (2)$$

while, as before, the element of phase space $dp_\theta \, dp_\phi \, dp_\psi \, d\theta d\phi d\psi$ is given by $d\xi d\eta d\zeta \sin \theta \, d\theta d\phi d\psi$. Consequently we now have

$$(\text{p.f.})_{\text{o-rot}} = \frac{1}{h^3} \int \dots \int e^{-\epsilon/kT} \, d\xi d\eta d\zeta \sin \theta \, d\theta d\phi d\psi, \qquad (3)$$

where ϵ is given by (2). (Cf. equation (8) of Chapter IX.)

Since ϑ, a positional coordinate, is quite independent of p_θ, p_ϕ, and p_ψ, and therefore of ξ, η, and ζ, the integrations over these three coordinates can be performed exactly as before, and we obtain

$$(\text{p.f.})_{\text{o-rot}} = \frac{(2\pi kT)^{\frac{3}{2}}(ABC)^{\frac{1}{2}}}{h^3} \int\int\int e^{\mu F \cos \vartheta/kT} \sin \theta \, d\theta d\phi d\psi, \quad (4)$$

where θ runs from 0 to π and ϕ and ψ both run from 0 to 2π (see Fig. 24). In fact, it now appears that we may write, formally,

$$(\text{p.f.})_{\text{o-rot}} = (\text{p.f.})_{\text{rot}}(\text{p.f.})_{\text{o}},$$

where
$$(\text{p.f.})_{\text{o}} = \frac{1}{8\pi^2} \int_0^{2\pi}\int_0^{2\pi}\int_0^{\pi} e^{\mu F \cos \vartheta/kT} \sin \theta \, d\theta d\phi d\psi; \qquad (5)$$

but we must recognize that $(\text{p.f.})_{\text{o}}$ is not a true partition function, it is merely the factor by which $(\text{p.f.})_{\text{rot}}$ is modified due to the orientating effect of an external electric field.

Before proceeding to evaluate (5), it remains to add only that the new factor introduced into the rotational partition function is still given by this expression even when the molecule concerned is a diatomic or linear molecule. This being so, ϑ is then the same angle as θ, and (5) takes the apparently much simpler form

$$(\text{p.f.})_{\text{o}} = \frac{1}{8\pi^2} \int_0^{2\pi}\int_0^{2\pi}\int_0^{\pi} e^{\mu F \cos \theta/kT} \sin \theta \, d\theta d\phi d\psi, \qquad (6)$$

in which the integrations over ϕ and ψ can be performed at once to give

$$(\text{p.f.})_{\text{o}} = \tfrac{1}{2} \int_0^{\pi} e^{\mu F \cos \theta/kT} \sin \theta \, d\theta. \qquad (7)$$

But we shall postpone further discussion of this formula until we have more fully discussed the general case covered by equation (5).

4. At first sight equation (5) looks distinctly awkward mathematically. For if we assume that the electric dipole associated with the molecule points in a direction having direction cosines (l, m, n) w.r.t. the principal axes of the molecule, then it can be shown that

$$\cos \vartheta = -\sin \theta \cos \psi . l + \sin \theta \sin \psi . m + \cos \theta . n. \qquad (8)$$

In (8), l, m, and n are, of course, constants since the dipole is rigidly attached to the molecule (i.e. part of it): but even so the resulting integral still appears somewhat unmanageable. However, if we take another set of mutually perpendicular axes in the molecule, say $O1'$, $O2'$, and $O3'$, and if the Eulerian angles which specify $O1'$, $O2'$, and $O3'$ with respect to Ox, Oy, and Oz are called θ', ϕ', and ψ', then it can be shown that†

$$\sin \theta \, d\theta d\phi d\psi = \sin \theta' \, d\theta' d\phi' d\psi'. \qquad (9)$$

We have thus only to choose any set of axes $O1'$, $O2'$, and $O3'$ (fixed in the molecule) for which $O3'$ has the direction of the electric dipole, and change from the coordinates θ, ϕ, and ψ to the analogous coordinates θ', ϕ', and ψ'. For then ϑ is the same angle as θ' (angle between $O3'$ and Oz) and, using (9), (5) becomes

$$(\text{p.f.})_0 = \frac{1}{8\pi^2} \int_0^{2\pi} \int_0^{2\pi} \int_0^{\pi} e^{\mu F' \cos \vartheta / kT} \sin \vartheta \, d\vartheta d\phi' d\psi', \qquad (6')$$

which has precisely the same form as (6). Integrating over ϕ' and ψ' we obtain

$$(\text{p.f.})_0 = \tfrac{1}{2} \int_0^{\pi} e^{\mu F \cos \vartheta / kT} \sin \vartheta \, d\vartheta, \qquad (7')$$

which, of course, is indistinguishable from (7) (we have simply written ϑ for θ).

We have thus proved the somewhat surprising theorem that the factor by which $(\text{p.f.})_{\text{rot}}$ is modified due to the orientating effect of an external field on an electric dipole carried by a molecule is

† In mathematical terms, the Jacobian of the transformation,

$$\frac{\partial(\theta', \phi', \psi')}{\partial(\theta, \phi, \psi)} = \frac{\sin \theta}{\sin \theta'}.$$

Unfortunately a proof of this rather beautiful result is outside the scope of this book.

independent of the internal orientation of this dipole with respect to the principal axes of inertia of the molecule: moreover this factor is the same whether we are dealing with a linear or non-linear rigid molecule.

It is now an easy matter to complete the calculation. Putting $\cos\vartheta = x$, so that $\sin\vartheta\, d\vartheta = -dx$, $(7')$ becomes

$$
\begin{aligned}
(\text{p.f.})_{\text{o}} &= \tfrac{1}{2} \int_{-1}^{1} e^{\mu Fx/kT}\, dx \\
&= \frac{kT}{\mu F}\, \frac{1}{2}\, e^{\mu Fx/kT} \Big]_{-1}^{1} \\
&= \frac{kT}{\mu F}\, \frac{e^{\mu F/kT} - e^{-\mu F/kT}}{2}.
\end{aligned}
$$

But $(e^{z} - e^{-z})/2$ is the mathematical function known as $\sinh z$. Therefore, finally,

$$(\text{p.f.})_{\text{o}} = \frac{\sinh y}{y}, \tag{10}$$

where
$$y = \mu F/kT.$$

5. It follows now, from our previous work on internal distribution functions, in Chapters IV and V, that the equilibrium number of dipoles whose orientation is specified by ϑ, ϕ', and ψ', whatever the simultaneous values of their angular momenta may be, is given by

$$n(\vartheta, \phi', \psi')\, d\vartheta d\phi' d\psi' = N\, \frac{1}{8\pi^2}\, \frac{e^{\mu F\cos\vartheta/kT}\sin\vartheta\, d\vartheta d\phi' d\psi'}{(\text{p.f.})_{\text{o}}}.$$

Hence, since ϕ' and ψ' can have any values between 0 and 2π, the equilibrium number of dipoles making an angle between ϑ and $\vartheta + d\vartheta$ with the external field is given by

$$n(\vartheta)\, d\vartheta = N\, \frac{1}{2}\, \frac{e^{\mu F\cos\vartheta/kT}\sin\vartheta\, d\vartheta}{(\text{p.f.})_{\text{o}}}. \tag{11}$$

The reader should observe that when $F = 0$, (11) becomes

$$n(\vartheta)\, d\vartheta = N\tfrac{1}{2}\sin\vartheta\, d\vartheta = N\, \frac{2\pi\sin\vartheta\, d\vartheta}{4\pi}.$$

Now $2\pi\sin\vartheta\, d\vartheta$ is the area cut off from the surface of a sphere of unit radius, centre O, between two cones having Oz as axis and semi-vertical angles ϑ and $\vartheta + d\vartheta$ (Fig. 30). And the total surface area of a unit sphere is 4π. Consequently equation (11) could have been obtained on the assumptions that the axis of the dipole is, in the absence of an external field, equally likely to cut this unit sphere at any point and that the effect of the external field is to weight these *a priori* equally probable positions (orientations) with the Boltzmann factor $\exp(-W/kT)$.

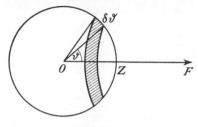

FIG. 30.

Equation (11) is often derived in this way: but the method obscures the essential dependence of the formula on the basic principles of statistical mechanics, and should therefore be regarded as more sophisticated and not more elementary.

Having obtained the required formula for $n(\vartheta)$, we shall now use it to discuss some macroscopic effects due to this partial orientation of the molecular dipoles in an external field. To obtain further insight into equation (11), the reader should plot $n(\vartheta)$ as a function of ϑ for various values of $\mu F/kT$.

6. For any one molecule, its dipole moment, μ, can be resolved into components with magnitudes $\mu \cos \vartheta$ along the direction of F and $\mu \sin \vartheta$ in a direction perpendicular to F. The latter direction is not, of course, the same for all the molecules; but since $n(\vartheta, \phi', \psi')$ is independent of the angle ϕ', a moment's thought (assisted by Fig. 31) shows that, for all the molecules of the assembly, the components perpendicular to F cancel out. Con-

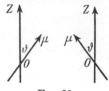

FIG. 31.

sequently the average dipole moment per molecule is directed along F and given by the average value of $\mu \cos \vartheta$: in other words, in an external field the assembly will behave as if each molecule carried a dipole of strength $\bar{\mu}$, directed along F and of magnitude given by the average value of $\mu \cos \vartheta$. We proceed first to calculate $\bar{\mu}$.

4973   M

From equations (11) and (5) we have at once

$$\bar{\mu} = \frac{\frac{1}{2}\int_0^\pi \mu \cos\vartheta \, e^{\mu F \cos\vartheta/kT} \sin\vartheta \, d\vartheta}{\frac{1}{2}\int_0^\pi e^{\mu F \cos\vartheta/kT} \sin\vartheta \, d\vartheta}.$$

We have already evaluated the integral in the denominator, and shown it to be given by

$$\frac{\sinh y}{y}, \quad \text{where } y = \frac{\mu F}{kT}.$$

The integral in the numerator follows at once, since

$$\int_0^\pi \cos\vartheta \, e^{y\cos\vartheta} \sin\vartheta \, d\vartheta = \frac{d}{dy}\int_0^\pi e^{y\cos\vartheta} \sin\vartheta \, d\vartheta.$$

We thus obtain†

$$\begin{aligned}
\bar{\mu} &= \mu \frac{d}{dy}\left(\frac{\sinh y}{y}\right) \Big/ \left(\frac{\sinh y}{y}\right) \\
&= \mu \left[\frac{y\cosh y - \sinh y}{y^2}\right]\frac{y}{\sinh y} \\
&= \mu \left[\coth y - \frac{1}{y}\right] \quad \left(\text{where } y = \frac{\mu F}{kT}\right).
\end{aligned} \tag{12}$$

(The function $\coth y - 1/y$ is usually denoted by $L(y)$ and called the Langevin function, of y, after P. Langevin who first showed its importance in the theory of ferromagnetism.)

Equation (12), which we may rewrite as

$$\bar{\mu} = \mu L\left(\frac{\mu F}{kT}\right), \quad \text{where } L(y) \equiv \coth y - \frac{1}{y}, \tag{12'}$$

shows at once that $\mu F/k$ behaves as a characteristic temperature as far as orientation (of a dipole of strength μ in a field of strength F) is concerned—a result which could have been foreseen from equation (5) since the temperature enters into (p.f.)$_0$ only through the combination $\mu F/kT$. To interpret our result further we must consider the behaviour of $L(y)$ as a function of y.

† $\cosh z$ stands for $(e^z + e^{-z})/2$, and $\coth z$ stands for $\cosh z/\sinh z$.

When y is small, we have

$$
\begin{aligned}
L(y) &= \frac{e^y + e^{-y}}{e^y - e^{-y}} - \frac{1}{y} \\
&= \frac{1 + \frac{1}{2}y^2 + \frac{1}{24}y^4 + \dots}{y + \frac{1}{6}y^3 + \frac{1}{120}y^5 + \dots} - \frac{1}{y} \\
&= \frac{1}{y}\left[(1 + \tfrac{1}{2}y^2 + \tfrac{1}{24}y^4 + \dots)(1 + \tfrac{1}{6}y^2 + \tfrac{1}{120}y^4 + \dots)^{-1} - 1\right] \\
&= \frac{1}{y}\left[(1 + \tfrac{1}{2}y^2 + \tfrac{1}{24}y^4 + \dots)(1 - \tfrac{1}{6}y^2 - \tfrac{1}{120}y^4 + \tfrac{1}{36}y^4 - \dots) - 1\right] \\
&= \frac{1}{y}(1 + \tfrac{1}{3}y^2 - \tfrac{1}{45}y^4 + \dots - 1) \\
&= \tfrac{1}{3}y - \tfrac{1}{45}y^3 + \dots,
\end{aligned}
$$

i.e. when y is sufficiently small $L(y)$ behaves like $\frac{1}{3}y$.

On the other hand, when y is large, e^{-y} is negligible compared with e^y and the term $1/y$ is also very small, so that

$$L(y) \to 1 \quad \text{for large } y.$$

In fact the function $L(y)$ has the form shown in Fig. 32. It is usefully described as a *saturation function* since, no matter how large y may be, $L(y)$ can never exceed the value unity.

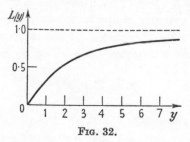

Fig. 32.

This saturation property could, of course, have been predicted on purely physical grounds, since obviously $\bar{\mu}$ can never exceed μ. But it is the behaviour of $L(y)$ for *small* y that we shall find of most immediate interest, and for the proof that this behaves as $\frac{1}{3}y$ we require the detailed investigation of the present paragraph. In terms of $\bar{\mu}$, the result may be written

$$\bar{\mu} = \frac{1}{3}\frac{\mu^2 F}{kT} \quad \text{when} \quad \mu F \ll kT. \tag{13}$$

7. Our purpose in calculating $\bar{\mu}$ was avowedly preparatory to our discussing a macroscopic manifestation of the orientational effect of the external field on the electric dipoles carried by the microscopic systems of the gaseous assembly. Speaking physically, we can now say that the effect of this field is to *polarize* the gas, producing a polarization (or dipole moment per unit volume) in the direction of F and of magnitude, P, given by

$$P = \frac{N}{V}\bar{\mu}. \tag{14}$$

At this point, however, we must pause to criticize the casual assumption made so far that F, the field acting on any particular dipole, is simply identical in magnitude with the strength of the external electric field in which the whole assembly is supposed situated. For the very fact that a polarization, P, is set up in the gas means that the microscopic dipoles, by tending to point along the external field, succeed in so aligning their own local fields as to produce a physically important polarization field within the body of the gas. This appears to conflict with our original decision to treat the dipoles as independent systems, but it can be shown that for a sufficiently dilute gas (i.e. for sufficiently low pressures) the above treatment is substantially correct provided that F, instead of being equated to the strength of the external field (which we may temporarily denote by E), is taken to be given by

$$F = E + \frac{4\pi}{3}P. \tag{15}$$

Here, too, we can further improve the physical plausibility of our model assembly by assuming that the effect of F on a system of the assembly is not only partially to *orientate* any permanent dipole moment that the system may carry, but also to *induce* an extra dipole moment in the system by distorting the electronic distribution of the molecule concerned. We shall suppose, in fact, that each molecule is *itself* polarized by the field F so that, besides bearing its permanent dipole moment μ, it has also an induced dipole moment, μ_i, given by

$$\mu_i = \alpha F, \tag{16}$$

in the direction of, and proportional to, the field F. The constant of proportionality, α in equation (16), is known as the *polarizability* of the molecule—and it will be noticed that we are here assuming that the molecule is equally polarizable in any direction. Since μ_i is, *ipso facto*, in the direction of F, this induced dipole moment will not affect the orientational effect of F on the permanent dipole moment; and the only modification in the above formulae, consequent on assuming the molecules to be themselves polarizable in this way, is in (14), which will now become

$$P = \frac{N}{V}(\bar{\mu}+\mu_i). \tag{14'}$$

Now it is a matter of physics that if the ratio of P to E is denoted by κ (the electrical susceptibility of the medium), then K, the dielectric constant of the medium, is given by

$$K = 1+4\pi\kappa. \tag{17}$$

In general, when $\bar{\mu}$ is given by (12'), K will not be independent of E and we shall have the phenomenon known as dielectric saturation. But, in practice, it is virtually impossible to observe dielectric saturation for a gaseous assembly since, as we shall see below, $\mu F/kT$ is always very small. Consequently (12') may be replaced by (13) and we have (from equations (13), (15), (16), and (14'))

$$P = \frac{N}{V}\left(\frac{1}{3}\frac{\mu^2}{kT}+\alpha\right)\left(E+\frac{4\pi}{3}P\right),$$

i.e.

$$\frac{\kappa}{1+\frac{4\pi}{3}\kappa} = \frac{N}{V}\left(\frac{1}{3}\frac{\mu^2}{kT}+\alpha\right). \tag{18}$$

For any particular sample of gas N/V is known: therefore measurement of the dielectric constant, K, enables us, on the basis of (17) and (18), to estimate the quantity

$$\frac{1}{3}\frac{\mu^2}{kT}+\alpha.$$

Actually, for all gases at pressures for which the above theory may be applied, κ turns out to be very small, of the order of 10^{-3}, so that we may legitimately ignore the denominator in the l.h.s.

of equation (18) and, on account of equation (17), use the simpler formula

$$\frac{1}{3}\frac{\mu^2}{kT}+\alpha = \frac{K-1}{4\pi}\frac{V}{N}. \tag{19}$$

The quantity on the l.h.s. of equation (19) may be called the total polarizability of the gas, per molecule, at the temperature T. On the basis of the above theory it consists of two terms: a temperature-dependent term involving the magnitude of the permanent electric dipole-moment, μ, of a molecule and a temperature-independent term which is simply the intrinsic molecular polarizability.

8. Since the r.h.s. of equation (19) can be determined experimentally, it is convenient to plot these experimental magnitudes

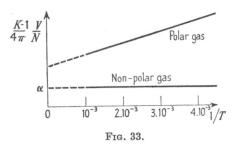

FIG. 33.

against the reciprocal temperature, $1/T$. For all gases, at not too great pressure, the plots are of the linear form predicted by the theory and shown schematically in Fig. 33. Extrapolation of these lines to the ordinate $1/T = 0$, determines α (the molecular polarizability) while the slope of the line enables us to calculate μ (the permanent dipole moment of the molecule concerned). When μ has a finite, non-zero, value we speak of a polar molecule, while when $\mu = 0$ the molecule is said to be non-polar.

Values of the constants μ and α determined in this way for a number of molecules are given in Table IX.

The first thing to notice is the units in which μ and α are expressed. If kT is expressed in ergs, and V in cubic centimetres then (regarding K as a pure number) μ is automatically given by equation (19) in electrostatic units (e.s.u.). The e.s.u., however, is an inconveniently large unit in which to express the electric

TABLE IX

Gas	$\mu \times 10^{18}$ in e.s.u.	$\alpha \times 10^{24}$ c.c./mole
HCl	1·03	2·63
HBr	0·79	3·58
HI	0·38	5·4
H_2	0	0·79
H_2O	1·84	1·68
CO_2	0	2·65
CH_4	0	2·61
CH_3Cl	1·86	4·56

dipole moment of a molecule, and the numbers actually listed in Table IX are given in terms of 10^{-18} of an e.s.u., i.e. in terms of so-called Debye units, where 1 Debye unit $= 10^{-18}$ e.s.u. This convenient unit in which to measure the electric dipole moment of a molecule is named after P. Debye, to whom the theory outlined in this chapter is due (1912).

It is also evident at once from equation (19) that α has the dimensions of cubic centimetres per mole.

Before commenting further on the data of Table IX, however, it is convenient here to verify numerically that the quantity y $(\equiv \mu F/kT)$ with which we were concerned in the general theory above is indeed small compared with unity—so that the linear approximation to $L(y)$ may be used legitimately. To verify this we shall calculate the value of F which would make $y = 1$ at room temperature when $\mu = 1$ Debye unit. We have

$$F = \frac{kT}{\mu}$$

$$= \frac{(1\cdot38 \cdot 10^{-16})(300)}{10^{-18}}$$

$$\approx 4\cdot1 \cdot 10^4 \text{ e.s.u.,}$$

i.e. we require

$$F \approx 4\cdot1 \cdot 10^4 \text{ dynes per unit charge}$$

$$= 12\cdot3 \cdot 10^6 \text{ volts per cm. (since 1 e.s.u.} = 300 \text{ volts).}$$

And an external field of the order of 10 million volts per cm. is certainly far beyond anything ever employed in the measurement of the dielectric constant of a gas. The approximation of replacing $L(y)$ by $\frac{1}{3}y$ is therefore legitimate.

Returning now to the data of Table IX, it is, for our present purpose, principally important to notice that whilst H_2O is a polar molecule, CO_2 is non-polar. This is strong evidence that H_2O has the well-known triangular structure, while CO_2 is a symmetrical linear molecule of the form O=C=O. Similarly, the fact that methane is non-polar provides evidence for the assumed tetrahedral symmetry of the CH_4 molecule. We thus see again how statistical theory, by relating together apparently unconnected matters (in this case the shape of a molecule and the variation of dielectric constant with temperature) can throw light on the basic problems of molecular structure.

We have dealt in this chapter only with assemblies of rigid systems (in the sense of Chapter IX) in the gaseous state. For non-rigid molecules a more elaborate discussion is necessary. Nor can the present theory be applied satisfactorily to describe the temperature variation of the dielectric constant of a liquid or solid. For in a condensed phase intermolecular distances are so small that the local polar fields of the molecules become extremely large. Dielectric saturation certainly occurs, but a more elaborate theory than the present one is required to give satisfactory quantitative agreement with the experimental data: and for this the reader must be referred to more advanced treatises.

EXAMPLES

1. Show that if we define an orientational energy by

$$E_0 = kT^2 \frac{\partial}{\partial T} \ln(\text{p.f.})_0$$

then $E_0 = -F\bar{\mu},$

where $\bar{\mu}$ is given by equation (12).

2. Show that the orientational specific heat, $C_{v,0}$, is given by

$$C_{v,0} = R\left[1 - \frac{y^2}{\sinh^2 y}\right], \quad \text{per mole, where } y = \frac{\mu F}{kT},$$

i.e. $C_{v,0} = R(\tfrac{1}{3}y^2 - \tfrac{1}{15}y^4 + ...)$, when $y \ll 1$, and thus that $C_{v,0}$ is generally completely negligible.

MIXED GASES AND THE LAW OF MASS ACTION

1. In the first ten chapters of this book we have considered a variety of problems in statistical mechanics, deriving the properties of assemblies (i.e. measurable thermodynamic quantities) in terms of the attributes of the systems (atoms, molecules, etc.) of which these assemblies are composed. In particular, we have dealt, if only briefly, with

(1) the specific heats of solids—Einstein model,
(2) the specific heats of gases—monatomic, diatomic, and poly-atomic,
(3) the dielectric constants of gases.

But all the assemblies with which we have been concerned have fulfilled three important conditions, apart from which we should not have been able to deal with them on the basis of the theory so far developed (Chapters I to V). They have been

(i) one-phase assemblies,
(ii) composed of identical systems (systems of one kind only), and
(iii) composed of independent systems.

Now as long as the third of these conditions is satisfied, i.e. as long as we are concerned only with essentially independent systems, there is no difficulty in extending the previous formulae to include multi-phase assemblies of mixed systems. It is only when the energy of the whole assembly is not simply the sum of independent contributions from the separate systems but involves also energies of interaction *between* the systems (as, for instance, in an imperfect gas) that real difficulties arise and an essentially more powerful technique is required.

It would, of course, be practicable to build up the tools of this more powerful technique at the present stage and then to use them to deal with problems for which they are not really needed. To do so would, indeed, effect some shortening of the statistical proofs of the formulae of the next two or three chapters. But it seems preferable to proceed more slowly, and to obtain greater insight into our present methods before enlarging their scope in any very fundamental way. We shall, therefore, proceed first to relax the conditions (i) and (ii) above, retaining the restriction to independent systems and retaining also the simple procedural technique to which we are accustomed.

The reader will, however, observe from henceforth a certain change of emphasis, which is quite deliberate. So far we have tended, especially in Chapters VI to X, to concentrate on the construction of partition functions appropriate to particular systems. For instance, we have evaluated

$$(\text{p.f.}) = \sum_i \omega_i \, e^{-\epsilon_i/kT} \tag{1}$$

for the rotational energies of a diatomic molecule, both on the basis of quantum mechanics and on the basis of classical mechanics. In future we shall generally not particularize partition functions in this way, but shall rather refer, for example, to $(\text{p.f.})_1$ and $(\text{p.f.})_2$ as the partition functions for species of types 1 and 2, respectively, leaving them further unspecified. These partition functions will each, of course, be given by an equation of type (1) (they are, indeed, merely abbreviations for sums like the r.h.s. of (1)), but we shall not usually evaluate them further. Consequently our statistical formulae will be quite general. The detailed application of these formulae to particular problems (such, for example, as the numerical evaluation of the equilibrium constant for the reaction between certain specific gases) is not our present concern. Such applications of the formulae which we shall derive, employing the partition functions evaluated in the past chapters, present no special difficulties; and many illustrations of their use are to be found in longer treatises and current literature. Our immediate aims are rather to reveal the basic structure of the fundamental statistical equations and to explain the statistical methods, and basic techniques, by means of which these equations can be derived.

2. Let us consider first the problem of two gases in separate containers but in thermal contact, so that they can exchange energy but cannot exchange systems. Then the assembly, i.e. the whole thermodynamic system with which we are dealing, can be represented diagrammatically by Fig. 34: it consists of two sub-assemblies,† labelled 1 and 2 and containing, say, N and M systems, respectively.

Let the systems of assembly 1 have allowed energies $\epsilon_1, \epsilon_2,..., \epsilon_i,...$ (for simplicity we shall put all degeneracy factors equal to unity)

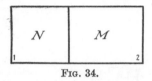

FIG. 34.

and let a state (strictly, a set of states) of this assembly be specified by the set of distribution numbers $n_1, n_2,..., n_i,...$, exactly as in § 1 of Chapter II. Similarly, let the systems of assembly 2 have allowed energies $\epsilon'_1, \epsilon'_2,..., \epsilon'_i,...$, and let a state of assembly 2 be specified by the distribution numbers $m_1, m_2,..., m_i,...$.

Then for given values of the n's there are

$$\frac{1}{N!}\frac{N!}{\prod_i n_i!} \tag{2}$$

distinguishable states of assembly 1: the factor $1/N!$ arises from the non-localization of the indistinguishable systems of this assembly, and the second factor is the number of ways n_1 systems can be given energy ϵ_1, n_2 systems given energy ϵ_2, and so on, it being supposed that the systems have first been rendered distinguishable in some way. Similarly, for given values of the m's there are

$$\frac{1}{M!}\frac{M!}{\prod_i m_i!} \tag{3}$$

distinguishable states of assembly 2. But these two distributions are independent (apart from a restrictive condition on the total energy of the whole assembly with which we shall deal in a moment) and any one of the distinguishable states (2) can be associated with any one of the distinguishable states (3) to give

† When no confusion is likely to arise, we shall usually refer to a sub-assembly of this kind simply as an assembly.

a certain definite state of the whole assembly. Thus, for the whole assembly, the number of states corresponding to the given distribution numbers is given by

$$t(n_1, n_2,..., n_i,...; \; m_1, m_2,..., m_i,...) = \frac{1}{N! \, M!} \, \frac{N!}{\prod_i n_i!} \, \frac{M!}{\prod_i m_i!}. \quad (4)$$

Therefore Ω, the total number of distinguishable states for the whole assembly, is given by

$$\Omega = \sum_{\substack{\text{(allowed } n\text{'s} \\ \text{and } m\text{'s)}}} t(n_1, n_2,..., n_i,...; \; m_1, m_2,..., m_i,...)$$

$$= \sum_{\substack{\text{(allowed } n\text{'s} \\ \text{and } m\text{'s)}}} \frac{1}{\prod_i n_i! \, \prod_i m_i!}. \quad (5)$$

We have still to lay down the restrictive conditions on the distribution numbers: but these are simply

$$\sum_i n_i = N, \qquad \sum_i m_i = M \quad (6)$$

and
$$\sum_i n_i \, \epsilon_i + \sum_i m_i \, \epsilon_i' = E. \quad (7)$$

The equations (6) hold since the two gases cannot exchange systems, and equation (7) holds since they *can* exchange energy and in dealing with Ω according to the methods of Chapter II we have to suppose that the total energy, E, of the whole assembly is given.

We assume now, as always, that only the greatest term in the sum on the r.h.s. of (5) contributes appreciably to Ω, and proceed to pick out this term, subject to the restrictive conditions (6) and (7), by the use of Lagrange's undetermined multipliers. We have, using Stirling's theorem,

$$\ln t = - \sum_i n_i (\ln n_i - 1) - \sum_i m_i (\ln m_i - 1),$$

$$\delta \ln t = - \sum_i \ln n_i \, \delta n_i - \sum_i \ln m_i \, \delta m_i = 0, \quad (8)$$

where
$$\sum \delta n_i = 0, \quad (9)$$

$$\sum \delta m_i = 0, \quad (10)$$

and
$$\sum \epsilon_i \, \delta n_i + \sum \epsilon_i' \, \delta m_i = 0. \quad (11)$$

Adding $\alpha_1(9)+\alpha_2(10)+\beta(11)$ to (8) we obtain

$$\sum_i (\alpha_1+\beta\epsilon_i-\ln n_i)\delta n_i + \sum_i (\alpha_2+\beta\epsilon_i'-\ln m_i)\delta m_i = 0,$$

whence

$$\alpha_1+\beta\epsilon_i-\ln n_i^* = 0,$$
$$\alpha_2+\beta\epsilon_i'-\ln m_i^* = 0,$$

i.e.

and

$$\left.\begin{matrix} n_i^* = e^{\alpha_1}e^{\beta\epsilon_i} \\ m_i^* = e^{\alpha_2}e^{\beta\epsilon_i'} \end{matrix}\right\} \quad (i = 1, 2,...), \tag{12}$$

where n_i^* and m_i^* give the important values, i.e. the equilibrium values, of the distribution numbers. Combining equations (12) and (6) we find, therefore,

and

$$\left.\begin{matrix} n_i^* = Ne^{\beta\epsilon_i}\Big/ \sum_i e^{\beta\epsilon_i} \\ m_i^* = Me^{\beta\epsilon_i'}\Big/ \sum_i e^{\beta\epsilon_i'} \end{matrix}\right\} \quad (i = 1, 2,...). \tag{13}$$

Returning now to the expression for Ω, and equating Ω to $t(n_1^*, n_2^*,..., n_i^*,...; m_1^*, m_2^*,..., m_i^*,...)$, we obtain, by using (12),

$$\ln\Omega = -\beta E - \alpha_1 N - \alpha_2 M + N + M \tag{14}$$

or, by using (13),

$$\ln\Omega = -\beta E + N\ln\sum_i e^{\beta\epsilon_i} - \ln N! + M\ln\sum_i e^{\beta\epsilon_i'} - \ln M!. \tag{14'}$$

Equating $k\ln\Omega$ to S, the entropy of the assembly, the thermodynamic formula

$$\left(\frac{\partial S}{\partial E}\right)_{V_1,V_2,N,M} = \frac{1}{T}$$

leads to the equation (see equation (21) of Chapter II)

$$\beta = -1/kT, \tag{15}$$

while the thermodynamic formulae

$$\left(\frac{\partial S}{\partial N}\right)_{E,V_1,V_2,M} = -\mu_1/T \quad \left(\frac{\partial S}{\partial M}\right)_{E,V_1,V_2,N} = -\mu_2/T$$

lead to the equations (see equation (25) of Chapter III)

$$\mu_1 = kT\alpha_1, \qquad \mu_2 = kT\alpha_2. \tag{16}$$

The reader should complete the steps in the derivations of equations (15) and (16), remembering that β is itself a function of E on account of equation (7).

Once again we can, without difficulty, identify k with Boltzmann's constant $\mathbf{k}$, given by the gas constant divided by Avogadro's number (see § 5 of Chapter III). Finally, therefore, returning to equation (14'), we have

$$S = \frac{E}{T} + k \ln \frac{(\text{p.f.})_1^N}{N!} + k \ln \frac{(\text{p.f.})_2^M}{M!}$$

or, in terms of the Helmholtz free energy, F,

$$F = -kT \ln \frac{(\text{p.f.})_1^N (\text{p.f.})_2^M}{N! \, M!}, \qquad (17)$$

where (introducing now the degeneracy factors ω_i and ω_i' for the sake of completeness)

$$(\text{p.f.})_1 = \sum_i \omega_i e^{-\epsilon_i/kT}, \qquad (\text{p.f.})_2 = \sum_i \omega_i' e^{-\epsilon_i'/kT}.$$

We have given the derivation of equation (17) at some length in order to remind the reader of the procedural methods developed in Chapters II and III. In future, however, to avoid wearisome repetition and inordinate wordiness we shall progressively reduce such arguments to the barest scaffolding of equations. The reader is advised to complete these arguments by carrying through any algebraic manipulations that have been suppressed: for only in this way can the basic structure of the equations be properly appreciated.

From equation (17) we see at once that we can write

$$F = F_1 + F_2,$$

where

$$F_1 = -kT \ln \frac{(\text{p.f.})_1^N}{N!}$$

and

$$F_2 = -kT \ln \frac{(\text{p.f.})_2^M}{M!},$$

i.e. where F_1 and F_2 are the free energies of the two separate 'phases' *evaluated at the same temperature* T. The result appears to be almost trivial, but it is not so. For we did not start from the assumption that the two sub-assemblies were at the same temperature, but merely assumed that they could *exchange energy*. If they had not been able to exchange energy (so that we dealt

with two completely separate phases) then in place of (7) we should
have had

$$\sum_i n_i \epsilon_i = E_1, \qquad \sum m_i \epsilon'_i = E_2$$

and (14) would have read

$$\ln \Omega = -\beta_1 E_1 - \beta_2 E_2 - \alpha_1 N - \alpha_2 M + N + M,$$

where β_1 and β_2 are the two parameters by which we should have
had to multiply the two new restrictive conditions which would
replace (11), i.e.

$$\sum_i \epsilon_i \delta n_i = 0 \quad \text{and} \quad \sum_i \epsilon'_i \delta m_i = 0.$$

We cannot then speak of $\partial \ln \Omega / \partial E$, but only of $\partial \ln \Omega / \partial E_1$ and
$\partial \ln \Omega / \partial E_2$, and there is no reason why the two separate sub-
assemblies should not be at different temperatures.

3. At first sight the substance of the last section has little to
do with the alleged topics of this chapter, i.e. with mixed gases
and the law of mass action. But suppose now that we have *a
single gas-phase of two components*, i.e. that we have

N identical non-localized systems having individually allowed
   energies $\epsilon_1, \epsilon_2, \ldots, \epsilon_i, \ldots$

and

M identical non-localized systems (of another kind) having
   individually allowed energies $\epsilon'_1, \epsilon'_2, \ldots, \epsilon'_i, \ldots$

in the same enclosure. We assume that thermal equilibrium can
be attained (say, by collisions) so that there is only one restrictive
condition on the total energy of the assembly, namely

$$\sum_i n_i \epsilon_i + \sum_i m_i \epsilon'_i = E,$$

where the distribution numbers have the same meanings as before.
Then a little thought will assure us that nothing has changed,
essentially, from the example of the last section, and that we
therefore still have, for this mixed gas,

$$F = -kT \ln \frac{(\text{p.f.})_1^N (\text{p.f.})_2^M}{N! \, M!}. \tag{17'}$$

At first sight this is a rather remarkable result, and perhaps
two comments will help to remove the apparent mystery. First,

we must not forget that the partition functions $(p.f.)_1$ and $(p.f.)_2$ involve as factors the volumes available to species of types 1 and 2, respectively. If the volumes, V_1 and V_2, of the two sub-assemblies of Fig. 34 are each precisely equal to the total volume, V, available to the mixed gas of the present section, then indeed there is no difference in free-energy or entropy between the two cases. The total free-energy or entropy of an assembly consisting of two different perfect gases, each at temperature T and volume V, is entirely unaffected by whether they are in the same container or in different containers. On the other hand, destroying the partition between the two sub-assemblies of Fig. 34 will certainly produce what is normally (though perhaps inadvisedly) called an entropy of mixing between the two different gases. For before the partition is removed, F contains the terms

$$-NkT\ln V_1 - MkT\ln V_2 \quad \text{(from equation (17))},$$

while after the partition is removed F contains the terms

$$-NkT\ln(V_1 + V_2) - MkT\ln(V_1 + V_2) \quad \text{(from equation (17'))}.$$

Thus on removing the partition we have a gain of entropy, ΔS, given by

$$\frac{\Delta S}{k} = (N+M)\ln(V_1 + V_2) - N\ln V_1 - M\ln V_2. \tag{18}$$

Although we normally call this an entropy of mixing it is essentially due to the lowering of the partial pressures† of the two gases concerned when the volumes available to them are increased.

Secondly, we must comment that equation (17') is *not* correct when the two species of system are *identical*, i.e. when the gas consists of only one component. For we know already that for a gas-phase of $N+M$ identical systems

$$F = -kT\ln\frac{(p.f.)^{N+M}}{(N+M)!}, \tag{19}$$

which is not the result obtained by identifying $(p.f.)_1$ and $(p.f.)_2$ in equation (17').

Equation (17), of course, is not affected by whether the two sub-assemblies do or do not consist of the same kind of species.

† See the Sackur–Tetrode equation, p. 136.

The argument of paragraph 2 above is certainly correct whether or not the set of levels ϵ_i is the same as the set ϵ_i'. But examination of this argument shows at once why, for a single gas-phase, equation (17') is valid only if we are concerned with two distinct species. In the case of the assembly of Fig. 34, even if the systems are all alike we still know that there are N on one side of the partition and M on the other side. To this extent then the systems are not completely non-localized. Similarly, for a single gas-phase containing N systems of type 1 and M systems of type 2 there are only N systems to which we can give any of the energies ϵ_i and in assigning these energies to the systems we can conveniently ignore the other M systems which are incapable of receiving them. On the other hand, when all the systems are alike the analogy between the two problems completely fails and it is not surprising that we then require to replace equation (17') by equation (19).

The fact that equation (17') has to be replaced by (19) when the gas phase contains only one instead of two distinct species of systems is known as the Gibbs paradox since, in essence, it was first pointed out by Willard Gibbs. Physically it produces the not very surprising result that if the two sub-assemblies of Fig. 34 contain the same gas *at the same pressure*, then there is no 'entropy of mixing' on removing the partition between them. For we now have (from (17) and (18))

$$\frac{\Delta S}{k} = (N+M)\ln(V_1+V_2) - N\ln V_1 - M\ln V_2 - (N+M)\ln(N+M) +$$
$$+ N\ln N + M\ln M$$
$$= (N+M)\ln\frac{V_1+V_2}{N+M} - N\ln\frac{V_1}{N} - M\ln\frac{V_2}{M},$$

which vanishes if $$\frac{V_1}{N} = \frac{V_2}{M},$$

i.e. if $P_1 = P_2$, since $$\frac{P_1 V_1}{N} = \frac{P_2 V_2}{M} = kT.$$

In so far as there is a paradox, it can be expressed in the question, How do the species know whether they are identical or not? But we must remember that it is we who have to ask this question, and not the species themselves. If we can recognize that we are dealing with different species, then we shall also be able to detect their entropy of mixing. (See § 3, Chapter IX, for the discussion of analogous 'paradoxes'.)

4. The above results can, of course, be extended without difficulty to include any number of different species in the gas phase. Thus if there are three species, 1, 2, and 3, then the free energy of the gaseous assembly is given by

$$F = -kT \ln \frac{(\text{p.f.})_1^{N_1}(\text{p.f.})_2^{N_2}(\text{p.f.})_3^{N_3}}{N_1! \, N_2! \, N_3!}, \tag{20}$$

where $(\text{p.f.})_i$ stands for the partition function appropriate to the ith species, and N_1, N_2, and N_3 are the numbers of systems of types 1, 2, and 3, respectively. These three numbers, N_1, N_2, and N_3 are, of course, supposed to be *known*: indeed it is essential to the whole statistical method so far developed that these three numbers are *given*.

We shall now tackle a different, and chemically more interesting problem. Suppose that we know that within a given volume, V, we have N_A A-atoms (or molecules, but we can conveniently speak of atoms) and N_B B-atoms, existing as a mixed gas. And suppose that the A-atoms and B-atoms can exist either independently, as such, or conjoined into AB-molecules. Then, *a priori*, we do not know the equilibrium number of AB-molecules (at any given temperature), but we shall find that this information is provided by the statistical theory. We require the thermodynamic properties of the assembly.

In order to make a direct statistical attack on this problem we have simply to introduce an appropriate notation and then go ahead in the usual way.

Let

$$\left. \begin{array}{l} \text{each } A\text{-atom have possible energies}\dagger \quad \epsilon_1^a, \ \epsilon_2^a, \dots, \ \epsilon_i^a, \dots \\ \text{and each } B\text{-atom have possible energies} \quad \epsilon_1^b, \ \epsilon_2^b, \dots, \ \epsilon_i^b, \dots \\ \text{and each } AB\text{-molecule have possible energies} \ \epsilon_1^{ab}, \ \epsilon_2^{ab}, \dots, \ \epsilon_i^{ab}, \dots \end{array} \right\} . \text{ (i)}$$

We may suppose that these energies are measured from the ground-state (i.e. the lowest energy state) of the appropriate system at

---

† For brevity we shall always assume that such energy-levels are non-degenerate. Note: a, b, and ab in (i) etc., are superscripts, and not indices.

rest: but if so then we must further let w be the energy of formation of a molecule AB from atoms A and B when all three systems
are in their lowest energy states. Thus we assume further that
AB has energy w less than $A+B$.

Then a specification of the assembly is given by the distribution
numbers

$$\left.\begin{array}{l} n_1^a,\ n_2^a,...,\ n_i^a,... \\ n_1^b,\ n_2^b,...,\ n_i^b,... \\ n_1^{ab},\ n_2^{ab},...,\ n_i^{ab},... \end{array}\right\}, \tag{ii}$$

and the number of different states of the whole assembly corresponding to the specification (ii) is (note the abbreviated notation)

$$t(n_i^a, n_i^b, n_i^{ab}) = \frac{1}{N_1!\,N_2!\,N_{12}!}\ \frac{N_1!}{\prod_i n_i^a!}\ \frac{N_2!}{\prod_i n_i^b!}\ \frac{N_{12}!}{\prod_i n_i^{ab}!}, \tag{21}$$

where

$N_1 =$ number of uncombined A-atoms in $= \sum_i n_i^a$
the given specification

$N_2 =$ number of uncombined B-atoms in $= \sum_i n_i^b$
the given specification

and $N_{12} =$ number of AB-molecules in the $= \sum_i n_i^{ab}$.
given specification

Then $$\Omega(E, V, N_A, N_B) = \sum_{(n_i^a, n_i^b, n_i^{ab})} t(n_i^a, n_i^b, n_i^{ab}), \tag{22}$$

where the distribution numbers have always to satisfy

$$\begin{aligned} N_1 + N_{12} &= N_A, \\ N_2 + N_{12} &= N_B, \end{aligned} \tag{23}$$

and $$\sum_i n_i^a \epsilon_i^a + \sum_i n_i^b \epsilon_i^b + \sum_i n_i^{ab} \epsilon_i^{ab} - N_{12} w = E. \tag{24}$$

The equations (23) ensure that the given N_A A-atoms and N_B
B-atoms are all accounted for (and no more), while equation (24)
fixes the total energy of the assembly as E. The last term on the
l.h.s. of (24) arises from the fact that every AB-molecule implies
a decrease w in the total energy.

We now proceed on the usual basic assumption that only the
greatest term, $t_{\max}$, in the sum on the r.h.s. of (22) contributes
appreciably to Ω. There are two ways in which we can pick out
this greatest term, and we shall consider them in turn.

Method 1. We first find the largest term for given values of N_1, N_2, and N_{12}, and then find those values of N_1, N_2, and N_{12} for which this term (so found) is itself a maximum. This means that, for simplicity, we attack the problem of finding the largest term in Ω in two steps.

Applying Stirling's theorem, equation (21) gives

$$\delta \ln t = -\sum_i \ln n_i^a \, \delta n_i^a - \sum_i \ln n_i^b \, \delta n_i^b - \sum_i \ln n_i^{ab} \, \delta n_i^{ab} \qquad (25)$$

and, when N_1, N_2, and N_{12} are fixed, the differential forms of the restrictive conditions are simply

$$\sum_i \delta n_i^a = 0, \qquad (26)$$

$$\sum_i \delta n_i^b = 0, \qquad (27)$$

$$\sum_i \delta n_i^{ab} = 0, \qquad (28)$$

and $$\sum_i \epsilon_i^a \, \delta n_i^a + \sum_i \epsilon_i^b \, \delta n_i^b + \sum_i \epsilon_i^{ab} \, \delta n_i^{ab} = 0. \qquad (29)$$

Using the method of Lagrange's undetermined multipliers, we multiply (26), (27), (28), and (29) by α_a, α_b, α_{ab}, and β, respectively, and add to (25), so obtaining the equations

$$\left.\begin{array}{r} \alpha_a + \beta \epsilon_i^a - \ln n_i^a = 0 \\ \alpha_b + \beta \epsilon_i^b - \ln n_i^b = 0 \\ \alpha_{ab} + \beta \epsilon_i^{ab} - \ln n_i^{ab} = 0 \end{array}\right\} \quad (i = 1,2,\dots) \qquad (30)$$

and

for the important values of the distribution numbers.

Substituting these values of n_i^a, n_i^b, and n_i^{ab} into the expression for $\ln t$, we find (cf. equation (14′)),

$$\ln t = -\beta(E + N_{12}w) + N_1 \ln \sum_i e^{\beta \epsilon_i^a} + N_2 \ln \sum_i e^{\beta \epsilon_i^b} + N_{12} \ln \sum_i e^{\beta \epsilon_i^{ab}} - $$
$$- \ln N_1! - \ln N_2! - \ln N_{12}! \quad (31)$$

where, on account of (24), β is given by

$$\frac{N_1 \sum_i \epsilon_i^a e^{\beta \epsilon_i^a}}{\sum_i e^{\beta \epsilon_i^a}} + \frac{N_2 \sum_i \epsilon_i^b e^{\beta \epsilon_i^b}}{\sum_i e^{\beta \epsilon_i^b}} + \frac{N_{12} \sum_i \epsilon_i^{ab} e^{\beta \epsilon_i^{ab}}}{\sum_i e^{\beta \epsilon_i^{ab}}} - N_{12}w = E. \qquad (32)$$

We first observe that $\left(\dfrac{\partial \ln t}{\partial \beta}\right)_{N_1,N_2,N_{12}} = 0$, since differentiating

(31) formally w.r.t. β reproduces (32). Consequently, in subsequent differentiation of (31), β may be treated as a constant. Then we proceed to the second step in finding t_{max}, namely to choose N_1, N_2, and N_{12} so that the expression on the r.h.s. of (31) is largest.

Since N_1, N_2, and N_{12} satisfy the restrictive conditions (23) we have

$$\delta \ln t = \left(\ln \sum_i e^{\beta \epsilon_i^a} - \ln N_1 \right) \delta N_1 + \left(\ln \sum_i e^{\beta \epsilon_i^b} - \ln N_2 \right) \delta N_2 +$$

$$+ \left(-\beta w + \ln \sum_i e^{\beta \epsilon_i^{ab}} - \ln N_{12} \right) \delta N_{12} = 0 \quad (33)$$

subject to

$$\delta N_1 + \delta N_{12} = 0 \quad (34)$$

and

$$\delta N_2 + \delta N_{12} = 0. \quad (35)$$

Again using the method of Lagrange's undetermined multipliers, we multiply (34) and (35) by a and b, respectively, and add to (33), so obtaining the equations

$$\left. \begin{aligned} a + \ln \sum_i e^{\beta \epsilon_i^a} - \ln N_1^* &= 0 \\ b + \ln \sum_i e^{\beta \epsilon_i^b} - \ln N_2^* &= 0 \\ a + b - \beta w + \ln \sum_i e^{\beta \epsilon_i^{ab}} - \ln N_{12}^* &= 0 \end{aligned} \right\} \quad (36)$$

and

If now we get rid of a and b between the equations (36), we obtain the equation

$$\frac{N_{12}^*}{N_1^* N_2^*} = \frac{\sum_i e^{\beta \epsilon_i^{ab}} e^{-\beta w}}{\sum_i e^{\beta \epsilon_i^a} \sum_i e^{\beta \epsilon_i^b}} \quad (37)$$

which, together with the two equations (23), suffices to determine N_1^*, N_2^*, and N_{12}^* in terms of N_A, N_B, and β.

Moreover, equating Ω to t_{max}, the equation $S = k \ln \Omega$ gives

$$\frac{1}{k} S(E, V, N_A, N_B) = -\beta(E + N_{12}^* w) + N_1^* \ln \sum_i e^{\beta \epsilon_i^a} + N_2^* \ln \sum_i e^{\beta \epsilon_i^b} +$$

$$+ N_{12}^* \ln \sum e^{\beta \epsilon_i^{ab}} - \ln N_1^*! - \ln N_2^*! - \ln N_{12}^*!,$$

whence, as always, the thermodynamical equation $\partial S/\partial E = 1/T$ leads to $\beta = -1/kT$. Consequently we obtain, finally,

$$E - TS = F = -kT \ln\left\{\frac{(\text{p.f.})_A^{N_1^*}(\text{p.f.})_B^{N_2^*}[(\text{p.f.})_{AB}\, e^{w/kT}]^{N_{12}^*}}{N_1^*! \; N_2^*! \; N_{12}^*!}\right\}, \quad (38)$$

where N_1^*, N_2^*, and N_{12}^* are given, in terms of N_A, N_B, and T, by

$$\frac{N_{12}^*}{N_1^* N_2^*} = \frac{(\text{p.f.})_{AB}\, e^{w/kT}}{(\text{p.f.})_A (\text{p.f.})_B} \quad (37')$$

together with

$$\left.\begin{array}{c} N_1^* + N_{12}^* = N_A \\ N_2^* + N_{12}^* = N_B \end{array}\right\}. \quad (23')$$

The partition functions occurring in (38) and (37') are, of course, given by

$$(\text{p.f.})_A = \sum_i \omega_i^a e^{-\epsilon_i^a/kT}, \qquad (\text{p.f.})_B = \sum_i \omega_i^b e^{-\epsilon_i^b/kT},$$

$$(\text{p.f.})_{AB} = \sum_i \omega_i^{ab} e^{-\epsilon_i^{ab}/kT},$$

where we have now introduced weight factors, for the sake of complete generality.

Before proceeding to the second method of obtaining these formulae, and then to discuss their physical significance, there is one comment which should obviously be made immediately. For we notice at once that the above equations would have been both simpler and more elegant in form had we decided initially to *measure all energies from the same energy zero*. To do so we have (see Fig. 35) merely to subtract w from all the energies at present occurring in $(\text{p.f.})_{AB}$. Our formulae then become

$$F = -kT \ln\left\{\frac{(\text{p.f.})_A^{N_1^*}(\text{p.f.})_B^{N_2^*}(\text{p.f.})_{AB}^{N_{12}^*}}{N_1^*! \; N_2^*! \; N_{12}^*!}\right\}, \quad (\text{I})$$

where

$$\frac{N_{12}^*}{N_1^* N_2^*} = \frac{(\text{p.f.})_{AB}}{(\text{p.f.})_A (\text{p.f.})_B} \quad (\text{II})$$

and

$$\left.\begin{array}{c} N_1^* + N_{12}^* = N_A \\ N_2^* + N_{12}^* = N_B \end{array}\right\} \quad (\text{III})$$

(where now, in all three partition functions, the energies are measured from the same energy zero). We shall adopt this better convention when describing the second way of obtaining the equations (I), (II), and (III). The heat of formation, w, was introduced explicitly above partly in deference to common custom and partly lest otherwise it should appear to have been entirely omitted from consideration.

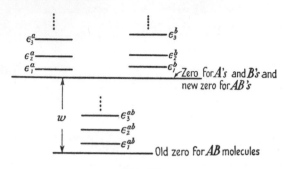

FIG. 35.

5. *Method* 2. The second method of deriving the above formulae is to go straight for t_{max} in one step instead of in two. We derive equation (25) as before, i.e.

$$\delta \ln t = -\sum_i \ln n_i^a \, \delta n_i^a - \sum_i \ln n_i^b \, \delta n_i^b - \sum_i \ln n_i^{ab} \, \delta n_i^{ab}, \qquad (25)$$

but now we deal only with the ultimate restrictive conditions

$$\left. \begin{array}{l} \sum_i n_i^a + \sum_i n_i^{ab} = N_A \\ \sum_i n_i^b + \sum_i n_i^{ab} = N_B \end{array} \right\}, \qquad (23'')$$

and

$$\sum_i n_i^a \epsilon_i^a + \sum_i n_i^b \epsilon_i^b + \sum_i n_i^{ab} \epsilon_i^{ab} = E. \qquad (24')$$

In equation (24') we have, of course, used the new, and preferable, convention in which all energies are measured from the same zero. The equations (23'') ensure that there are precisely N_A A-systems and N_B B-systems (combined or uncombined), and nothing more.

In differential form, the restrictive conditions read

$$\sum_i \delta n_i^a + \sum_i \delta n_i^{ab} = 0, \qquad (39)$$

$$\sum_i \delta n_i^b + \sum_i \delta n_i^{ab} = 0, \qquad (40)$$

and

$$\sum_i \epsilon_i^a \, \delta n_i^a + \sum_i \epsilon_i^b \, \delta n_i^b + \sum_i \epsilon_i^{ab} \, \delta n_i^{ab} = 0. \qquad (41)$$

Multiplying (39), (40), and (41) by $\bar{\alpha}_a$, $\bar{\alpha}_b$, and β, respectively, and adding to (25), we obtain the equations

$$\left.\begin{aligned}
\bar{\alpha}_a + \beta\epsilon_i^a - \ln n_i^{a*} &= 0 \\
\bar{\alpha}_b + \beta\epsilon_i^b - \ln n_i^{b*} &= 0 \\
\bar{\alpha}_a + \bar{\alpha}_b + \beta\epsilon_i^{ab} - \ln n_i^{ab*} &= 0
\end{aligned}\right\} \quad (i = 1, 2, \ldots) \qquad (42)$$

for the important values of the distribution numbers. Introducing the symbols

$$N_1^* \equiv \sum_i n_i^{a*}, \qquad N_2^* \equiv \sum_i n_i^{b*} \quad \text{and} \quad N_{12}^* \equiv \sum_i n_i^{ab*},$$

we obtain from (42) the formulae

$$n_i^{a*} = N_1^* \frac{e^{\beta\epsilon_i^a}}{\sum_i e^{\beta\epsilon_i^a}}, \qquad n_i^{b*} = N_2^* \frac{e^{\beta\epsilon_i^b}}{\sum_i e^{\beta\epsilon_i^b}}, \qquad n_i^{ab*} = N_{12}^* \frac{e^{\beta\epsilon_i^{ab}}}{\sum_i e^{\beta\epsilon_i^{ab}}}$$

$$(43)$$

and

$$\left.\begin{aligned}
N_1^* &= e^{\bar{\alpha}_a} \sum_i e^{\beta\epsilon_i^a} \\
N_2^* &= e^{\bar{\alpha}_b} \sum_i e^{\beta\epsilon_i^b} \\
N_{12}^* &= e^{\bar{\alpha}_a + \bar{\alpha}_b} \sum_i e^{\beta\epsilon_i^{ab}}
\end{aligned}\right\}. \qquad (44)$$

Substituting from (43) into the formula for t (equation (21)), we find

$$\ln t_{\max} = -\beta E + N_1^* \ln \sum_i e^{\beta\epsilon_i^a} + N_2^* \ln \sum_i e^{\beta\epsilon_i^b} +$$

$$+ N_{12}^* \ln \sum e^{\beta\epsilon_i^{ab}} - \ln N_1^*! - \ln N_2^*! - \ln N_{12}^*! \quad (45)$$

while from the equations (44) we obtain immediately

$$\frac{N_{12}^*}{N_1^* N_2^*} = \frac{\sum_i e^{\beta\epsilon_i^{ab}}}{\sum_i e^{\beta\epsilon_i^a} \sum_i e^{\beta\epsilon_i^b}}. \qquad (46)$$

On comparing equations (45) and (46) with the previous equations (31) and (37) we see that, apart from the new convention of a common energy zero, we have precisely the same equations as before. The identification of β with $-1/kT$ is unchanged, and from equations (45) and (46) we derive immediately the equations (I) and (II) above. The equations (III) follow from equations (23″) as a matter of course.

This second derivation of the crucial equations, (I), (II), and (III), has been given in bare outline only, and the reader should make certain that he can complete the arguments in detail before proceeding further. It is, essentially, a shorter method than the first, if only because one step is generally shorter than two. On the other hand the longer method perhaps better reveals the essential structure of the equations. In particular, it is instructive to compare the equations (30), (36), and (42): a matter to which we shall return later (see next chapter).

6. To appreciate the physical significance of the equations (I), (II), and (III) we need only refer back to equation (20) which gives the free energy of a gaseous assembly of three distinct non-combining species, i.e. of a mixed gas containing N_1 systems of type 1, N_2 systems of type 2, and N_3 systems of type 3. Equations (I) and (20) have precisely the same form. Consequently, we have proved that when equilibrium has been attained, then the free energy of the present gaseous assembly, of A-systems and B-systems capable of uniting to form AB-systems, is precisely the same as for a gas mixture of the three species *in their equilibrium amounts* (i.e. with N_1^* A-atoms, N_2^* B-atoms, and N_{12}^* AB-molecules).

This result is of the greatest theoretical, and practical, importance. For it means that if we know the equilibrium composition of the gaseous assembly at *a given temperature*, then we can entirely ignore the continuous interchange $A + B \rightleftarrows AB$ when calculating the free energy of the equilibrium state of the assembly *at that temperature*. If, however, we do not know the equilibrium composition of the assembly at the temperature concerned, but do know the partition functions for the three types of species, A, B, and AB, then we can calculate this equilibrium composition from the equation

$$\frac{N_{12}^*}{N_1^* N_2^*} = \frac{(\text{p.f.})_{AB}}{(\text{p.f.})_A (\text{p.f.})_B} \tag{II}$$

together with the constitutive equations

$$N_1^* + N_{12}^* = N_A \quad \text{and} \quad N_2^* + N_{12}^* = N_B. \tag{III}$$

Equation (II) is said to express the *Law of Mass Action* for the reaction $A + B \rightleftarrows AB$. The r.h.s. depends on T and also, through the energies ϵ, on V: in fact each partition function involves a factor V. We may therefore write

$$\frac{N_{12}^*}{N_1^* N_2^*} = K(V, T) = \frac{(\text{p.f.})_{AB}}{(\text{p.f.})_A (\text{p.f.})_B}, \tag{47}$$

where K, which is called the *equilibrium constant* of the reaction, is, for given V and T, independent of the amounts N_A and N_B of the two components concerned.†

EXAMPLES

1. Complete the steps, omitted above, in the derivation of equations (15) and (16).

2. Use equation (17') to prove that a perfect gaseous mixture, containing N systems of type 1 and M systems of type 2, satisfies the equation of state $PV = (N+M)kT$.

3. Two different gases, A and B, both at a pressure of 1 atm. are allowed to mix and the resulting mixed gas attains the pressure of 1 atm. The temperature is constant throughout. The mixed gas satisfies the equation of state $PV = nRT$. Calculate the entropy of mixing

(a) if, before mixing, there are equal volumes of A and B;

(b) if, before mixing, there are 2 volumes of A to 1 of B.

$$((a) \ \Delta S = 0 \cdot 69nR, \quad (b) \ \Delta S = 0 \cdot 64nR.)$$

4. Two different gases, each at the same pressure, are in adjacent containers (as in Fig. 34). The partition is then removed, the temperature remaining constant. Show that the entropy of mixing may be written

$$\Delta S = (N+M)(-x_1 \ln x_1 - x_2 \ln x_2)k,$$

where $x_1 = N/(N+M)$, $x_2 = M/(N+M)$.

5. Complete the details of the analysis of § 5 above.

6. At a given temperature and volume, a gas of AB-molecules is 50 per cent. dissociated into A's and B's. The volume is doubled, the temperature remaining constant. Find the new equilibrium dissociation. By how much is the original pressure reduced? (61·8 per cent.; 46·1 per cent.)

† This is true, of course, only as long as we are dealing with perfect gases.

LAW OF MASS ACTION (*contd.*): CHEMICAL POTENTIALS OF GASEOUS ASSEMBLIES

1. In the last chapter we proved that if N_A A-systems and N_B B-systems, capable of combining to form AB-systems, exist in a gaseous phase of volume V and at temperature T, then the Helmholtz free energy of the assembly is given by

$$F = -kT \ln \left\{ \frac{(\text{p.f.})_A^{N_1^*}(\text{p.f.})_B^{N_2^*}(\text{p.f.})_{AB}^{N_{12}^*}}{N_1^*! \, N_2^*! \, N_{12}^*!} \right\}, \tag{I}$$

where $(\text{p.f.})_A$, $(\text{p.f.})_B$, and $(\text{p.f.})_{AB}$ are the partition functions for an A-system, a B-system, and an AB-system, respectively, and N_1^*, N_2^*, and N_{12}^* are the numbers of systems of these three types in the equilibrium state of the assembly. Moreover, N_1^*, N_2^*, and N_{12}^*, which define the equilibrium composition of the assembly, are given by the three equations

$$\frac{N_{12}^*}{N_1^* \, N_2^*} = \frac{(\text{p.f.})_{AB}}{(\text{p.f.})_A (\text{p.f.})_B}, \tag{II}$$

and
$$\left. \begin{array}{l} N_1^* + N_{12}^* = N_A \\ N_2^* + N_{12}^* = N_B \end{array} \right\}. \tag{III}$$

We have already briefly discussed the physical meaning of these results, but we must now proceed to derive further consequences of these equations before their full significance can be appreciated.

First, let us calculate the pressure of the assembly from the thermodynamic formula

$$P = -\left(\frac{\partial F}{\partial V}\right)_{N_A, N_B, T}.$$

We remember that, on account of the translational motions of the systems, all the partition functions will contain V as a factor (and they will not otherwise involve V if we are dealing with perfect gases): therefore
$$\frac{\partial \ln(\text{p.f.})}{\partial V} = \frac{d \ln V}{d V} = \frac{1}{V} \tag{1}$$

in each case. Consequently,

$$\left(\frac{\partial F}{\partial V}\right)_{N_A,N_B,T} = -kT\frac{\partial}{\partial V}\{N_1^*\ln(\text{p.f.})_A + N_2^*\ln(\text{p.f.})_B +$$
$$+ N_{12}^*\ln(\text{p.f.})_{AB} - N_1^*(\ln N_1^* - 1) -$$
$$- N_2^*(\ln N_2^* - 1) - N_{12}^*(\ln N_{12}^* - 1)\}_{N_A,N_B,T}$$

$$= -kT\left\{\frac{N_1^*}{V} + \frac{N_2^*}{V} + \frac{N_{12}^*}{V}\right\} - \quad \text{(by use of (1))}$$
$$- kT\left(\frac{\partial N_1^*}{\partial V}\right)_{N_A,N_B,T}(\ln(\text{p.f.})_A - \ln N_1^*) -$$
$$- kT\left(\frac{\partial N_2^*}{\partial V}\right)_{N_A,N_B,T}(\ln(\text{p.f.})_B - \ln N_2^*) -$$
$$- kT\left(\frac{\partial N_{12}^*}{\partial V}\right)_{N_A,N_B,T}(\ln(\text{p.f.})_{AB} - \ln N_{12}^*).$$

But, by (III),

$$\left(\frac{\partial N_1^*}{\partial V}\right)_{N_A,N_B,T} = -\left(\frac{\partial N_{12}^*}{\partial V}\right)_{N_A,N_B,T} = \left(\frac{\partial N_2^*}{\partial V}\right)_{N_A,N_B,T}.$$

Therefore,

$$\left(\frac{\partial F}{\partial V}\right)_{N_A,N_B,T} = -\frac{kT}{V}(N_1^* + N_2^* + N_{12}^*) +$$
$$+ kT\left(\frac{\partial N_{12}^*}{\partial V}\right)_{N_A,N_B,T}\{\ln(\text{p.f.})_A + \ln(\text{p.f.})_B -$$
$$- \ln(\text{p.f.})_{AB} - \ln N_1^* - \ln N_2^* + \ln N_{12}^*\},$$

and the quantity in the curly brackets vanishes on account of (II). Thus we have

$$P = -\left(\frac{\partial F}{\partial V}\right)_{N_A,N_B,T} = \frac{kT}{V}(N_1^* + N_2^* + N_{12}^*),$$

i.e.
$$PV = (N_1^* + N_2^* + N_{12}^*)kT. \tag{2}$$

Since $N_1^* + N_2^* + N_{12}^*$ is not a constant, the assembly does not satisfy Boyle's law. Nevertheless, $N_1^* + N_2^* + N_{12}^*$ is the equilibrium number of systems in the assembly at temperature T (and volume V), and therefore equation (2) is closely analogous to the equation of state

$$PV = NkT$$

for a perfect gas (as we might, perhaps, have guessed on kinetic grounds—though kinetic arguments are strictly outside our present purview).

2. At this point it is necessary, for clarity, to make use of the technical distinction between species and components defined in Chapter I. We shall take A-systems and B-systems, wherever they are to be found, for the two *components* of the assembly, and then, as distinct *species* we have A-atoms (uncombined), B-atoms (uncombined), and AB-molecules. Thus the systems of the components A and B number N_A and N_B, respectively, while in the equilibrium state of the assembly, we have

N_1^* systems of the species 1 (uncombined A-atoms),

N_2^* systems of the species 2 (uncombined B-atoms), and

N_{12}^* systems of the species 12 (AB-molecules).

Let us now ask, What is the chemical potential of the component A in the assembly? We have, thermodynamically (from (I)),

$$\mu_A = \left(\frac{\partial F}{\partial N_A}\right)_{N_B,V,T} = -kT\left\{\left(\frac{\partial N_1^*}{\partial N_A}\right)_{N_B,V,T}(\ln(\text{p.f.})_A - \ln N_1^*) + \right.$$

$$+ \left(\frac{\partial N_2^*}{\partial N_A}\right)_{N_B,V,T}(\ln(\text{p.f.})_B - \ln N_2^*) +$$

$$\left. + \left(\frac{\partial N_{12}^*}{\partial N_A}\right)_{N_B,V,T}(\ln(\text{p.f.})_{AB} - \ln N_{12}^*)\right\}.$$

But, by III, $\quad \left(\frac{\partial N_1^*}{\partial N_A}\right)_{N_B,V,T} + \left(\frac{\partial N_{12}^*}{\partial N_A}\right)_{N_B,V,T} = 1$

and $\quad \left(\frac{\partial N_2^*}{\partial N_A}\right)_{N_B,V,T} + \left(\frac{\partial N_{12}^*}{\partial N_A}\right)_{N_B,V,T} = 0.$

Therefore, getting rid of $\frac{\partial N_1^*}{\partial N_A}$ and $\frac{\partial N_2^*}{\partial N_A}$, we have

$$\mu_A = -kT(\ln(\text{p.f.})_A - \ln N_1^*) +$$

$$+ kT\left(\frac{\partial N_{12}^*}{\partial N_A}\right)_{N_B,V,T}\{\ln(\text{p.f.})_A + \ln(\text{p.f.})_B - \ln(\text{p.f.})_{AB} -$$

$$- \ln N_1^* - \ln N_2^* + \ln N_{12}^*\}.$$

The last term on the r.h.s. again vanishes, on account of II, and we obtain simply

$$\mu_A = -kT(\ln(\text{p.f.})_A - \ln N_1^*). \tag{3}$$

Similarly, $$\mu_B = -kT(\ln(\text{p.f.})_B - \ln N_2^*). \tag{4}$$

Adding (3) and (4), and using II, we find

$$\mu_A + \mu_B = -kT(\ln(\text{p.f.})_{AB} - \ln N_{12}^*). \tag{5}$$

The significance of these equations, (3), (4), and (5), can best be appreciated when we recall that for a perfect gas of just one species, for which

$$F = -kT \ln\frac{(\text{p.f.})^N}{N!},$$

we have $$\mu = -kT(\ln(\text{p.f.}) - \ln N) \tag{6}$$

(see end of Chapter III). We then see that equations (3) and (4) tell us that the chemical potentials of the two components, A and B, are the chemical potentials of the species 1 and 2 (A-atoms and B-atoms) supposed to exist as independent perfect gases with pressures equal to the partial pressures of the species 1 and 2 (A-atoms and B-atoms) in the mixed gas phase. For not only does equation (2) enable us to identify $N_1^* kT/V$ and $N_2^* kT/V$ with the partial pressures of species 1 (A-atoms) and species 2 (B-atoms), but also, of course, if we calculate, quite formally, the quantities

$$\mu_1 \equiv \left(\frac{\partial F}{\partial N_1^*}\right)_{N_2^*,N_{12}^*,V,T} \quad \text{and} \quad \mu_2 \equiv \left(\frac{\partial F}{\partial N_2^*}\right)_{N_1^*,N_{12}^*,V,T},$$

we obtain $$\mu_1 = -kT(\ln(\text{p.f.})_A - \ln N_1^*)$$

and $$\mu_2 = -kT(\ln(\text{p.f.})_B - \ln N_2^*),$$

whence $$\mu_A = \mu_1 \quad \text{and} \quad \mu_B = \mu_2. \tag{7}$$

These quantities, μ_1 and μ_2, defined as above, may be called the chemical potentials of the species 1 and 2: and our result can be expressed by saying that the chemical potential of an A-atom (or B-atom) is the same whether it is uncombined or combined with a B-atom (or A-atom).

If now, in exactly the same way, we define the chemical potential of the species 12 by the formula

$$\mu_{12} \equiv \left(\frac{\partial F}{\partial N_{12}^*}\right)_{N_1^*,N_2^*,V,T},$$

we find $\qquad\qquad \mu_{12} = -kT(\ln(\text{p.f.})_{AB} - \ln N_{12}^*),$

i.e., by (5), $\qquad\qquad\qquad \mu_{12} = \mu_A + \mu_B,$ $\qquad\qquad$ (8)

or, alternatively, $\qquad\qquad\quad \mu_{12} = \mu_1 + \mu_2.$ $\qquad\qquad$ (8′)

Equation (8), or (8′), may be regarded as the crux of the whole matter. For it tells us that the chemical potential of a complex system is the sum of the chemical potentials of the parts from which it is constructed. Had we had three completely *independent* species, 1, 2, and 3 say, then there would have been no such connexion between their chemical potentials: equation (8′) is an expression of the Law of Mass Action, controlling the reaction $A + B \rightleftarrows AB$.

3. Next it is instructive to investigate just how this important law, expressed in equation (8′), first made its appearance in the statistical mechanics underlying the equations (I), (II), and (III). It is very easy to see how the equation arises. If we return to equations (44) of the last chapter, and take the logarithm of both sides, we find

$$\bar{\alpha}_a = -(\ln(\text{p.f.})_A - \ln N_1^*),$$

$$\bar{\alpha}_b = -(\ln(\text{p.f.})_B - \ln N_2^*),$$

and $\qquad \bar{\alpha}_a + \bar{\alpha}_b = -(\ln(\text{p.f.})_{AB} - \ln N_{12}^*),$

so that

$$\left. \begin{aligned} \mu_1 &= kT\bar{\alpha}_a \\ \mu_2 &= kT\bar{\alpha}_b \\ \mu_{12} &= kT(\bar{\alpha}_a + \bar{\alpha}_b) = \mu_1 + \mu_2 \end{aligned} \right\}. \qquad (9)$$

Thus equation (8′) goes right to the heart of the statistical treatment, and expresses nothing more or less than the influence of the two restrictive conditions

$$\sum_i n_i^a + \sum_i n_i^{ab} = N_A$$

and $\qquad\qquad\qquad \sum_i n_i^b + \sum_i n_i^{ab} = N_B.$

Indeed, the position is still further clarified if we look again at the first method of obtaining equations (I), (II), and (III), given in § 4 of Chapter XI. (To avoid the old energy convention, simply treat w as zero.) For the equations (30), obtained from the restrictive conditions

$$\sum_i n_i^a = N_1, \quad \sum_i n_i^b = N_2, \quad \text{and} \quad \sum_i n_i^{ab} = N_{12},$$

give

$$\alpha_a = -(\ln(\text{p.f.})_A - \ln N_1),$$

$$\alpha_b = -(\ln(\text{p.f.})_B - \ln N_2),$$

and

$$\alpha_{ab} = -(\ln(\text{p.f.})_{AB} - \ln N_{12})$$

with no connexion between α_a, α_b, and α_{ab}. It is the *second* step in this first method, in which N_1, N_2, and N_{12} are chosen to make $t(N_1, N_2, N_{12})$ itself a maximum (subject to $N_1 + N_{12} = N_A$ and $N_2 + N_{12} = N_B$), which then makes $\alpha_{ab} = \alpha_a + \alpha_b$ when $N_1 = N_1^*$, $N_2 = N_2^*$, and $N_{12} = N_{12}^*$. And it is just this second step, of course, which brings in the chemical reaction $A + B \rightleftarrows AB$.

The reader should also observe that the important values of α_a and α_b, which correspond to the true equilibrium state of the assembly, are simply the quantities a and b of equation (36) (of Chapter XI).

Thus the law of mass action or, more precisely, the reflection of this law in the equation connecting the chemical potentials of the various species, is a direct consequence of those restrictive conditions which express the indestructibility of matter in the chemical reaction under consideration.

4. Returning now to equation (I), and using the results of paragraphs 2 and 3 above, we find

$$
\begin{aligned}
F = -kT\{ & N_1^* \ln(\text{p.f.})_A - N_1^*(\ln N_1^* - 1) + \\
& + N_2^* \ln(\text{p.f.})_B - N_2^*(\ln N_2^* - 1) + \\
& + N_{12}^* \ln(\text{p.f.})_{AB} - N_{12}^*(\ln N_{12}^* - 1)\} \\
= -kT\{ & N_1^*(\ln(\text{p.f.})_A - \ln N_1^*) + \\
& + N_2^*(\ln(\text{p.f.})_B - \ln N_2^*) + \\
& + N_{12}^*(\ln(\text{p.f.})_{AB} - \ln N_{12}^*) + \\
& + (N_1^* + N_2^* + N_{12}^*)\} \\
= N_1^* & \mu_A + N_2^* \mu_B + N_{12}^*(\mu_A + \mu_B) - PV,
\end{aligned}
$$

whence

$$G = F + PV$$
$$= \mu_A(N_1^* + N_{12}^*) + \mu_B(N_2^* + N_{12}^*),$$

i.e. $$G = N_A\mu_A + N_B\mu_B, \qquad (10)$$

showing that the chemical potentials are actually partial Gibbs free energies—as we should expect thermodynamically. Moreover, from (7) and (8), we see that we can also write

$$G = N_1^*\mu_1 + N_2^*\mu_2 + N_{12}^*\mu_{12}$$

subject to $$\mu_{12} = \mu_1 + \mu_2. \qquad (10')$$

These equations are of considerable thermodynamic importance, but we shall not pursue them further here.

5. At this point, and in view of developments to be described later, it is convenient to introduce the quantities

$$\lambda_A \equiv e^{\mu_A/kT} \quad \text{and} \quad \lambda_B \equiv e^{\mu_B/kT}. \qquad (11)$$

By the equations (9) above, we have

$$\lambda_A = e^{\bar{\alpha}_a}, \qquad \lambda_B = e^{\bar{\alpha}_b},$$

and, therefore, the formulae (42) of Chapter XI become, in terms of λ_A and λ_B,

$$\left.\begin{array}{l} n_i^{a*} = \lambda_A e^{-\epsilon_i^a/kT} \\ n_i^{b*} = \lambda_B e^{-\epsilon_i^b/kT} \\ n_i^{ab*} = \lambda_A \lambda_B e^{-\epsilon_i^{ab}/kT} \end{array}\right\} \quad (i = 1, 2, ...), \qquad (12)$$

whence, summing over all values of i,

$$N_1^* = \lambda_A(\text{p.f.})_A,$$
$$N_2^* = \lambda_B(\text{p.f.})_B, \qquad (13)$$
$$N_{12}^* = \lambda_A\lambda_B(\text{p.f.})_{AB}.$$

Thus the restrictive conditions

$$\begin{array}{l} N_1^* + N_{12}^* = N_A, \\ N_2^* + N_{12}^* = N_B \end{array} \qquad (\text{III})$$

yield the equations

$$\left.\begin{array}{l} N_A = \lambda_A[(\text{p.f.})_A + \lambda_B(\text{p.f.})_{AB}] \\ N_B = \lambda_B[(\text{p.f.})_B + \lambda_A(\text{p.f.})_{AB}] \end{array}\right\}, \qquad (14)$$

whilst equations (13) and (2) give

$$PV = kT[\lambda_A(\text{p.f.})_A + \lambda_B(\text{p.f.})_B + \lambda_A\lambda_B(\text{p.f.})_{AB}]. \qquad (15)$$

6. Before commenting at all on equations (14) and (15), it is convenient to consider just what happens to the formulae of this chapter when the A and B systems are *alike* (so that there is only one *component* in the assembly) and we are concerned with a dissociative equilibrium between atoms and diatomic molecules represented by $A + A \rightleftarrows A_2$.

If $(p.f.)_A$ and $(p.f.)_{AA}$, where all energies are measured from the same zero, refer to systems of the species A and A_2, respectively, and if, in any specification of the assembly with total energy E, we let N_1 = number of uncombined A's,

N_{11} = number of A_2 molecules, and

N_A = total number of A's, combined or uncombined,

then, following Method I above, we can easily prove that, for this specification, we have effectively

$$\ln t = E/kT + N_1 \ln(p.f.)_A - N_1 \ln N_1 + N_1 +$$
$$+ N_{11} \ln(p.f.)_{AA} - N_{11} \ln N_{11} + N_{11} \qquad (16)$$

(see equation (31) of Chapter XI).

We have now to choose N_1 and N_{11} so that the r.h.s. of (16) is a maximum, subject to N_A fixed. But, stoichiometrically,

$$N_1 + 2N_{11} = N_A \qquad (17)$$

and therefore we require

$$\delta \ln t = (\ln(p.f.)_A - \ln N_1)\delta N_1 + (\ln(p.f.)_{AA} - \ln N_{11})\delta N_{11}$$
$$= 0 \qquad (18)$$

subject to $$\delta N_1 + 2\delta N_{11} = 0. \qquad (19)$$

Multiplying (19) by a and adding to (18) we obtain, for the equilibrium values of N_1 and N_{11}, the equations

$$\left. \begin{array}{l} a = -(\ln(p.f.)_A - \ln N_1^*) \\ 2a = -(\ln(p.f.)_{AA} - \ln N_{11}^*) \end{array} \right\}, \qquad (20)$$

whence we obtain the Law of Mass Action

$$\frac{N_{11}^*}{(N_1^*)^2} = \frac{(p.f.)_{AA}}{(p.f.)_A^2}. \qquad (21)$$

In place of equations (I), (II), and (III), therefore, we now have

$$F = -kT \ln\left\{\frac{(\text{p.f.})_A^{N_1^*}(\text{p.f.})_{AA}^{N_{11}^*}}{N_1^*!\,N_{11}^*!}\right\}, \qquad \text{(I}')$$

where

$$\frac{N_{11}^*}{(N_1^*)^2} = \frac{(\text{p.f.})_{AA}}{(\text{p.f.})_A^2} \qquad \text{(II}')$$

and

$$N_1^* + 2N_{11}^* = N_A. \qquad \text{(III}')$$

It is important to recognize that these equations are *not* obtained if we simply identify B-systems with A-systems in the equations (I), (II), and (III). (Equation (II′) could be obtained in this way, but not either equation (I′) or equation (III′).)

Proceeding with the analysis of this new problem, we can derive, without difficulty, the formulae

$$PV = kT(N_1^* + N_{11}^*), \qquad (22)$$

$$\mu_A = -kT(\ln(\text{p.f.})_A - \ln N_1^*) = kTa, \qquad (23)$$

and

$$\mu_1 = \mu_A, \qquad \mu_{11} = 2\mu_1 = 2\mu_A. \qquad (24)$$

Consequently, introducing

$$\lambda_A \equiv e^{\mu_A/kT},$$

we find, from (20)

and

$$\left.\begin{aligned} N_1^* &= \lambda_A(\text{p.f.})_A \\ N_{11}^* &= \lambda_A^2(\text{p.f.})_{AA} \end{aligned}\right\}, \qquad (25)$$

so that equations (III′) and (22) give us now (in place of (14) and (15))

$$N_A = \lambda_A[(\text{p.f.})_A + 2\lambda_A(\text{p.f.})_{AA}] \qquad (26)$$

and

$$PV = kT[\lambda_A(\text{p.f.})_A + \lambda_A^2(\text{p.f.})_{AA}]. \qquad (27)$$

If now we compare equations (26) and (27) with equations (14) and (15) we notice two things. First, equations (27) and (15) are very closely analogous. In fact they both exemplify the general rule that if we take as components independent units (e.g. A-, B-, C-,... atoms) from which all the various species are built up, then, for any gaseous assembly (perfect, apart from the dissociative equilibria),

$$PV = kT\{\text{sum for all species of } [(\text{p.f.})_{\text{species}} \times \text{product of } \lambda\text{'s for all}$$
$$\text{the units occurring in the species}]\}. \qquad (28)$$

It is not difficult to prove equation (28) by the methods of this chapter: we have only to introduce a sufficiently general notation and proceed along lines which have already led, in two particular cases, to equations (15) and (27), respectively.

Secondly, looking now at equations (14) and (26), we observe that the equations (14) may be written

$$\left. \begin{aligned} N_A &= \lambda_A \frac{\partial}{\partial \lambda_A} \left(\frac{PV}{kT} \right)_{\lambda_B, V, T} \\ N_B &= \lambda_B \frac{\partial}{\partial \lambda_B} \left(\frac{PV}{kT} \right)_{\lambda_A, V, T} \end{aligned} \right\} \text{ where } PV \text{ is given by (15),}$$

while equation (26) may be written

$$N_A = \lambda_A \frac{\partial}{\partial \lambda_A} \left(\frac{PV}{kT} \right)_{V, T}, \quad \text{where } PV \text{ is given by (27).}$$

Thus, in each instance, we follow the general rule that, for each component (distinguished by a suffix i)

$$N_i = \lambda_i \frac{\partial}{\partial \lambda_i} \left(\frac{PV}{kT} \right)_{\lambda_{j(j \neq i)}, V, T} \qquad \begin{aligned} &\text{where } PV \text{ is given} \\ &\text{by (28).} \end{aligned} \qquad (29)$$

This equation, (29), can likewise be justified, in its complete generality, by a suitable extension of the methods of this chapter.

Here we must leave these equations for the moment, commenting in conclusion only that if there are altogether x components then (having written down (28) with appropriate values for the partition functions on the r.h.s.) the equations (29) give just x equations connecting the x quantities N_i with the x quantities λ_i. But each λ is related to the corresponding chemical potential by the formula
$$\lambda = e^{\mu/kT} \quad \text{or} \quad \mu = kT \ln \lambda, \qquad (30)$$

and consequently we have just sufficient equations to determine the chemical potential of each component as a function of the composition of the gaseous assembly. It should also be noted that the technical name for the quantity λ, connected with the chemical potential, μ, by equation (30), is *absolute activity*.

We shall return to the formulae of this last section in Chapter XVII.

EXAMPLES

1. Show that the results of Example 6 of Chapter XI are unchanged if instead of dealing with the dissociation of AB-molecules we deal with the dissociation of A_2-molecules.

2. N_{AB} AB-molecules and N_{CD} CD-molecules are introduced into a vessel (volume V and temperature T) in which they form a gaseous phase and where they can react according to the formula

$$AB + CD \rightleftarrows AC + BD.$$

Prove, by the methods of this chapter, that when equilibrium is attained

$$\frac{N_{AB}^* N_{CD}^*}{N_{AC}^* N_{BD}^*} = \frac{(\text{p.f.})_{AB}(\text{p.f.})_{CD}}{(\text{p.f.})_{AC}(\text{p.f.})_{BD}},$$

where

$$N_{AB}^* + N_{AC}^* = N_{AB},$$
$$N_{CD}^* + N_{BD}^* = N_{CD},$$

and

$$N_{AC}^* = N_{BD}^*.$$

(Note that the result is independent of the volume, V.)

TWO-PHASE ASSEMBLIES: SINGLE COMPONENT

1. In Chapters XI and XII we extended the methods previously developed for single-phase assemblies of identical systems to include also the statistical treatment of assemblies whose systems are of more than one kind. We shall devote the present chapter and the next to discussing the further extension of our methods, or formulae, necessary when we have to consider more than one *phase*, e.g. when we desire to discuss the equilibrium between a crystal and a gas. For simplicity, we shall assume throughout that there are only two possible phases (open to the systems of the assembly): further extension of the formulae to cover multiphase assemblies introduces no new principles. In the present chapter we shall discuss some simple two-phase problems in which only one component is concerned, and in Chapter XIV we shall deal with some similar problems for two-component assemblies.

It is, of course, necessary that we still deal with essentially *independent* systems and, therefore, when discussing a solid or liquid phase we must employ an Einstein model in which every system is assumed to have, in the condensed phase, a set of possible energy values which is unaffected by the energy states of neighbouring systems. We are not yet ready to approach the much more difficult problems presented by assemblies of non-independent systems.

It is convenient to adopt a distinctive notation in which we can easily distinguish the symbols which refer to non-localized systems in a gaseous phase from those which refer to localized systems in a condensed phase. For the systems of a gaseous phase we shall employ (with appropriate suffixes)

ϵ to denote a possible energy level of a system,

ω to denote the corresponding degeneracy (if any),

n to denote a distribution number, and   (a)

N to denote the number of systems of a species or component, while for the systems of a condensed phase we shall use (again with appropriate suffixes)

η to denote a possible energy level of a system,

ϖ to denote the corresponding degeneracy (if any),

m to denote a distribution number, and   (b)

M to denote the number of systems of a species or component.

Thus the symbols ϵ, ω, n, and N refer to non-localized systems, while the symbols η, ϖ, m, and M refer to localized systems. Finally, when we wish to denote, say, the total number of systems in a one-component two-phase assembly, given by $M+N$ in the above notation, we shall use the letter X. It is hoped that the reader will find this standardization of notation a help towards the ready recognition and appreciation of formulae in subsequent chapters.

2. The first problem we shall discuss may seem a slightly artificial one. It is the problem of (non-combining) systems which can distribute themselves between two different, perfect, gaseous assemblies. The whole assembly is, therefore, supposed to consist of two sub-assemblies, 1 and 2, between which the systems can migrate. It can be represented, dia-

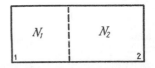

Fig. 36.

grammatically, by Fig. 36, and the problem differs from that represented by Fig. 34 only in that now systems, as well as energy, can be exchanged between the two parts of the assembly.

Suppose, then, that we have N systems each capable of being either

(i) in phase 1, when its allowed energies are ϵ_1, ϵ_2,..., ϵ_i,...,

or

(ii) in phase 2, when its allowed energies are ϵ'_1, ϵ'_2,..., ϵ'_i,... .

Let the corresponding distribution numbers, defining a specification of the assembly, be n_1, n_2,..., n_i,... and n'_1, n'_2,..., n'_i,..., respectively, and let

$$\sum_i n_i = N_1, \qquad \sum_i n'_i = N_2.$$

Then, if the total energy of the assembly is E, the restrictive conditions on the distribution numbers n_i and n_i' are

$$\sum_i n_i + \sum_i n_i' = N \tag{1}$$

and
$$\sum_i n_i \epsilon_i + \sum_i n_i' \epsilon_i' = E. \tag{2}$$

Moreover, the number of different complexions of the assembly for the given specification (i.e. for given values of the distribution numbers) is (see equation (4) of Chapter XI)

$$t(n_i, n_i') = \frac{1}{N_1!\, N_2!} \frac{N_1!\, N_2!}{\prod_i n_i! \prod_i n_i'!}, \tag{3}$$

so that, by Stirling's theorem,

$$\ln t = -\sum_i n_i(\ln n_i - 1) - \sum_i n_i'(\ln n_i' - 1)$$

and, for the maximum such term, we require

$$\delta \ln t = -\sum_i \ln n_i\, \delta n_i - \sum_i \ln n_i'\, \delta n_i' = 0 \tag{4}$$

where, on account of (1) and (2), δn_i and $\delta n_i'$ are subject to the restrictive conditions

$$\sum_i \delta n_i + \sum_i \delta n_i' = 0 \tag{5}$$

and
$$\sum_i \epsilon_i\, \delta n_i + \sum_i \epsilon_i'\, \delta n_i' = 0. \tag{6}$$

Adding $\alpha(5) + \beta(6)$ to (4) we find, in the usual way, that the important values of the distribution numbers are given by the equations

$$\left.\begin{array}{l} \alpha + \beta\epsilon_i - \ln n_i^* = 0 \\[2mm] \alpha + \beta\epsilon_i' - \ln n_i'^* = 0 \end{array}\right\} \quad (i = 1, 2, ...), \tag{7}$$

which have solutions

$$\left.\begin{array}{l} n_i^* = \lambda e^{\beta\epsilon_i} \\[2mm] n_i'^* = \lambda e^{\beta\epsilon_i'} \end{array}\right\} \quad (i = 1, 2, ...) \tag{8}$$

where $\lambda = e^{\alpha}$.

We can, forthwith, identify β with $-1/kT$, and introduce weight-factors ω_i and ω_i'. The equations (8) then become

$$\left.\begin{array}{l} n_i^* = \lambda \omega_i\, e^{-\epsilon_i/kT} \\[2mm] n_i'^* = \lambda \omega_i'\, e^{-\epsilon_i'/kT} \end{array}\right\} \quad (i = 1, 2, ...) \tag{9}$$

so that, summing over all values of i, we find

$$\left.\begin{array}{l} N_1^* = \lambda(\text{p.f.})_1 \\ N_2^* = \lambda(\text{p.f.})_2 \end{array}\right\}, \tag{10}$$

where

$$(\text{p.f.})_1 = \sum_i \omega_i e^{-\epsilon_i/kT}$$

and

$$(\text{p.f.})_2 = \sum_i \omega_i' e^{-\epsilon_i'/kT}.$$

Finally, identifying Ω with $t_{\max}$, and S with $k\ln\Omega$ we obtain, for the Helmholtz free energy of the whole assembly,

$$F = -kT \ln\left\{\frac{(\text{p.f.})_1^{N_1^*}(\text{p.f.})_2^{N_2^*}}{N_1^*! \, N_2^*!}\right\}, \tag{11}$$

where, from (1) and (10), N_1^* and N_2^* are given by

$$\left.\begin{array}{l} \dfrac{N_1^*}{N_2^*} = \dfrac{(\text{p.f.})_1}{(\text{p.f.})_2} \\[2mm] N_1^* + N_2^* = N \end{array}\right\} \tag{12}$$

and

The argument follows the traditional lines so closely that the reader who so desires should have no difficulty in completing the formal details of the proof.

Before proceeding to discuss these formulae further, we must first dispose of one rather intriguing matter. For it may, rightly, be argued that a much simpler approach would have been simply to have said

every system can have one of the possible energies $\epsilon_1, \epsilon_2,..., \epsilon_i,...,$ $\epsilon_1', \epsilon_2',..., \epsilon_i',...$ and if the system has one of the energies ϵ we shall say that it is in phase 1, while if it has one of the energies ϵ' we shall say that it is in phase 2. Consequently, since the systems are non-localized, we must have

$$F = -kT \ln\frac{(\text{p.f.})^N}{N!} \tag{13}$$

where

$$(\text{p.f.}) = \sum_i \omega_i e^{-\epsilon_i/kT} + \sum_i \omega_i' e^{-\epsilon_i'/kT},$$

i.e.

$$(\text{p.f.}) = (\text{p.f.})_1 + (\text{p.f.})_2.$$

And then, by the internal distribution properties of a partition function (Chapter V),

$$\frac{N_1^*}{N} = \frac{(\text{p.f.})_1}{(\text{p.f.})_1 + (\text{p.f.})_2} \quad\text{and}\quad \frac{N_2^*}{N} = \frac{(\text{p.f.})_2}{(\text{p.f.})_1 + (\text{p.f.})_2}. \tag{14}$$

Now this argument is quite sound. And, clearly, the equations (14) are entirely equivalent to the equations (12). The difficulty lies in recognizing that equation (13) is equivalent to equation (11).

On the basis of equation (13), we have

$$F = -kT \ln \frac{[(\text{p.f.})_1 + (\text{p.f.})_2]^N}{N!}$$

$$= -kT \ln \left\{ \sum_{(N_1 + N_2 = N)} \frac{N!}{N_1! \, N_2!} (\text{p.f.})_1^{N_1} (\text{p.f.})_2^{N_2} \frac{1}{N!} \right\}$$

(by the binomial theorem)

$$= -kT \ln \left\{ \sum_{(N_1 + N_2 = N)} \frac{(\text{p.f.})_1^{N_1} (\text{p.f.})_2^{N_2}}{N_1! \, N_2!} \right\}. \tag{13'}$$

Now in the sum on the r.h.s. of (13′) there are $N+1$ terms, corresponding to $N_1 = 0, 1, 2, \ldots, N$, respectively, and the greatest of these terms is easily determined. Writing

$$\tau = \frac{(\text{p.f.})_1^{N_1} (\text{p.f.})_2^{N_2}}{N_1! \, N_2!}$$

we have

$$\delta \ln \tau = (\ln (\text{p.f.})_1 - \ln N_1) \delta N_1 + (\ln (\text{p.f.})_2 - \ln N_2) \delta N_2, \tag{15}$$

where

$$\delta N_1 + \delta N_2 = 0. \tag{16}$$

Consequently, if N_1^+ and N_2^+ are the values of N_1 and N_2 leading to $\tau_{\max}$, we have (multiplying (16) by α and adding to (15))

$$\left. \begin{array}{l} \alpha + \ln (\text{p.f.})_1 - \ln N_1^+ = 0 \\ \alpha + \ln (\text{p.f.})_2 - \ln N_2^+ = 0 \end{array} \right\} \tag{17}$$

Also $N_1^+ + N_2^+ = N$. Hence comparison with the equations (14) shows that

$$N_1^+ = N_1^* \quad \text{and} \quad N_2^+ = N_2^*.$$

Moreover, since

$$\tau_{\max} < \sum_{(N_1 + N_2 = N)} \frac{(\text{p.f.})_1^{N_1} (\text{p.f.})_2^{N_2}}{N_1! \, N_2!} < (N+1) \tau_{\max},$$

we have, from (13′),

$$F = -kT \ln \tau_{\max} + \delta, \tag{18}$$

where

$$|\delta| < kT \ln(N+1).$$

But, from (13), F is proportional to N, when N is large, and then $\ln(N+1)$ is negligible compared with N. Thus, when N is large, δ is negligible compared with F and equation (18) gives

$$F = -kT \ln \tau_{\max} = -kT \ln \frac{(\text{p.f.})_1^{N_1^*}(\text{p.f.})_2^{N_2^*}}{N_1^*! \, N_2^*!}$$

in accordance with equation (11). Therefore equation (13) is entirely equivalent to equation (11).

The apparent difference between equations (11) and (13) may be expressed by saying that in deriving (11) we have already recognized that only the equilibrium distribution of the systems between the two phases contributes appreciably to the entropy (and, therefore, to the free energy) of the assembly, while in equation (13) we do not recognize this and so equation (13) involves a sum over all such distributions. But since in fact only the equilibrium distribution does matter, the two equations are entirely equivalent (when N is large and we can neglect $\ln N$ in comparison with N).

3. Having shown that both methods of attack lead to the same formulae, we must now discuss the significance of these results, summarized in equations (11) and (12).

We observe, first, that, from equation (11), we can write

$$F = F_1^* + F_2^*,$$

where

$$F_1^* = -kT \ln \frac{(\text{p.f.})_1^{N_1^*}}{N_1^*!} \quad \text{and} \quad F_2^* = -kT \ln \frac{(\text{p.f.})_2^{N_2^*}}{N_2^*!},$$

so that the free energy of the whole assembly may be regarded as the sum of the free energies of the two sub-assemblies. We have written F_1^* and F_2^*, instead of F_1 and F_2, simply to emphasize that these quantities have to be evaluated at the equilibrium composition of the assembly; i.e. if

$$F_1 = -kT \ln \frac{(\text{p.f.})_1^{N_1}}{N_1!} \quad \text{and} \quad F_2 = -kT \ln \frac{(\text{p.f.})_2^{N_2}}{N_2!},$$

then
$$F_1^* = (F_1 \text{ evaluated at } N_1 = N_1^*)$$
and
$$F_2^* = (F_2 \text{ evaluated at } N_2 = N_2^*).$$

Thus, first, then,

the free energy of the whole assembly is the sum of the
free energies of the two sub-assemblies, each sub-assembly   (a)
having its equilibrium composition,

and a similar statement is true of any other extensive thermodynamic property of the assembly.

Secondly, we notice that the equations (12), which serve to
fix the equilibrium composition of the assembly referred to above,
are equivalent to the equations

$$\left(\frac{\partial F_1}{\partial N_1}\right)_{V_1, T} = \left(\frac{\partial F_2}{\partial N_2}\right)_{V_2, T} \tag{19}$$

and
$$N_1 + N_2 = N. \tag{20}$$

For equation (19) gives

$$-kT(\ln(\text{p.f.})_1 - \ln N_1) = -kT(\ln(\text{p.f.})_2 - \ln N_2),$$

i.e.
$$\frac{N_1}{N_2} = \frac{(\text{p.f.})_1}{(\text{p.f.})_2} \tag{21}$$

and so, since equations (21) and (20) are identical with the
equations (12), the solutions of equations (19) and (20) are
$N_1 = N_1^*$ and $N_2 = N_2^*$. But

$$\left(\frac{\partial F_1}{\partial N_1}\right)_{V_1, T} = \mu_1 \quad \text{and} \quad \left(\frac{\partial F_2}{\partial N_2}\right)_{V_2, T} = \mu_2,$$

where μ_1 and μ_2 are the chemical potentials of systems in the
phases 1 and 2, respectively. Consequently,

the equilibrium composition of the assembly can be determined by equating the chemical potentials of systems   (b)
in the two sub-assemblies,

where, in conjunction with (b) we have, of course, to use the
equation of conservation of mass (see equations (12) and (20)
above).

Now these results, summarized in (a) and (b), express well-
known thermodynamic properties of poly-phase assemblies and
suggest an entirely new approach to statistical problems in which
more than one phase is involved. They suggest that we should
first calculate, statistically, expressions for the thermodynamic

properties of the *separate* phases, and then determine the equilibrium composition of the assembly (in particular, the equilibrium amounts of the various phases) by the method of equating chemical potentials—each component having the same chemical potential in every phase in which it occurs.

This is a perfectly valid method of approach, and we shall call it *the thermodynamic method* of dealing with poly-phase assemblies. Formally, it is usually shorter than the more thorough-going statistical methods used earlier in this chapter, but it is neither as fundamental nor as powerful a method. For the sake of obtaining insight into the statistical theory and acquiring practice in handling problems we shall proceed to develop the fully statistical method (in which different phases are regarded as providing different possible states for the systems of a single assembly), sometimes verifying that the thermodynamic method leads to the same results.

4. The second problem that we shall discuss under the heading of this chapter is that of a pure crystal in equilibrium with its own vapour. In accordance with the proposed general notation, we shall suppose that there are altogether X systems in the assembly, each of which can either

(i) exist in the gaseous phase, when its allowed energies are
$$\epsilon_1, \epsilon_2, ..., \epsilon_i, ...,$$

or

(ii) exist in the crystal phase, when its allowed energies are
$$\eta_1, \eta_2, ..., \eta_i, ...$$

We let the corresponding distribution numbers, defining a specification of the assembly, be $n_1, n_2, ..., n_i, ...$ and $m_1, m_2, ..., m_i, ...,$ respectively. Then, for the distribution numbers $n_1, n_2, ..., n_i, ...,$ there are

$$\frac{1}{N!} \frac{N!}{\prod_i n_i!}, \quad \text{where} \quad N = \sum_i n_i, \tag{22}$$

complexions of the non-localized, gaseous systems; and for the distribution numbers $m_1, m_2, ..., m_i, ...$ there are

$$\frac{M!}{\prod_i m_i!}, \quad \text{where} \quad M = \sum_i m_i, \tag{23}$$

complexions of the localized, crystalline systems. Each of the complexions numbered in (22) can be associated with each of the complexions in (23); consequently for the given distribution numbers there are

$$t(n_i, m_i) = \frac{\left(\sum_i m_i\right)!}{\prod_i n_i! \prod_i m_i!} \tag{24}$$

complexions of the whole assembly.

For given X and E, the restrictive conditions on the distribution numbers are

$$\sum_i n_i + \sum_i m_i = X \tag{25}$$

and

$$\sum_i n_i \epsilon_i + \sum_i m_i \eta_i = E. \tag{26}$$

From (24), and Stirling's theorem, we have, since

$$\delta \sum_i m_i = \sum_i \delta m_i,$$

$$\delta \ln t = \ln\left(\sum_i m_i\right) \sum_i \delta m_i - \sum_i \ln m_i \, \delta m_i - \sum_i \ln n_i \, \delta n_i,$$

and so, for the greatest term in $\Omega \{= \sum t(n_i, m_i)\}$, we require

$$\ln\left(\sum_i m_i\right) \sum_i \delta m_i - \sum_i \ln m_i \, \delta m_i - \sum_i \ln n_i \, \delta n_i = 0 \tag{27}$$

where, on account of (25) and (26),

$$\sum_i \delta n_i + \sum_i \delta m_i = 0 \tag{28}$$

and

$$\sum_i \epsilon_i \delta n_i + \sum_i \eta_i \delta m_i = 0. \tag{29}$$

Adding $\alpha(28) + \beta(29)$ to (27) we obtain, in the usual way, for the important values of the distribution numbers, the equations

$$\alpha + \beta \epsilon_i - \ln n_i^* = 0, \tag{30}$$

$$\alpha + \beta \eta_i - \ln m_i^* + \ln \sum_i m_i^* = 0, \tag{31}$$

which have the solutions $\quad n_i^* = \lambda e^{\beta \epsilon_i} \tag{32}$

and

$$\frac{m_i^*}{\sum_i m_i^*} = \lambda e^{\beta \eta_i}, \tag{33}$$

where $\lambda = e^{\alpha}$.

Equating now S with $k \ln \Omega$, or $k \ln t_{\max}$, we find

$$S/k = -\beta E - \alpha N^* + N^* - \alpha M^*, \tag{34}$$

whence we can identify β with $-1/kT$ and† α with μ/kT (so that $\mu = kT \ln \lambda$), where μ is the chemical potential of the systems of the assembly.

From equations (32) and (33), on summing over all i, we have

$$N^* = \lambda(\text{p.f.})_g \tag{35}$$

and

$$1 = \lambda(\text{p.f.})_c, \tag{36}$$

where (now introducing degeneracies for complete generality)

$$(\text{p.f.})_g = \sum_i \omega_i e^{-\epsilon_i/kT} \quad \text{and} \quad (\text{p.f.})_c = \sum_i \varpi_i e^{-\eta_i/kT},$$

i.e. $(\text{p.f.})_g$ and $(\text{p.f.})_c$ are the partition functions for a system in the gaseous and condensed phases, respectively. Then, from (34),

$$F = E - TS = -kT(N^* - \alpha N^* - \alpha M^*)$$
$$= -kT(N^* - (\ln N^* - \ln(\text{p.f.})_g)N^* + M^* \ln(\text{p.f.})_c)$$

by (35) and (36), i.e., using Stirling's theorem,

$$F = -kT \ln \left\{ (\text{p.f.})_c^{M^*} \frac{(\text{p.f.})_g^{N^*}}{N^*!} \right\}. \tag{37}$$

Equations (35), (36), and (37) epitomize the solution of this problem, and should be contrasted with equations (10) and (11) earlier in this chapter. Only two further comments are necessary. First, writing

$$F_c = -kT \ln(\text{p.f.})_c^M$$

and forgetting about the volume of the condensed phase,‡ we have

$$\mu_c = \left(\frac{\partial F_c}{\partial M} \right)_T = -kT \ln(\text{p.f.})_c = kT \ln \lambda$$

while, writing

$$F_g = -kT \ln \frac{(\text{p.f.})_g^N}{N!},$$

we have

$$\mu_g = \left(\frac{\partial F_g}{\partial N} \right)_{V,T} = -kT(\ln(\text{p.f.})_g - \ln N) \quad (= kT \ln \lambda \text{ when } N = N^*).$$

† The reader who refers back to Chapter II will notice that the α there introduced (see equation (17)) is *not* the α of the present paragraph. Consequently, in Chapter II, we did not deduce $\mu = kT\alpha$: in fact, in the notation of Chapter II, $\mu = kT(\alpha - \ln N)$, as may easily be verified. The apparent discrepancy is due to treating $N!$ as a constant when differentiating $\ln t$ in Chapter II. Of course, both treatments are perfectly correct, and it is well that the reader should realize that a little care is needed, in the handling of our equations, if we are to ensure that the 'undetermined multiplier', α, is equal to μ/kT.

‡ See paragraph 5, below.

Consequently the equations (35) and (36) are equivalent to the equation $\mu_c = \mu_g$. We could, therefore, have obtained the same results equally well by following the thermodynamic method described above (see (a) and (b)).

Secondly, we must examine the two equations (35) and (36) rather more closely, to see just how they differ from one another. We remember that $(\text{p.f.})_g$, for a perfect gas, involves the volume V of the assembly merely as a multiplicative factor. Distinguishing, for the moment, quite formally, between λ_g calculated from (35) and λ_c calculated from (36), and dropping the stars, we have

$$\lambda_g = \frac{N}{(\text{p.f.})_g} = \frac{N}{V_g g(T)}, \quad \text{where } g(T) \text{ is independent of } V_g,$$

i.e.
$$\lambda_g = \frac{1}{v_g g(T)}, \quad \text{where} \quad v_g = V_g/N.$$

Consequently λ_g, and hence μ_g, is an *intensive* property of the gas phase, independent of its extent: if we double V and double N (so that the density and pressure of the gas are unaltered) then λ_g remains unchanged. Similarly,

$$\lambda_c = \frac{1}{(\text{p.f.})_c} = \frac{1}{f(v_c, T)}, \quad \text{where} \quad v_c = V_c/M,$$

i.e. where v_c is the volume per system of the crystalline phase. For the moment the last statement here must be taken on trust: we shall deal with this matter more fully later when discussing the place of models in statistical mechanics. But, for the present, we may simply say that if λ_c, or μ_c, is to be an intensive property of the condensed phase, then $(\text{p.f.})_c$ must involve only v_c and not V_c independently of M. This being so, both equations lead to chemical potentials which are properly intensive properties of their respective phases, and the striking difference between equations (35) and (36) is due fundamentally to the fact that $(\text{p.f.})_g$ involves V as a factor while $(\text{p.f.})_c$ involves only v_c, the volume per system of the condensed phase. Indeed this is the real difference between gaseous and condensed phases, i.e. between assemblies of non-localized and localized systems, respectively.

5. Before proceeding to discuss briefly two more problems which fall under this same heading, it seems desirable here to consider rather more carefully how v_c, the volume per system of the condensed phase, enters into the above equations. So far it is fairly clear that we have neglected v_c in comparison with v_g, for from the equation

$$F = -kT(N^* - \alpha N^* - \alpha M^*)$$
$$= -kT(N^* - \mu X/kT)$$

we have, since $\mu X = G$, the Gibbs free energy of the whole assembly,

$$PV = G - F$$
$$= \mu X + N^* kT - \mu X$$
$$= N^* kT,$$

showing that we are treating v_g as V/N^*, i.e. neglecting the volume of the crystalline phase. We shall now proceed to take account of the volume of the crystalline phase on the assumption that when there are M systems therein the volume remaining for the gaseous phase is $V - Mv_c$.

If we assume to start with that M and N are fixed, so that the phases can exchange energy but not systems, then we readily find (see equation (34))

$$\ln t_{\max} = -\beta E + M \ln \sum_i e^{\beta \eta_i} + N \ln \sum_i e^{\beta \epsilon_i} - N \ln N + N.$$

Now, since $\partial \ln t_{\max}/\partial \beta = 0$ (formally) we can, in future, treat β as a constant, and we may as well forthwith identify β with $-1/kT$. Then

$$\ln t_{\max} = E/kT + M \ln(\text{p.f.})_c + N \ln(\text{p.f.})_g - N \ln N + N,$$

i.e.

$$\ln t_{\max} = E/kT + M \ln f(v_c, T) + N \ln (V - Mv_c) g(T) -$$
$$- N \ln N + N. \quad (38)$$

Now, choosing M and N, subject to $M + N = X$, so that the r.h.s. of (38) is a maximum, we have

$$\left(\ln f(v_c, T) - \frac{Nv_c}{V - Mv_c} \right) \delta M + [\ln\{(V - Mv_c)g(T)\} - \ln N]\delta N = 0,$$
$$(39)$$

subject to $\qquad\qquad \delta M + \delta N = 0. \qquad\qquad (40)$

Consequently, adding α(40) to (39) in the usual way, we find

$$\alpha + \ln f(v_c, T) - \frac{N^* v_c}{V - M^* v_c} = 0, \tag{41}$$

and $$\alpha + \ln[(V - M^* v_c) g(T)] - \ln N^* = 0, \tag{42}$$

i.e., writing $V - M^* v_c = V_g^*$ and $(\text{p.f.})_g^*$ for $(\text{p.f.})_g$ when $V_g = V_g^*$, from (42) and (41), respectively,

$$\left. \begin{aligned} N^* &= \lambda (\text{p.f.})_g^* \\ e^{N^* v_c / V_g^*} &= \lambda (\text{p.f.})_c \end{aligned} \right\} \tag{43}$$

and

where $\lambda = e^\alpha$. Now,

$$\frac{N^* v_c}{V_g^*} = \frac{P^* v_c}{kT}, \quad \text{where} \quad P^* V_g^* = N^* kT,$$

i.e. where P^* is the equilibrium pressure of the gas phase. Thus the equations (43) become

$$N^* = \lambda (\text{p.f.})_g^* \tag{35'}$$

and $$e^{P^* v_c / kT} = \lambda (\text{p.f.})_c. \tag{36'}$$

These equations, (35') and (36'), now replace (35) and (36) and, similarly, equation (37) becomes

$$F = -kT \ln\left[(\text{p.f.})_c^{M^*} \frac{(\text{p.f.})_g^{* N^*}}{N^*!} \right]. \tag{37'}$$

We now see, quite clearly, that previously, in the argument of paragraph 4, we were neglecting $P^* v_c$ in comparison with kT, i.e. in comparison with $P^* v_g^*$: consequently we were neglecting v_c in comparison with v_g—which is eminently reasonable in most circumstances.

On the other hand all the previous difficulty about μ_c (hidden by the words 'forgetting about the volume of the condensed phase') now disappears. We have

$$\mu_c = \left(\frac{\partial F_c}{\partial M} \right)_{V_c, T}, \quad \text{where} \quad \begin{aligned} F_c &= -M\, kT \ln(\text{p.f.})_c \\ &= -M\, kT \ln f(v_c, T) \\ &= -M\, kT \ln f(V_c/M, T). \end{aligned}$$

I.e.

$$\mu_c = -kT \ln(\text{p.f.})_c + MkT \frac{V_c}{M^2} \frac{f'}{f}, \quad \text{where} \quad f' = \frac{\partial f(v_c, T)}{\partial v_c},$$

$$= -kT \ln(\text{p.f.})_c + kTv_c \frac{f'}{f}.$$

But, similarly, $\quad P = -\left(\frac{\partial F_c}{\partial V_c}\right)_{M,T} = kT \frac{f'}{f}.$

Therefore, $\quad\quad \mu_c = -kT \ln(\text{p.f.})_c + Pv_c,$

i.e., by (36'), $\mu_c = kT \ln \lambda$ when $P = P^*$, as we should expect.

Moreover, it is now apparent that if any external pressure, P, hinders the growth of the crystalline phase, whether or not P is merely the pressure of the crystal's own vapour, equation (36') will read

$$e^{Pv_c/kT} = \lambda(\text{p.f.})_c. \tag{44}$$

But the l.h.s. of equation (44) is almost always very nearly unity. For, numerically, we have, taking

$$v_c = 10 \text{ A}^3 = 10^{-23} \text{ c.c.} \quad \text{and} \quad T = 300° \text{ K.},$$

since $\quad\quad\quad\quad k \approx 1{\cdot}4 \,.\, 10^{-16} \text{ erg/deg.,}$

$$\frac{Pv_c}{kT} \sim \frac{P\,10^{-23}}{4\,.\,10^{-14}} \sim \frac{1}{40} \quad \text{when} \quad P \approx 10^8 \text{ dynes/c.c.}$$

Now 1 atm. = $1{\cdot}013\,.\,10^6$ dynes/c.c. Therefore $Pv_c/kT \sim 1/40$, and $e^{Pv_c/kT}$ differs from unity only by some 2 per cent., even when $P \approx 100$ atm.

Since the l.h.s. of equation (44) is always, in practice, so nearly unity we shall, in further illustrative examples of the statistical methods, generally ignore the volume of the crystalline phase. But we shall refer to this problem again at the end of Chapter XVII.

6. Next we shall discuss briefly the problem of the adsorption of a perfect gas upon a surface, supposing that there is no dissociation of the systems on adsorption (we may think of the adsorption of a monatomic gas if we wish, though this restriction is not necessary). We shall also suppose that on adsorption each system occupies a definite *site* on the adsorbing surface: consequently we are dealing with immobile rather than mobile adsorbed films.

Finally, we shall suppose that all the sites on the surface capable of adsorbing a system are equivalent, and that the adsorbed systems can be treated as *independent* systems, which implies that there are no interactions between them. We shall show that the statistical treatment of this problem leads to the well-known Langmuir adsorption isotherm.

Diagrammatically, the adsorbed phase can be represented by

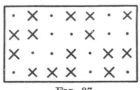

Fig. 37, where each cross signifies an adsorbed system and each dot a possible site for adsorption. We shall denote the *total* number of sites on which adsorption is possible by M_s, and let M denote the number of adsorbed systems in any particular specification of the

FIG. 37.

assembly. M^* will, of course, denote the equilibrium number of adsorbed systems.

If altogether there are X systems, and each can exist either

(i) in the gaseous phase, with possible energies $\epsilon_1, \epsilon_2, ..., \epsilon_i, ...,$ or

(ii) in the adsorbed phase, with possible energies $\eta_1, \eta_2, ..., \eta_i, ...,$ and if the corresponding distribution numbers are $n_1, n_2, ..., n_i, ...$ and $m_1, m_2, ..., m_i, ...,$ respectively, where

$$\sum_i n_i = N, \quad \sum_i m_i = M, \quad \text{and} \quad N+M = X,$$

then for this specification of the assembly there are

$$\frac{1}{N!} \frac{N!}{\prod_i n_i!} \quad \text{complexions of the gaseous systems} \quad (45)$$

and

$$\frac{M_s!}{M!(M_s-M)!} \frac{M!}{\prod_i m_i!} \quad \text{complexions of the adsorbed systems.} \quad (46)$$

The first factor in (46) gives the number of ways in which M identical systems can be localized upon M out of M_s possible sites on the adsorbing surface (see Appendix II, §a). For any such localization, we have then the problem of the number of complexions of M localized systems, the well-known solution of which is given by the second factor in (46).

Since each complexion of the gas phase, numbered in (45), can be associated with each complexion of the adsorbed phase in (46), we have

$$\Omega = \sum t(n_i, m_i),$$

where
$$t(n_i, m_i) = \frac{M_s!}{(M_s - M)!} \frac{1}{\prod_i m_i!} \frac{1}{\prod_i n_i!} \tag{47}$$

while, if E is the total energy of the assembly,

$$\sum_i n_i + \sum_i m_i = X \tag{48}$$

and
$$\sum_i n_i \epsilon_i + \sum_i m_i \eta_i = E. \tag{49}$$

Now M_s is constant, and therefore

$$\delta(M_s - M) = \delta(M_s - \sum_i m_i) = -\delta \sum_i m_i = -\sum_i \delta m_i;$$

consequently,

$$\delta \ln t = \ln(M_s - \sum_i m_i) . \sum_i \delta m_i - \sum_i \ln m_i . \delta m_i - \sum_i \ln n_i . \delta n_i, \tag{50}$$

where
$$\sum_i \delta n_i + \sum_i \delta m_i = 0, \tag{51}$$

and
$$\sum_i \epsilon_i \delta n_i + \sum_i \eta_i \delta m_i = 0. \tag{52}$$

Adding $\alpha(51) + \beta(52)$ to (50), in the usual way, we find, for the important, equilibrium, values of the distribution numbers, the equations

$$\left. \begin{array}{l} \alpha + \beta\epsilon_i - \ln n_i^* = 0 \\ \alpha + \beta\eta_i - \ln m_i^* + \ln(M_s - M^*) = 0 \end{array} \right\} \quad (i = 1, 2, ...), \tag{53}$$

where $M^* = \sum_i m_i^*$. The equations (53) have solutions

$$n_i^* = \lambda e^{\beta\epsilon_i} \quad (i = 1, 2, ...), \tag{54}$$

$$\frac{m_i^*}{M_s - M^*} = \lambda e^{\beta\eta_i} \quad (i = 1, 2, ...) \tag{55}$$

where $\lambda = e^{\alpha}$. We can now identify β with $-1/kT$, and introduce weight factors if necessary. Summing (54) and (55) over all i, we then find

$$N^* = \lambda(\text{p.f.})_g, \quad \text{where} \quad (\text{p.f.})_g = \sum_i \omega_i e^{-\epsilon_i/kT}, \tag{56}$$

and
$$\frac{M^*}{M_s - M^*} = \lambda(\text{p.f.})_a, \quad \text{where} \quad (\text{p.f.})_a = \sum_i \varpi_i e^{-\eta_i/kT}, \tag{57}$$

i.e. where $(\text{p.f.})_g$ and $(\text{p.f.})_a$ are the partition functions appropriate to systems in the gaseous and adsorbed phases, respectively.

Eliminating λ between equations (56) and (57), and writing $M^*/M_s = \theta$, we obtain

$$N^* = \frac{\theta}{1-\theta} \frac{(\text{p.f.})_g}{(\text{p.f.})_a}, \qquad (58)$$

where θ is the equilibrium fraction of sites for adsorption which are occupied by adsorbed molecules. Now $(\text{p.f.})_g$ contains V, the volume of the gas-phase, as a factor, and $N^*/V = P/kT$, where P is the pressure of the gas. Consequently equation (58) gives

$$P = \frac{\theta}{1-\theta} f(T), \qquad (59)$$

which is Langmuir's isotherm equation. In equation (58), however, the function of temperature, $f(T)$, is specified quite definitely in terms of the partition functions of gaseous and adsorbed systems.

We shall not discuss this problem further here (see examples) except to state that when the results (54) and (55) are substituted into the equation for $\ln t$ we find (using

$$F = E - TS = E - kT.\ln\Omega = E - kT.\ln t_{\max})$$

the formula

$$F = -kT.\ln\left\{ \frac{M_s!}{M^*!(M_s - M^*)!} (\text{p.f.})_a^{M^*} \frac{(\text{p.f.})_g^{N^*}}{N^*!} \right\} \qquad (60)$$

as the equation for the Helmholtz free energy of the whole assembly.

7. As a final example in this chapter we shall sketch the statistical attack on the problem of the equilibrium between a gaseous and a condensed phase when the systems of either phase can dimerize, that is, can join together in pairs to form a new species. Apart from this allowed dimerization we shall assume that the gaseous phase is perfect and that the condensed phase can be treated on the basis of an Einstein model (i.e. as an assembly of independent localized systems). We shall further assume that *in the condensed phase monomers and dimers are interchangeable*. This implies (cf. the previous problem of adsorption)

that if we have M_1 monomers and M_2 dimers in a certain specification of the condensed phase then there are

$$\frac{(M_1+M_2)!}{M_1!\,M_2!} \tag{61}$$

mutual arrangements of these systems (all these arrangements being equally probable). After the systems have been localized in any one of these arrangements, we have still the familiar task of assigning to them their various allowed energy values.

It is convenient to set out the symbols occurring in the statistical theory in tabular form: i.e.

State of a system	Allowed energies	Distribution numbers
Monomer in gas phase	$\epsilon_1, \epsilon_2,..., \epsilon_i,...$	$n_1, n_2,..., n_i,...$
Dimer in gas phase	$\epsilon_1', \epsilon_2',..., \epsilon_i',...$	$n_1', n_2',..., n_i',...$
Monomer in condensed phase	$\eta_1, \eta_2,..., \eta_i,...$	$m_1, m_2,..., m_i,...$
Dimer in condensed phase	$\eta_1', \eta_2',..., \eta_i',...$	$m_1', m_2',..., m_i',...$

and to introduce the abbreviations

$$\sum_i n_i = N_1, \quad \sum_i n_i' = N_2, \quad \sum_i m_i = M_1, \quad \sum_i m_i' = M_2.$$

Then, if in the whole assembly there are X monomer units, since each dimer accounts for two such units we have

$$N_1+2N_2+M_1+2M_2 = X. \tag{62}$$

After the previous discussions of a mixed gas phase and of adsorption, we can write down, without further explanation, the expression for the number of different complexions of the assembly corresponding to a given set of distribution numbers. This is given by

$$t(n_i, n_i', m_i, m_i') = \frac{(M_1+M_2)!}{M_1!\,M_2!} \frac{M_1!}{\prod_i m_i!} \frac{M_2!}{\prod_i m_i'!} \frac{1}{\prod_i n_i!} \frac{1}{\prod_i n_i'!}$$

$$= \frac{\left(\sum_i m_i + \sum_i m_i'\right)!}{\prod_i m_i! \prod_i m_i'! \prod_i n_i! \prod_i n_i'!}. \tag{63}$$

The restrictive conditions on the distribution numbers are

$$\sum_i n_i + 2\sum_i n_i' + \sum_i m_i + 2\sum_i m_i' = X \tag{64}$$

and

$$\sum_i n_i \epsilon_i + \sum_i n_i' \epsilon_i' + \sum_i m_i \eta_i + \sum_i m_i' \eta_i' = E, \tag{65}$$

where E is the total energy of the assembly.

Therefore we have

$$\delta \ln t = \ln\left(\sum_i m_i + \sum_i m_i'\right)\left(\sum_i \delta m_i + \sum_i \delta m_i'\right) - \sum_i \ln m_i . \delta m_i -$$
$$- \sum_i \ln m_i' . \delta m_i' - \sum_i \ln n_i . \delta n_i - \sum_i \ln n_i' . \delta n_i', \quad (66)$$

where the changes in the distribution numbers are subject to

$$\sum_i \delta n_i + 2\sum_i \delta n_i' + \sum_i \delta m_i + 2\sum_i \delta m_i' = 0 \quad (67)$$

and

$$\sum_i \epsilon_i \delta n_i + \sum_i \epsilon_i' \delta n_i' + \sum_i \eta_i \delta m_i + \sum_i \eta_i' \delta m_i' = 0. \quad (68)$$

Adding $\alpha(67) + \beta(68)$ to (66) we obtain, for the important values of the distribution numbers, the equations

$$\alpha + \beta\epsilon_i - \ln n_i^* = 0 \qquad \text{i.e.} \qquad n_i^* = \lambda e^{\beta\epsilon_i} \quad (69)$$

$$2\alpha + \beta\epsilon_i' - \ln n_i'^* = 0 \qquad \text{i.e.} \qquad n_i'^* = \lambda^2 e^{\beta\epsilon_i'} \quad (70)$$

$$\alpha + \beta\eta_i - \ln m_i^* + \ln(M_1^* + M_2^*) = 0 \quad \text{i.e.} \quad \frac{m_i^*}{M_1^* + M_2^*} = \lambda e^{\beta\eta_i} \quad (71)$$

$$2\alpha + \beta\eta_i' - \ln m_i'^* + \ln(M_1^* + M_2^*) = 0 \quad \text{i.e.} \quad \frac{m_i'^*}{M_1^* + M_2^*} = \lambda^2 e^{\beta\eta_i'} \quad (72)$$

where $\lambda = e^\alpha$.

Identifying β with $-1/kT$, and summing (69), (70), (71), and (72) for all i, we find

$$N_1^* = \lambda(\text{p.f.})_1^g, \quad (73)$$

$$N_2^* = \lambda^2(\text{p.f.})_2^g, \quad (74)$$

$$\frac{M_1^*}{M_1^* + M_2^*} = \lambda(\text{p.f.})_1^c, \quad (75)$$

$$\frac{M_2^*}{M_1^* + M_2^*} = \lambda^2(\text{p.f.})_2^c. \quad (76)$$

Here $(\text{p.f.})_1^g$ and $(\text{p.f.})_1^c$ are the partition functions appropriate to monomer systems in the gaseous and condensed phases, respectively, and $(\text{p.f.})_2^g$ and $(\text{p.f.})_2^c$ are the corresponding partition functions for dimer systems.

From the equations (73) and (74) we obtain, on eliminating λ,

$$\frac{N_2^*}{N_1^{*2}} = \frac{(\text{p.f.})_2^g}{[(\text{p.f.})_1^g]^2}, \quad (77)$$

which expresses the Law of Mass Action for the vapour phase. Similarly, eliminating λ from equations (75) and (76), we find

$$\frac{M_2^*(M_1^* + M_2^*)}{M_1^{*2}} = \frac{(\text{p.f.})_2^c}{[(\text{p.f.})_1^c]^2}. \quad (78)$$

Equation (78) expresses the Law of Mass Action for the condensed phase. Its meaning is, perhaps, better revealed if we write

$$\frac{M_1^*}{M_1^*+M_2^*} = x_1 \quad \text{and} \quad \frac{M_2^*}{M_1^*+M_2^*} = x_2,$$

so that x_1 and x_2 are, respectively, the equilibrium mole fractions of monomers and dimers in the condensed phase. Then equation (78) becomes

$$\frac{x_2}{x_1^2} = \frac{(\text{p.f.})_2^c}{[(\text{p.f.})_1^c]^2} \tag{78'}$$

and shows that the Law of Mass Action for the condensed phase is expressed by an equation which, while analogous to that for the gas phase (equation (77)), involves *mole fractions*, and not numbers of systems (as in the gas phase).

Again we shall not discuss this problem in further detail here, save only to record that the usual procedure now leads to the equation

$$F =$$

$$-kT \ln \left\{ \frac{(M_1^*+M_2^*)!}{M_1^*!\,M_2^*!} [(\text{p.f.})_1^c]^{M_1^*}[(\text{p.f.})_2^c]^{M_2^*} \frac{[(\text{p.f.})_1^g]^{N_1^*}[(\text{p.f.})_2^g]^{N_2^*}}{N_1^*!\,N_2^*!} \right\}, \tag{79}$$

as the reader can easily verify.

EXAMPLES

1. Derive equation (60), using the results (54) and (55).

2. Writing

$$F_a = -kT \ln \left(\frac{M_s!}{M!\,(M_s-M)!} (\text{p.f.})_a^M \right), \qquad F_g = -kT \ln \frac{(\text{p.f.})_g^N}{N!},$$

derive Langmuir's isotherm equation by the method of equating chemical potentials.

3. Prove that the free energy of the adsorbed phase may be written

$$F_a = -kT[M \ln(\text{p.f.})_a - M_s \{(1-\theta)\ln(1-\theta) + \theta \ln \theta\}].$$

4. If, in the problem of immobile adsorption, the gas consists of diatomic molecules, A_2 (whose dissociation in the gas phase may be ignored) which are adsorbed as single, A, atoms (between which interactions may be neglected), prove that Langmuir's isotherm equation then becomes

$$P^{\frac{1}{2}} = \frac{\theta}{1-\theta} f(T).$$

5. Derive equation (79).

TWO-PHASE ASSEMBLIES: TWO COMPONENTS

1. EXTENSION of the methods of the last chapter to the slightly more complex problems, of the same type, in which there are several different components present in the assembly presents no difficulty and we shall illustrate the procedure by considering just two problems in each of which we are concerned with two components only.

First, we shall consider the problem of a perfect mixed crystal in equilibrium with its own vapour phase: in place of the mixed crystal we can substitute instead any condensed phase (solid or liquid) provided we may treat it on the basis of an Einstein model of essentially independent systems and provided also that a second physical condition, implied in the word *perfect* is satisfied (see paragraph 3 below). Secondly, we shall consider the rather more elaborate problem in which one of the two components is capable of dimerization in the condensed phase, and shall discuss the effect of this dimerization on the corresponding partial vapour-pressure curves.

After the several examples which we have worked through in fair detail in the previous and preceding chapters, the reader will recognize that the application of our standard procedure (to the simple problems with which it is capable of dealing) is merely a matter of routine. In fact it is now possible to predict with confidence what the result will be, even without carrying through the mathematical derivation of many of the intermediate formulae. To appreciate this let us collect, in tabular form, some of the results we have already obtained (using the notation of § 1, Chapter XIII).

These results, see Table X, should be studied carefully: it will be seen that very little effort is required to memorize them, since all subsequent formulae follow logically from the first one according to the rule that each new factor in the general term in Ω gives rise to an appropriate corresponding factor in $\exp(-F/kT)$. The equations fixing the equilibrium extent, or composition, of

TABLE X

Problem	General term in Ω	Essential result (Helmholtz free energy)
Perfect crystal	$\dfrac{M!}{\prod_i m_i!}$	$F = -kT\ln(\text{p.f.})_c^M$
Perfect gas	$\dfrac{1}{\prod_i n_i!}$	$F = -kT\ln\dfrac{(\text{p.f.})_g^N}{N!}$
Mixed gas (two components)	$\dfrac{1}{\prod_i n_i! \prod_i n_i'!}$	$F = -kT\ln\left[\dfrac{(\text{p.f.})_1^{N_1}(\text{p.f.})_2^{N_2}}{N_1!\,N_2!}\right]$
Crystal-gas	$\dfrac{M!}{\prod_i m_i! \prod_i n_i!}$	$F = -kT\ln\left[(\text{p.f.})_c^{M^*}(\text{p.f.})_g^{N^*}\dfrac{i^*!}{N^*!}\right]$
Immobile adsorption	$\dfrac{M_s!}{M!(M_s-M)!}\dfrac{M!}{\prod_i m_i!}\dfrac{1}{\prod_i n_i!}$	$F = -kT\ln\left[\dfrac{M_s!}{M^*!(M_s-M^*)!}(\text{p.f.})_a^{M^*}\dfrac{i^*!}{N^*!}(\text{p.f.})_g^{N^*}\right]$
Crystal-gas, with dimerization	$\dfrac{(M_1+M_2)!}{M_1!\,M_2!}\dfrac{M_1!\,M_2!}{\prod_i m_i! \prod_i m_i'!}\dfrac{1}{\prod_i n_i! \prod_i n_i'!}$	$F = -kT\ln\left[\dfrac{(M_1^*+M_2^*)!}{M_1^*!\,M_2^*!}(\text{p.f.})_1^{M_1^*}[(\text{p.f.})_1']^{M_1^*}[(\text{p.f.})_2]^{M_2^*}[(\text{p.f.})_2']^{M_2^*}\dfrac{[(\text{p.f.})_1^*]^{N_1^*}[(\text{p.f.})_2^*]^{N_2^*}}{N_1^*!\,N_2^*!}\right]$

Note that each distinctive factor of the general term in Ω gives rise to an equally characteristic factor in $e^{-F/kT}$.

the various phases (when there is more than one phase) are not given in Table X. Whilst these equations are produced automatically on carrying through the full statistical treatment (as above), they can also be obtained by the alternative method, already discussed, of equating chemical potentials. Thus, for instance, in the case of immobile adsorption we should write

$$F = F_a + F_g,$$

where
$$F_a = -kT \ln\left[\frac{M_s!}{M^*!(M_s - M^*)!}(\text{p.f.})_a^{M^*}\right]$$

and
$$F_g = -kT \ln\left[\frac{(\text{p.f.})_g^{N^*}}{N^*!}\right],$$

and then write down explicitly the equation $\mu_a = \mu_g$, where

$$\mu_a = \frac{\partial F_a}{\partial M^*} \quad \text{and} \quad \mu_g = \frac{\partial F_g}{\partial N^*}.$$

This gives

$$kT \ln M^* - kT \ln(M_s - M^*) - kT \ln(\text{p.f.})_a$$
$$= kT \ln N^* - kT \ln(\text{p.f.})_g$$

(see equations (56) and (57) of Chapter XIII), which determines M^* and N^* when $M^* + N^* (= X)$ is known.

We shall employ this short-cut method in discussing the two problems of the present chapter: but the reader should bear in mind that, from the standpoint of statistical mechanics, the justification of the results so obtained lies in the fully statistical derivation which, though sometimes a little tedious, can always be supplied. Indeed, if in doubt the reader should always return to the full-length statistical treatment.

2. Considering now a mixed crystal, of two components, in equilibrium with its own vapour phase, let there be altogether

$$X_A \text{ systems of type } A,$$

$$X_B \text{ systems of type } B,$$

and suppose that any system of type A can have energies

$$\epsilon_1^a, \epsilon_2^a, ..., \epsilon_i^a, ... \text{ in the vapour phase}$$

and energies

$$\eta_1^a, \eta_2^a, ..., \eta_i^a, ... \text{ in the condensed phase,}$$

whilst the corresponding energy levels available to a system of type B are $\epsilon_1^b, \epsilon_2^b,..., \epsilon_i^b,...$ and $\eta_1^b, \eta_2^b,..., \eta_i^b,...,$

respectively. Weight factors ω_i^a, ϖ_i^a, ω_i^b, ϖ_i^b, can be introduced if necessary.

Let any specification of the assembly be described by the distribution numbers

$$n_1^a, n_2^a,..., n_i^a,...; \quad m_1^a, m_2^a,..., m_i^a,...$$

$$n_1^b, n_2^b,..., n_i^b,...; \quad m_1^b, m_2^b,..., m_i^b,...$$

in accordance with the notation of Chapter XIII. We shall also write

$$\sum_i n_i^a = N_A, \qquad \sum_i m_i^a = M_A,$$

$$\sum_i n_i^b = N_B, \qquad \sum_i m_i^b = M_B,$$

and then, of course, $N_A + M_A = X_A$

and $N_B + M_B = X_B.$ (1)

For given M_A and M_B, the crystalline phase comprises $M_A + M_B$ systems. We shall suppose (cf. § 7, Chapter XIII) that these systems, of the two types A and B, are sufficiently alike in size and shape to be entirely equivalent as far as arrangements within the crystal lattice are concerned. More precisely, we shall suppose that the M_A systems of type A and the M_B systems of type B can be permuted at random among the $M_A + M_B$ available lattice-sites, so that there are

$$\frac{(M_A + M_B)!}{M_A! \, M_B!}$$ (2)

equivalent ways of localizing the systems of the condensed phase (see § 3, below). Having localized these systems in any one of the possible ways enumerated in (2), the energies η^a and η^b can then be assigned to the systems, on the basis of the distribution numbers m^a and m^b in

$$\frac{M_A!}{\prod_i m_i^a!} \frac{M_B!}{\prod_i m_i^b!}$$ (3)

ways. Finally, we can assign the energies ϵ^a and ϵ^b to the non-localized systems on the basis of the distribution numbers n^a and n^b in

$$\frac{1}{\prod\limits_i n_i^a!} \frac{1}{\prod\limits_i n_i^b!} \tag{4}$$

ways (see equation (5), Chapter XI).

Now each of the equivalent arrangements enumerated in (2) can be associated with any of the energy distributions enumerated in (3), and any such complexion of the condensed phase can then be associated with any complexion of the gas phase (enumerated in (4)). Consequently, the total number of complexions of the assembly corresponding to the given distribution numbers is given by

$$\frac{(M_A+M_B)!}{M_A!\,M_B!}\,\frac{M_A!}{\prod\limits_i m_i^a!}\,\frac{M_B!}{\prod\limits_i m_i^b!}\,\frac{1}{\prod\limits_i n_i^a!}\,\frac{1}{\prod\limits_i n_i^b!}. \tag{5}$$

The expression (5) gives the general term in Ω for the present problem. We can now take the proposed short cut, on the basis of past experience, to the result that the Helmholtz free energy of the assembly is given by

$$F = -kT \ln\left[\frac{(M_A^*+M_B^*)!}{M_A^*!\,M_B^*!}[(\text{p.f.})_A^c]^{M_A^*}[(\text{p.f.})_B^c]^{M_B^*} \times\right.$$

$$\left.\times \frac{[(\text{p.f.})_A^g]^{N_A^*}[(\text{p.f.})_B^g]^{N_B^*}}{N_A^*!\,N_B^*!}\right], \tag{6}$$

where

$$(\text{p.f.})_A^c = \sum_i \varpi_i^a e^{-\eta_i^a/kT}, \qquad (\text{p.f.})_B^c = \sum_i \varpi_i^b e^{-\eta_i^b/kT},$$

$$(\text{p.f.})_A^g = \sum_i \omega_i^a e^{-\epsilon_i^a/kT}, \qquad (\text{p.f.})_B^g = \sum_i \omega_i^b e^{-\epsilon_i^b/kT},$$

and M_A^*, M_B^*, N_A^*, and N_B^* are the equilibrium values of M_A, M_B, N_A, and N_B.

To find these equilibrium values of M_A, M_B, N_A, and N_B, by the method of equating chemical potentials, we write

$$F = F_c + F_g,$$

where

$$F_c = -kT \ln\left[\frac{(M_A^*+M_B^*)!}{M_A^*!\,M_B^*!}[(\text{p.f.})_A^c]^{M_A^*}[(\text{p.f.})_B^c]^{M_B^*}\right] \tag{7}$$

and

$$F_g = -kT \ln\left[\frac{[(\text{p.f.})_A^g]^{N_A^*}[(\text{p.f.})_B^g]^{N_B^*}}{N_A^*!\,N_B^*!}\right]. \tag{8}$$

Then

$$\mu_A^c = \left(\frac{\partial F_c}{\partial M_A^*}\right)_{M_B^*} = kT \ln M_A^* - kT \ln(M_A^* + M_B^*) - kT \ln(\text{p.f.})_A^c,$$

$$\mu_A^g = \left(\frac{\partial F_g}{\partial N_A^*}\right)_{N_B^*} = kT \ln N_A^* - kT \ln(\text{p.f.})_A^g,$$

so that the equation $\mu_A^c = \mu_A^g$ gives

$$N_A^* = \frac{M_A^*}{M_A^* + M_B^*} \frac{(\text{p.f.})_A^g}{(\text{p.f.})_A^c}. \tag{9}$$

Similarly, the equation $\mu_B^c = \mu_B^g$ gives

$$N_B^* = \frac{M_B^*}{M_A^* + M_B^*} \frac{(\text{p.f.})_B^g}{(\text{p.f.})_B^c}. \tag{10}$$

To find M_A^*, M_B^*, N_A^*, and N_B^* we require, besides the equations (9) and (10), the two constitutive equations (see equations (1))

$$\left.\begin{array}{c} N_A^* + M_A^* = X_A \\ N_B^* + M_B^* = X_B \end{array}\right\}; \tag{11}$$

but equations (9) and (10) themselves express the most important properties of a perfect binary solution. Before discussing their content further, however, we must examine, rather more carefully than in § 1 above, the physical assumptions underlying the model from which these equations have been derived.

3. The basis of equations (9) and (10) is to be found in the expression (5): given the expression (5), equations (9) and (10) follow automatically. In the expression (5) there are three distinct factors, (2), (3), and (4), with each of which is associated a definite physical assumption.

Taking first the factor (4), concerned simply with the gas phase, we need comment only that

   (i) the assumption of independent systems implies a perfect (mixed) gas,
   (ii) the assumption that ϵ^a and ϵ^b are independent of M_A and M_B implies that we are ignoring the volume of the condensed phase compared with that of the vapour phase.

Neither of these assumptions, however, is particularly important. We have already discussed (ii) in paragraph 4 of Chapter XIII (and shall treat the matter in more detail later); whilst (i), although essential to equations (9) and (10), simply enables us to give explicit values to μ_A^g and μ_B^g. If we are unable to treat the vapour phase as perfect, then we shall still have

$$\left.\begin{aligned}\mu_A^g = \mu_A^c = kT\ln\frac{M_A^*}{M_A^*+M_B^*} - kT\ln(\text{p.f.})_A^c \\[2mm] \mu_B^g = \mu_B^c = kT\ln\frac{M_B^*}{M_A^*+M_B^*} - kT\ln(\text{p.f.})_B^c\end{aligned}\right\}. \tag{12}$$

But since the physical interpretation of the equations (12) is less simple and striking than that of equations (9) and (10), we shall continue to make the assumption that the vapour phase may be treated as perfect.

The assumption underlying the factor (3) is that entailed in any simple Einstein model, namely that the systems of the condensed phase may be regarded as essentially independent; more precisely (since obviously the systems of a crystal or liquid are far from being physically independent), that there is a model comprising essentially independent systems which can do justice to the real condensed phase. Now for a condensed phase of one component only we can always write, formally,

$$F = -kT\ln(\text{p.f.})_c^M;$$

for since F is, thermodynamically, an extensive property of the assembly it is necessarily proportional to M. Thus, in one sense, an Einstein model always exists for a pure phase: although we may know very little about the actual set of energy levels, η, which would lead to the correct behaviour of F. For a mixed phase the situation is less simple. But we have certainly assumed that the energy levels, η^a and η^b, besides being the same for all systems of types A and B, respectively, are also quite unaffected by the relative arrangement of A and B systems in the condensed phase. Thus we assume that we can mutually rearrange the systems, keeping M_A and M_B fixed, without upsetting the distribution of energies to these systems, and so without affecting the total energy possessed by the condensed phase as a whole. Physically, this certainly implies that, effectively, there are no preferential interaction energies between systems of the same or opposite types. Indeed, we shall see below that zero heat of mixing (in the thermodynamical sense) is one of the necessary consequences of equation (6), and so of the expression (5).

So much, then, for the assumption which underlies our inclusion of the factor (3): briefly, we may say that we are supposing the systems of types A and B to be sufficiently similar for there to be no preferential interaction-energies between them.

Finally, there is the assumption underlying the use of the expression (2) for the number of mutual arrangements of M_A A-systems and M_B B-systems. If the systems can (pictorially) be regarded as spherical and all of the same size, then clearly any two systems can always be interchanged (whether of the same kind or not), and corresponding to any one positional arrangement of the systems there are altogether $(M_A+M_B)!/M_A!\,M_B!$ arrangements (including the first one) obtained simply by permuting the systems among the given positions. Moreover, it may be expected that small differences of size or shape will not greatly affect the validity of the expression (2) for the number of mutual arrangements. But the validity of expression (2) is more general than this. Equal, or roughly equal, molecules, whatever their shape, will also be capable of this number of mutual rearrangements: for if the species of types A and B are equal in size, any two such systems can be interchanged without the necessity of disturbing the other systems of the assembly.

Thus we may, provisionally, claim that the physical assumption underlying the use of the expression (2), and so implied in the epithet *perfect solution*, is that of equality (or very near equality) in the size and shape of the two species concerned. There is, however, certainly one exception to this rule: if we have a mixture of two matchlike species, of the same thickness but of two different lengths, and if the only significant arrangements of these systems are those in which they are all aligned with their axes parallel (see Fig. 38) then, provided that the condition of no preferential interactions is fulfilled, we can always interchange two systems by simply pushing others further along the line if necessary (this having no effect on the energy of the assembly). Consequently,

Q

in such circumstances the expression (2) will again be valid,† and the solution will exhibit all the consequences of equations (9) and (10).

To sum up, then, we may say that for the validity of equations (9) and (10) we require that

 (a) the vapour phase behaves as a mixture of perfect gases,
 (b) there are no preferential interactions between the different systems within the condensed phase,
 (c) the systems (in the condensed phase) are of approximately equal size and shape.

We have noted an exception to the condition (c), but it is

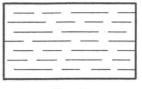

FIG. 38.

comparatively unimportant. Moreover, (a) concerns only the gas phase and is not, essentially, a restriction on the nature of the solution itself. When the conditions (b) and (c) are satisfied or, more accurately, when the equations (12) are satisfied for all values of the mole-ratio M_A^*/M_B^*, we speak of a *perfect* solution. The condensed phase concerned may be either solid or liquid.

Having thus defined more precisely the microscopic physical conditions, or assumptions, underlying the equations (6) to (10) above, derived somewhat uncritically in paragraph 2, we may now proceed to examine the content and consequences of these equations with respect to the macroscopic behaviour of any solution for which they may hold true.

4. We shall consider first the equations (9) and (10), i.e.

$$N_A^* = \frac{M_A^*}{M_A^*+M_B^*} \frac{(\text{p.f.})_A^g}{(\text{p.f.})_A^c} \quad \text{and} \quad N_B^* = \frac{M_B^*}{M_A^*+M_B^*} \frac{(\text{p.f.})_B^g}{(\text{p.f.})_B^c}.$$

If V and P be the volume and pressure, respectively, of the gas phase then

$$\begin{aligned}(\text{p.f.})_A^g &= V g_A(T) \\ (\text{p.f.})_B^g &= V g_B(T)\end{aligned} \right\} \tag{13}$$

and
$$(N_A^*+N_B^*)kT = PV. \tag{14}$$

† This particular exception to the rule of equal size and shape seems to occur with mixtures of certain linear hydrocarbon molecules of different lengths.

But in place of (14) we may write

$$\left. \begin{array}{l} N_A^* kT = p_A V \\ N_B^* kT = p_B V \end{array} \right\} \quad \text{where } p_A + p_B = P. \tag{15}$$

Here p_A and p_B are the *partial* vapour pressures, of A and B systems respectively, in the gas phase. Using (13) and (15), the equations (9) and (10) then become

$$p_A = \frac{M_A^*}{M_A^* + M_B^*} \frac{kT g_A(T)}{(\text{p.f.})_A^c} \tag{16}$$

and

$$p_B = \frac{M_B^*}{M_A^* + M_B^*} \frac{kT g_B(T)}{(\text{p.f.})_B^c}. \tag{17}$$

Putting $M_B^* = 0$ in (16) we find

$$\frac{kT g_A(T)}{(\text{p.f.})_A^c} = p_A^0(T),$$

where $p_A^0(T)$ denotes the vapour pressure, at the temperature T, of the condensed phase of the pure A-component. Similarly, putting $M_A^* = 0$ in (17) we find

$$\frac{kT g_B(T)}{(\text{p.f.})_B^c} = p_B^0(T).$$

Consequently (16) and (17) may be written

$$\left. \begin{array}{l} p_A = \dfrac{M_A^*}{M_A^* + M_B^*} p_A^0(T) \\[2ex] p_B = \dfrac{M_B^*}{M_A^* + M_B^*} p_B^0(T) \end{array} \right\} \tag{18}$$

showing that, at any given temperature, p_A and p_B, the partial vapour pressures of the two components in the gas phase, are linear functions of the mole fraction,

$$M_A^*/(M_A^* + M_B^*) \quad \text{or} \quad M_B^*/(M_A^* + M_B^*),$$

defining the composition of the solution. Experimentally, this law, that the partial vapour pressure in the gas phase is proportional to the mole fraction in the condensed phase, is known as Raoult's law: the above statistical theory shows that a solution obeys Raoult's law when the three conditions (a), (b), and (c), of § 3, are satisfied.

The equations (18) are represented graphically in Fig. 39 (i), where the straight lines describe the behaviour of the partial vapour pressures at a constant temperature, as functions of the ↦

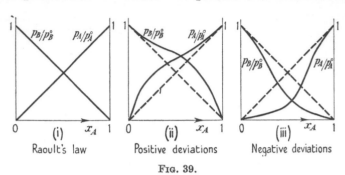

(i) Raoult's law   (ii) Positive deviations   (iii) Negative deviations

Fig. 39.

composition of the condensed phase. This composition is specified by x_A or x_B, where

$$x_A = \frac{M_A^*}{M_A^* + M_B^*}, \quad x_B = \frac{M_B^*}{M_A^* + M_B^*} \quad \text{and} \quad x_A + x_B = 1.$$

So much for the equations (9) and (10). From equation (7), however, we can easily determine two other interesting properties of a perfect solution, namely expressions for the free energy and entropy of mixing. For, from (7), we know that the free energy of a *mixed* condensed phase of M_A^* A-systems and M_B^* B-systems (forming a perfect solution) is given by

$$F_c = -kT \ln \left[\frac{(M_A^* + M_B^*)!}{M_A^*! \, M_B^*!} [(\text{p.f.})_A^c]^{M_A^*} [(\text{p.f.})_B^c]^{M_B^*} \right],$$

whereas the sum of the free energies of two pure condensed phases containing, respectively, M_A^* A-systems and M_B^* B-systems is

$$F_A + F_B = -kT \ln[(\text{p.f.})_A^c]^{M_A^*} - kT \ln[(\text{p.f.})_B^c]^{M_B^*}.$$

Consequently, the gain in Helmholtz free energy on mixing the two pure phases, to form the perfect solution, is

$$\Delta F = F_c - F_A - F_B$$
$$= -kT \ln \frac{(M_A^* + M_B^*)!}{M_A^*! \, M_B^*!}$$

(a negative quantity, showing that there is a loss of free energy on mixing), i.e. by Stirling's theorem,

$$\Delta F = -kT\,(M_A^* + M_B^*)\ln(M_A^* + M_B^*) +$$
$$+ kT\,M_A^*\ln M_A^* + kT\,M_B^*\ln M_B^*$$
$$= kTM_A^*\ln\frac{M_A^*}{M_A^* + M_B^*} + kTM_B^*\ln\frac{M_B^*}{M_A^* + M_B^*},$$

i.e. $$\Delta F = (M_A^* + M_B^*)kT(x_A \ln x_A + x_B \ln x_B). \qquad (19)$$

It follows at once, from the Gibbs–Helmholtz equation

$$\Delta E = -T^2\frac{\partial}{\partial T}\!\left(\frac{\Delta F}{T}\right),$$

that $$\Delta E = 0, \qquad (20)$$

and thence, since $\Delta F = \Delta E - T\Delta S$, that the entropy of mixing is given by

$$\Delta S = -(M_A^* + M_B^*)k(x_A \ln x_A + x_B \ln x_B)$$
$$= k\ln\frac{(M_A^* + M_B^*)!}{M_A^*!\,M_B^*!}. \qquad (21)$$

The equations (20) and (21) are, of course, direct macroscopic consequences of the two molecular physical conditions, (b) and (c), which a perfect solution must satisfy. Not all the solutions of chemistry or metallurgy, however, are perfect solutions: indeed, comparatively few of them obey Raoult's law at all accurately. When the actual, experimental, partial vapour-pressures lie above the corresponding straight lines of Fig. 39 (i), as in Fig. 39 (ii), we speak of *positive* deviations from Raoult's law; when they lie below, as in Fig. 39 (iii), we speak of *negative* deviations. Partial vapour-pressure curves lying partly above and partly below the Raoult's law lines are quite possible. An important field of statistical mechanics, in which much work remains yet to be done, may be defined as the correlation of deviations from Raoult's law with the progressive breakdown, or relaxation, of the conditions (b) and (c). This, however, is not the place to enter upon an extensive treatment of the theory of solutions (but see §5 below and Chapter XVIII). This is, however, perhaps a convenient place to remind the reader that the two partial vapour-pressure curves depicted in any diagram such as Fig. 39 are not independent: they are necessarily connected by the Duhem–Margules equation (see Appendix V)

$$\frac{x_A}{p_A}\frac{\partial p_A}{\partial x}+\frac{x_B}{p_B}\frac{\partial p_B}{\partial x}=0, \tag{22}$$

where x stands for either x_A or x_B and the symbol of partial differentiation signifies that the changes are at constant temperature. Equation (22) provides a useful check on the internal consistency of all approximate statistical treatments.

5. The second problem which we have proposed to discuss in this chapter may be called the problem of dimerization in an otherwise perfect solution. We suppose that all the physical conditions are just as in the last example (i.e. as for a perfect binary solution) except that now one of the two species is capable of forming dimers in the condensed phase. The dimers so formed are assumed to be roughly equivalent, in size and shape, to the other systems of the condensed phase (see § 7, Chapter XIII) so that we have in fact three species therein capable of mutual interchanges of position. We shall refer to the non-dimerizing component and the dimerizing component as the solvent and solute, respectively: the solute then comprises both monomer and dimer species.

We shall further assume, for simplicity, that no dimerization occurs in the vapour phase: but it is not necessary that we introduce the vapour phase explicitly to start with, and we shall consider first simply the appropriate expression for the free energy of the condensed phase. Again we shall use the short-cut method employed already in this chapter, though the reader is strongly urged to carry through the full statistical treatment without this appeal to past experience.

The notational symbols may conveniently be exhibited in tabular form:

Species	Allowed energies	(Degeneracies)	Distribution numbers
Solvent	$\eta_1,\ \eta_2,...,\ \eta_i,...$	(ϖ_i)	$m_1,\ m_2,...,\ m_i,...$
Monomer solute	$\eta_1',\ \eta_2',...,\ \eta_i',...$	(ϖ_i')	$m_1',\ m_2',...,\ \dot{m}_i',...$
Dimer solute	$\eta_1'',\ \eta_2'',...,\ \eta_i'',...$	(ϖ_i'')	$m_1'',\ m_2'',...,\ m_i'',...$

and we shall further write

$$\sum_i m_i = M_v, \qquad \sum_i m_i' = M_1, \qquad \sum_i m_i'' = M_2,$$

and
$$M_1 + 2M_2 = M_u. \tag{23}$$

Thus M_v is the total number of solvent species and M_u the total number of monomer units in either of the two solute species (i.e. whether occurring as monomers or as dimers).

Now M_1 species of type 1, M_2 species of type 2, and M_v species of type 3 can, if mutually interchangeable, be arranged spacially in

$$\frac{(M_1 + M_2 + M_v)!}{M_1! \, M_2! \, M_v!} \tag{24}$$

different ways. (This is a direct generalization of (2): see Appendix II, §a.) Consequently the general term in Ω, for the condensed phase, corresponding to the given distribution numbers, is

$$\frac{(M_1 + M_2 + M_v)!}{M_1! \, M_2! \, M_v!} \frac{M_1!}{\prod_i m_i'!} \frac{M_2!}{\prod_i m_i''!} \frac{M_v!}{\prod_i m_i!}, \tag{25}$$

and we may now jump to the result that the Helmholtz free energy of the condensed phase is given by

$$F_c = -kT \ln\left[\frac{(M_1^* + M_2^* + M_v^*)!}{M_1^*! \, M_2^*! \, M_v^*!} (\text{p.f.})_1^{M_1^*} (\text{p.f.})_2^{M_2^*} [(\text{p.f.})_v^c]^{M_v^*}\right], \tag{26}$$

where

$$(\text{p.f.})_1 = \sum_i \varpi_i' e^{-\eta_i'/kT}, \qquad (\text{p.f.})_2 = \sum_i \varpi_i'' e^{-\eta_i''/kT},$$

$$(\text{p.f.})_v^c = \sum_i \varpi_i e^{-\eta_i/kT}.$$

The formula (26) may, by Stirling's theorem, be written

$$F_c = -kT[M_1^* \ln(\text{p.f.})_1 + M_2^* \ln(\text{p.f.})_2 + M_v^* \ln(\text{p.f.})_v^c +$$
$$+ (M_1^* + M_2^* + M_v^*) \ln(M_1^* + M_2^* + M_v^*) -$$
$$- M_1^* \ln M_1^* - M_2^* \ln M_2^* - M_v^* \ln M_v^*], \tag{26'}$$

from which we can immediately derive expressions for the three chemical potentials given by

$$\mu_1 = \left(\frac{\partial F_c}{\partial M_1^*}\right)_{M_2^*, M_v^*} = kT\left[\ln \frac{M_1^*}{M_1^* + M_2^* + M_v^*} - \ln(\text{p.f.})_1\right], \tag{27}$$

$$\mu_2 = \left(\frac{\partial F_c}{\partial M_2^*}\right)_{M_v^*, M_1^*} = kT\left[\ln \frac{M_2^*}{M_1^* + M_2^* + M_v^*} - \ln(\text{p.f.})_2\right], \tag{28}$$

$$\mu_v^c = \left(\frac{\partial F_c}{\partial M_v^*}\right)_{M_1^*, M_2^*} = kT\left[\ln \frac{M_v^*}{M_1^* + M_2^* + M_v^*} - \ln(\text{p.f.})_v^c\right]. \tag{29}$$

For the vapour phase, assuming this to be a mixture of perfect gases, without dimerization, we have, as always,

$$\mu_u = kT[\ln N_u^* - \ln(\text{p.f.})_u^g] \tag{30}$$

and
$$\mu_v^g = kT[\ln N_v^* - \ln(\text{p.f.})_v^g]. \tag{31}$$

The equations expressing thermodynamic equilibrium and which, together with the constitutive equations, fix the values of M_1^*, M_2^*, M_v^*, N_u^*, and N_v^*, are now

$$\left. \begin{aligned} \mu_v^c &= \mu_v^g \quad (= \mu_v \text{ say}) \\ \mu_u &= \mu_1 \\ \mu_2 &= 2\mu_1 \end{aligned} \right\}. \tag{32}$$

and

From the viewpoint of thermodynamics these equations, (32), may be regarded as self-evident. Statistically they are produced automatically in the full treatment, and in writing them down without proof we presume an appeal to past experience (see § 7 of Chapter XIII).

Before making full use of these equations it is desirable that we should note, from (26′), (27), (28), and (29), that

$$F = M_1^* \mu_1 + M_2^* \mu_2 + M_v^* \mu_v \tag{33}$$

which, by (32) and (23), becomes

$$F = M_u^* \mu_u + M_v^* \mu_v. \tag{33'}$$

These equations show that what we have here been regarding as a Helmholtz free energy is, in reality, a Gibbs free energy: but the anomaly is due simply to our customary disregard of Pv/kT for a condensed phase.

Using the above explicit formulae for the various chemical potentials, the equations (32) become

$$N_v^* = \frac{M_v^*}{M_1^* + M_2^* + M_v^*} \frac{(\text{p.f.})_v^g}{(\text{p.f.})_v^c}, \tag{34}$$

$$N_u^* = \frac{M_1^*}{M_1^* + M_2^* + M_v^*} \frac{(\text{p.f.})_u^g}{(\text{p.f.})_1}, \tag{35}$$

and
$$\frac{M_2^*(M_1^* + M_2^* + M_v^*)}{M_1^{*2}} = \frac{(\text{p.f.})_2}{(\text{p.f.})_1^2} = K(T), \text{ say.} \tag{36}$$

Equation (36) expresses the law of mass action for dimerization in an otherwise perfect solution (cf. equation (78), Chapter XIII). The equations (34) and (35) are the analogues, for the present problem, of equations (9) and (10) above, and we may proceed to discuss them along the lines which led from those equations to Raoult's law. With a self-explanatory notation, we have immediately

$$p_v = \frac{M_v^*}{M_1^* + M_2^* + M_v^*} \frac{kTg_v(T)}{(\mathrm{p.f.})_v^c} \tag{37}$$

and

$$p_u = \frac{M_1^*}{M_1^* + M_2^* + M_v^*} \frac{kTg_u(T)}{(\mathrm{p.f.})_1}. \tag{38}$$

Now when $M_u^* = 0$ it necessarily follows that $M_1^* = M_2^* = 0$. Therefore, putting $M_u^* = 0$ in (37) we obtain the equation

$$\frac{kTg_v(T)}{(\mathrm{p.f.})_v^c} = p_v^0,$$

where p_v^0 is the vapour pressure of a condensed phase of the pure solvent species. Thus equation (37) may be written

$$p_v = \frac{M_v^*}{M_1^* + M_2^* + M_v^*} p_v^0. \tag{39}$$

On the other hand, when $M_v^* = 0$, the equation (38) gives

$$p_u^0 = x_1^0 \frac{kTg_u(T)}{(\mathrm{p.f.})_1}, \tag{40}$$

where x_1^0 denotes the value of $M_1^*/(M_1^* + M_2^* + M_v^*)$ when $M_v^* = 0$, and we must proceed with caution.

To find x_1^0 we must use equation (36). Putting $M_v^* = 0$, equation (36) becomes

$$\frac{1 - x_1^0}{(x_1^0)^2} = K,$$

whence

$$x_1^0 = \frac{\sqrt{(1 + 4K)} - 1}{2K}.$$

Consequently, from (40), we have

$$\frac{kTg_u(T)}{(\mathrm{p.f.})_1} = \frac{2K}{\sqrt{(1 + 4K)} - 1} p_u^0$$

and equation (38) becomes

$$p_u = \frac{M_1^*}{M_1^* + M_2^* + M_v^*} \frac{2K}{\sqrt{(1 + 4K)} - 1} p_u^0, \tag{41}$$

where p_u^0 denotes the vapour pressure of a condensed phase of pure solute (within which a measure of dimerization necessarily occurs).

In terms of M_u^* and M_v^* the equations (39) and (40) become

$$p_v = \frac{M_v^*}{M_u^* + M_v^* - M_2^*} \, p_v^0$$

and

$$p_u = \frac{M_u^* - 2M_2^*}{M_u^* + M_v^* - M_2^*} \, \frac{2K}{\sqrt{(1+4K)} - 1} \, p_u^0$$

$$\left. \right\} \qquad (42)$$

where, from (36), M_2^* is given by

$$\frac{M_2^*(M_u^* + M_v^* - M_2^*)}{(M_u^* - 2M_2^*)^2} = K(T).$$

It is left to the reader to show, which is not difficult, that if p_v/p_v^0 and p_u/p_u^0 are plotted, at constant temperature, against the mole fraction $M_u^*/(M_u^* + M_v^*)$ then the resulting partial vapour-pressure curves exhibit everywhere positive deviations from the straight lines corresponding to Raoult's law.

EXAMPLES

1. Starting from equation (5), and the appropriate restrictive conditions on the distribution numbers, derive equation (6) by the full-length method of picking out the greatest term in Ω.

2. For a perfect binary solution, the entropy of mixing is given by

$$\Delta S = -R(x_A \ln x_A + x_B \ln x_B)$$

per mole of solution. Plot ΔS against x_A, and show that ΔS is greatest when $x_A = \frac{1}{2}$. (Note: $x_A + x_B = 1$.)

3. Derive equations analogous to (16) and (17) for the three partial vapour pressures of a perfect ternary solution. And thus prove that the partial vapour pressures of the components of a given perfect binary solution are always lowered by the addition of a third component which forms a perfect ternary solution with them.

4. Prove that for a perfect ternary solution the entropy of mixing, per mole of solution, is given by

$$\Delta S = -R(x_A \ln x_A + x_B \ln x_B + x_C \ln x_C)$$

(where $x_A + x_B + x_C = 1$); and that this is greatest when $x_A = x_B = x_C = \frac{1}{3}$.

5. Show that the partial vapour pressures given by the equations (42) satisfy the Duhem–Margules equation, (22).

6. Prove that the partial vapour pressures given by (42) exhibit everywhere positive deviations from Raoult's law.

7. Prove that the Duhem-Margules equation is necessarily satisfied whenever

$$F_c(M_A, M_B) = (M_A + M_B) f(M_A/(M_A + M_B)).$$

XV

CONSTANT-TEMPERATURE PARTITION FUNCTIONS

1. ALL the examples of the preceding chapters have, in principle, been worked out by the same technique and from the same starting-point. Admittedly we have sometimes employed short cuts, when the main road was in danger of becoming rather tiresomely familiar, and sometimes we have dealt with the integrals appropriate to classical mechanics instead of quantal sums of which the significance is more easily appreciated, particularly in formal work. But throughout we have built on the foundations laid down in Chapters I and II, namely the equation

$$S(E, V, N) = k \ln \Omega(E, V, N) \tag{1}$$

which links the macroscopic, thermodynamical properties of the equilibrium state of an assembly with its microscopic, molecular attributes.

There are, however, besides that expressed in equation (1), other bridges from the mechanical to the thermodynamical states of an assembly, two of which are of particular importance. Indeed, these other two bridges provide stronger and broader thoroughfares, than that with which we are already familiar. We could, perhaps, have built all these bridges first, before proceeding to cross any of them: we might even have confined our attention to the strongest. But it has seemed wisest first to explore the simplest, if also the narrowest, route and only afterwards to approach the broader, and more elaborate, structures. In this chapter and the next we shall build, and use, the second bridge: in Chapter XVII we shall proceed to the third. It will then be seen that while these three bridges are progressively wider, and more useful, they are by no means mutually independent.

Perhaps the simplest approach to the second basic formula of statistical mechanics (abandoning the bridge metaphor) starts from the familiar equation†

$$E = N\left(\sum_i \epsilon_i \omega_i e^{-\epsilon_i/kT} \Big/ \sum_i \omega_i e^{-\epsilon_i/kT} \right). \tag{2}$$

† We shall drop the special ϖ, η, M notation of the last few chapters, and use ω, ϵ, N whether dealing with non-localized or localized systems.

Writing $E/N = \bar{\epsilon}$, so that (2) becomes

$$\bar{\epsilon} = kT^2 \frac{\partial}{\partial T} \ln(\text{p.f.}), \tag{3}$$

where

$$(\text{p.f.}) = \sum_i \omega_i e^{-\epsilon_i/kT}, \tag{4}$$

we may interpret this equation as giving the mean (effective, or equilibrium) energy of any particular *system* in the assembly. Now let us consider a very large collection of identical assemblies (each of volume V and containing N systems) in thermal contact, and equilibrium, with each other. We consider in fact an assembly of assemblies, which, to avoid linguistic confusion, we shall call an *ensemble* of assemblies: so that each of our original assemblies is, as it were, a system in the ensemble. (The reader may find it helpful to think of a block of lead weighing ten tons divided mentally into 10^7 separate little cubes—clearly in thermal contact with each other—each weighing about one gram.) Then, according to quantum mechanics, each assembly, which consists of N definite microscopic systems within a given volume V, is capable of any one of a certain set of energies

$$E_1, E_2,..., E_i,... \, .$$

In practice, of course, these levels lie extremely close together and form, to all intents and purposes, a continuum. But since all mechanical systems are, strictly speaking, quantal systems it is legitimate, as well as convenient, to employ the discrete, quantal notation. (The energy, E, in equation (1) is, necessarily, one of these energies.) Now we may suppose that the whole ensemble of assemblies is thermally isolated, so that its total energy is fixed, and so we can forthwith apply the formulae (3) and (4), with the appropriate change of notation, to determine the equilibrium value of the energy of any particular assembly in the ensemble. We thus obtain

$$\bar{E} = kT^2 \frac{\partial}{\partial T} \ln(\text{P.F.}), \tag{5}$$

where

$$(\text{P.F.}) = \sum_i \Omega_i e^{-E_i/kT}. \tag{6}$$

In the expression (6), Ω_i is the degeneracy, or weight-factor, pertaining to the energy level E_i of an assembly: i.e. it is the number of distinguishable states of the assembly corresponding to this energy level, and the given values of V and N. Consequently Ω in (6) has precisely the same meaning as has Ω in (1).

Before commenting at all on the above argument, we shall next derive an immediate consequence of equation (5). From the Gibbs–Helmholtz equation

$$E = -T^2 \frac{\partial}{\partial T}\left(\frac{F}{T}\right)_{V,N}$$

we deduce that (5) implies that

$$\bar{F} = -kT[\ln(\text{P.F.}) + \text{constant}]. \tag{7}$$

The 'constant' in (7) is independent of the temperature, T, and we shall take it to be zero: a procedure which could be justified along the lines of our previous discussion of the third law of thermodynamics, were the foregoing argument intended to be other than tentative. As it is we shall take as the second fundamental formula of statistical mechanics the equation (dropping the unnecessary bar)

$$F = -kT \ln(\text{P.F.}), \tag{8}$$

where
$$(\text{P.F.}) = \sum_i \Omega_i e^{-E_i/kT},$$

and (P.F.) will be called the partition function for the assembly.†

The consequences of equation (8) will be developed in the next section and the remainder of this chapter. Before proceeding to derive them, however, further comment on the argument immediately preceding equation (5) above is certainly called for. The argument is not intended to be more than suggestive, and we must regard the validity of equation (8) as something still to be justified *a posteriori*. Nevertheless it is perhaps worth emphasizing (*a*) that, on physical grounds, the temperature of the ensemble, T in (6), will be the same as the temperature of an assembly within the ensemble, and (*b*) that the thermodynamical properties of an assembly (its free energy, for instance) are not dependent on its environment (for any actual thermodynamic assembly possesses

† In contradistinction to (p.f.), the partition function for a system, which has meaning only when the assembly comprises essentially independent systems.

a definite equation of state) and consequently if (8) is true at all it is true whether the assembly is or is not part of an actual physical ensemble of assemblies in the way imagined. If it is complained that an isolated assembly has a fixed and definite energy, so that it is hard to see why all the energies of which the assembly is capable should occur in the expression for its free energy, then we may reply first that the adiabatic isolation of a body is not known to affect its thermodynamical properties and, secondly, that if an assembly has a definite temperature it has also a very well defined internal energy: a point which will become clearer in the discussion below.

2. The first thing to observe about equation (8) is that, supposing the partition function, (P.F.), to have been evaluated, the r.h.s. is an explicit function of T, V, and N, which are just the independent variables appropriate to the thermodynamic function F (see equation (23), Chapter II). Secondly, however, we must observe an apparent contradiction with previous results. For the equation (1),

$$S = k \ln \Omega,$$

combined with the thermodynamic equation

$$F = E - TS,$$

leads to the result (see equations (1) and (2) of Chapter III)

$$F = -kT \ln \Omega e^{-E/kT}:$$

and, of course, $\Omega e^{-E/kT}$ is only one of the many terms included in the sum $\sum_i \Omega_i e^{-E_i/kT}$. We must resolve this paradox before going any further.

That the antithesis is more apparent than real can be seen by making explicit use of the expression for Ω already obtained for any assembly of identical independent systems. For definiteness, we shall take these systems to be localized: the extra factor $1/N!$ for non-localized systems, of course, makes no essential difference. Adopting the results obtained in Chapter II, but writing E_i for E since E is necessarily one of the allowed energies of the assembly, we have

$$\Omega_i = \left[\sum_j \omega_j e^{\beta_i \epsilon_j} \right]^N e^{-\beta_i E_i}, \tag{9}$$

where β_i is given by

$$E_i = N \frac{\sum_j \epsilon_j \, \omega_j \, e^{\beta_i \epsilon_j}}{\sum_j \omega_j \, e^{\beta_i \epsilon_j}}. \tag{10}$$

In the equations (9) and (10) we have given β a suffix i to emphasize that β is implicitly a function of the energy E, through equation (10); and we have had to adopt j instead of i as the summation suffix to avoid unnecessary confusion.

Using (9) and (10), we thus obtain

$$(\text{P.F.}) = \sum_i \Omega_i e^{-E_i/kT}$$

$$= \sum \mathfrak{T}_i, \tag{11}$$

where

$$\mathfrak{T}_i = \Big[\sum_j \omega_j \, e^{\beta_i \epsilon_j} \Big]^N e^{-(\beta_i + 1/kT)E_i}. \tag{12}$$

We shall now make the assumption, which can be justified mathematically, that only the greatest term, $\mathfrak{T}_{\max}$, in the sum on the r.h.s. of (11) contributes appreciably to this sum, and so to (P.F.). Proceeding to pick out this greatest term, we have

$$\ln \mathfrak{T}_i = N \ln \Big[\sum_j \omega_j \, e^{\beta_i \epsilon_j} \Big] - \Big(\beta_i + \frac{1}{kT} \Big) E_i,$$

$$\frac{\partial \ln \mathfrak{T}_i}{\partial E_i} = - \Big(\beta_i + \frac{1}{kT} \Big) + \frac{\partial \beta_i}{\partial E_i} \Bigg[N \frac{\sum_j \epsilon_j \, \omega_j \, e^{\beta_i \epsilon_j}}{\sum_j \omega_j \, e^{\beta_i \epsilon_j}} - E_i \Bigg]$$

$$= - \Big(\beta_i + \frac{1}{kT} \Big)$$

since the term enclosed in square brackets vanishes on account of (10). Consequently $\mathfrak{T}_{\max}$ corresponds to that energy E_i of the assembly for which

$$\beta_i = -1/kT$$

and the equations (11) and (12) lead to

$$(\text{P.F.}) = \mathfrak{T}_{\max} = \Big[\sum_j \omega_j \, e^{-\epsilon_j/kT} \Big]^N, \tag{13}$$

while the important value of E_i, which we shall denote simply by E, is given, from equation (10), by

$$E = N \frac{\sum_j \epsilon_j \, \omega_j \, e^{-\epsilon_j/kT}}{\sum \omega_j \, e^{-\epsilon_j/kT}}. \tag{14}$$

Thus the formula $\qquad F = -kT \ln(\text{P.F.})$

gives $\qquad\qquad\qquad F = -NkT \ln(\text{p.f.}),$

in identical agreement with the results of Chapter II for an assembly of independent localized systems.

The reader should study the above proof carefully. For though we shall proceed in the next section to improve upon it, it shows up very nicely the connexion between the first and second fundamental formulae of statistical mechanics. Putting into words the essence of the argument, we may say that we have shown that the only term, $\mathfrak{T}_i$, which contributes appreciably to (P.F.) is just that term for which E_i is related to the temperature in the manner demanded by the earlier theory, starting from $S = k \ln \Omega$.

3. The above demonstration, for an assembly of identical independent systems, of the equivalence of the two statistical methods based, respectively, on the formulae

$$S = k \ln \Omega$$

and $\qquad\qquad\qquad F = -kT \ln(\text{P.F.})$

suffers from a certain inelegance in that the technique of picking out the greatest term in a sum has been used twice, once in evaluating Ω and then again in evaluating (P.F.). While there is no mathematical objection to this, it is natural to try to avoid so elaborate a technique by attempting a more direct calculation of (P.F.).

We shall, therefore, consider again the case of an assembly of N identical, independent, localized systems. We shall, however, interchange the roles of the suffixes i and j above, so that most of our formulae may have their customary appearance. We thus suppose that any system is capable of the possible energies

$$\epsilon_1, \epsilon_2, ..., \epsilon_i, ...$$

with degeneracies $\qquad \omega_1, \omega_2, ..., \omega_i, ...$

and let $\qquad\qquad\quad n_1, n_2, ..., n_i, ...,$

where $\qquad\qquad\qquad \sum_i n_i = N, \qquad\qquad\qquad (15)$

be the set of distribution numbers corresponding to any particular specification of the assembly.

Then the number of distinct complexions of the assembly, corresponding to these distribution numbers, is

$$t(n_i) = \frac{N!}{\prod_i n_i!} \prod_i \omega_i^{n_i} \qquad (16)$$

(for formal completeness, we have introduced the degeneracy factors explicitly) while for these same distribution numbers the total energy of the assembly is given by

$$E_j = \sum_i n_i \epsilon_i. \qquad (17)$$

Consequently $\qquad \Omega_j = \sum_{(n_i)} t(n_i),$

where the allowed n_i are subject to the restrictive conditions

$$\sum_i n_i = N \qquad (15)$$

and $\qquad\qquad \sum_i n_i \epsilon_i = E_j, \qquad (17)$

while

$$\text{(P.F.)} = \sum_j \Omega_j e^{-E_j/kT} \qquad (18)$$

$$= \sum_{(n_i)} t(n_i) e^{-\sum_i n_i \epsilon_i/kT}, \qquad (19)$$

where, since all possible values of E_j are to occur in (18) the only restriction on the distribution numbers in (19) is simply that their sum shall equal N, the total number of systems in the assembly.

Thus, using the expression (16) for $t(n_i)$ we have, finally,

$$\text{(P.F.)} = \sum_{(n_i)} \frac{N!}{\prod_i n_i!} \prod_i \omega_i^{n_i} e^{-\sum_i n_i \epsilon_i/kT}, \qquad (20)$$

where $\qquad\qquad \sum n_i = N. \qquad (15)$

We can now proceed to pick out the greatest term in the sum on the r.h.s. of (20) on the legitimate assumption that only this greatest term contributes significantly to (P.F.). Denoting the general term by $\mathfrak{T}(n_i)$, we have, using Stirling's theorem,

$$\ln \mathfrak{T}(n_i) = \left(\sum_i n_i\right)\ln\left(\sum_i n_i\right) - \sum_i n_i \ln n_i + \sum_i n_i \ln \omega_i - \sum_i n_i \epsilon_i/kT,$$

whence

$$\delta \ln \mathfrak{T}(n_i) = \ln\left(\sum_i n_i\right)\left(\sum_i \delta n_i\right) - \sum_i \ln n_i \, \delta n_i +$$

$$+ \sum_i \ln \omega_i \, \delta n_i - \sum_i \frac{\epsilon_i}{kT} \delta n_i. \qquad (21)$$

The only restrictive condition on the variations δn_i now is that provided by (15), namely,

$$\sum_i \delta n_i = 0. \qquad (22)$$

Adding a constant multiple, α, times (22) to (21) in the usual way (method of Lagrange's undetermined multipliers) we find, for the important distribution numbers, the equation

$$\sum_i \left[\ln\left(\sum_i n_i^* \right) + \alpha + \ln \omega_i - \epsilon_i/kT - \ln n_i^* \right] \delta n_i = 0,$$

whence

$$\ln N + \alpha + \ln \omega_i - \epsilon_i/kT - \ln n_i^* = 0 \quad (i = 1, 2, ...),$$

i.e.

$$n_i^* = N \lambda \omega_i e^{-\epsilon_i/kT} \quad (i = 1, 2, ...), \qquad (23)$$

where $\lambda = e^{\alpha}$.

Summing (23) for all i, we find

$$\lambda \sum_i \omega_i e^{-\epsilon_i/kT} = 1$$

so that, getting rid of λ,

$$n_i^* = N \frac{\omega_i e^{-\epsilon_i/kT}}{\sum_i \omega_i e^{-\epsilon_i/kT}} \quad (i = 1, 2, ...). \qquad (24)$$

Finally, putting these values of n_i in the above expression for $\mathfrak{T}(n_i)$ we obtain

$$\ln \mathfrak{T}_{\max} = \ln \mathfrak{T}(n_i^*) = N \ln N - N \ln N - \sum_i n_i^* \ln \omega_i +$$

$$+ \sum_i n_i^* \epsilon_i/kT + N \ln\left(\sum_i \omega_i e^{-\epsilon_i/kT} \right) +$$

$$+ \sum_i n_i^* \ln \omega_i - \sum_i n_i^* \epsilon_i/kT$$

$$= N \ln\left(\sum_i \omega_i e^{-\epsilon_i/kT} \right);$$

i.e.

$$(\text{P.F.}) = \mathfrak{T}_{\max} = \left(\sum_i \omega_i e^{-\epsilon_i/kT} \right)^N$$

or

$$F = -kT \ln(\text{P.F.}) = -kT \ln(\text{p.f.})^N, \qquad (25)$$

where

$$(\text{p.f.}) = \sum_i \omega_i e^{-\epsilon_i/kT}.$$

This completes the proof, for we have now obtained precisely the same equations, (24) and (25), as we found formerly, starting from the equation $S = k \ln \Omega$. The two methods lead to identical results. And at this point the only further comment we would make is that the second method, based on $F = -kT \ln(\text{P.F.})$, has the advantage of introducing only *one* restrictive condition on the distribution numbers: we do not now have to bring in an unknown parameter β and afterwards identify this with $-1/kT$, where T is the absolute temperature.

4. We shall now show that the r.h.s. of equation (20) can be summed *exactly*: in other words, that for the expression (20) there was no need at all to adopt the technique of picking out the greatest term. This is surprising, and calls for subsequent comment, but we must first prove our assertion.

To readers familiar with the multinomial extension of the binomial theorem there is indeed very little to prove. But for those less well equipped algebraically, a statement of this theorem, or algebraic formula, is necessary.

We will start by recalling that the ordinary binomial theorem

$$(x+y)^n = x^n + {}^nC_1 x^{n-1}y + {}^nC_2 x^{n-2}y^2 + \ldots + y^n,$$

where

$$^nC_r = \frac{n(n-1)(n-2)\ldots(n-r+1)}{r!},$$

may be written in the alternative forms

$$(x+y)^n = \sum_r \frac{n!}{r!(n-r)!} x^{n-r}y^r,$$

or

$$(x+y)^n = \sum_{(r+s=n)} \frac{n!}{r!\,s!} x^s y^r = \sum_{(r+s=n)} \frac{n!}{r!\,s!} x^r y^s.$$

In three variables, x, y, and z, the multinomial theorem reads

$$(x+y+z)^n = \sum_{(r+s+t=n)} \frac{n!}{r!\,s!\,t!} x^r y^s z^t,$$

while with m variables, $x_1, x_2, ..., x_m$, we have

$$(x_1+x_2+...+x_m)^n = \sum_{(n_1+n_2+...+n_m=n)} \frac{n!}{n_1!\,n_2!...n_m!} x_1^{n_1} x_2^{n_2}...x_m^{n_m}.$$
(26)

This important theorem can be proved by the method of induction from the binomial theorem: an alternative and neater proof, depending on combinatory formulae with which we are already familiar, is given in Appendix II, §b.

We are going to apply the formula (26) to the case of an infinite number of variables, $x_1, x_2, ..., x_i, ...$—a step which really calls for justification, though we shall not attempt this here. When this is legitimate (26) takes the form

$$(x_1+x_2+...+x_i+...)^n = \sum_{(n_i)} \frac{n!}{\prod_i n_i!} \prod_i x_i^{n_i},$$
(26′)

where, in the sum on the r.h.s. of (26′), the n_i's are subject to

$$\sum_i n_i = n.$$

In the equation (26′) write N for n, and put

$$x_i = \omega_i e^{-\epsilon_i/kT}.$$

The equation then becomes

$$\left(\sum_i \omega_i e^{-\epsilon_i/kT}\right)^N = \sum_{(n_i)} \frac{N!}{\prod_i n_i!} \prod_i (\omega_i^{n_i} e^{-n_i \epsilon_i/kT})$$

$$= \sum_{(n_i)} \frac{N!}{\prod_i n_i!} \prod_i \omega_i^{n_i} e^{-\sum_i n_i \epsilon_i/kT},$$
(27)

where $\sum_i n_i = N$. The r.h.s. of (27) is identical with the r.h.s. of (20). Consequently, for the problem discussed in paragraph 3 above, we have, *identically*,

$$(\text{P.F.}) = \left(\sum_i \omega_i e^{-\epsilon_i/kT}\right)^N = (\text{p.f.})^N:$$
(28)

which is the somewhat surprising result already asserted. Indeed, not only can the partition function, (P.F.), be summed exactly but the result of so doing is precisely the same as that obtained by the technique of picking out the greatest term.

The significance of this rather remarkable conclusion is perhaps most easily appreciated if we summarize, in note form, the achievements of the three parallel attacks which we have made on this problem of an assembly of independent, localized systems. We have

I	II (a)	II (b)
$S = k \ln \Omega$	$F = -kT \ln(\text{P.F.})$	$F = -kT \ln(\text{P.F.})$
$\Omega = \sum_{(n_i)} \dfrac{N!}{\prod_i n_i!} \prod_i \omega_i^{n_i}$	$(\text{P.F.}) = \sum_{(n_i)} \dfrac{N!}{\prod_i n_i!} \prod_i \omega_i^{n_i} \exp\left(-\sum_i n_i \, \epsilon_i / kT\right)$	
where	where	where
(i) $\sum_i n_i = N$	(i) $\sum_i n_i = N.$	(i) $\sum_i n_i = N.$
(ii) $\sum_i n_i \epsilon_i = E.$		
Picking out the greatest term subject to (i) and (ii) leads to	Picking out the greatest term subject to (i) leads to	$(\text{P.F.}) \equiv (\text{p.f.})^N$
$F = -kT \ln(\text{p.f.})^N$	$F = -kT \ln(\text{p.f.})^N$	
where	where	where
$(\text{p.f.}) = \sum_i \omega_i \, e^{-\epsilon_i/kT}$	$(\text{p.f.}) = \sum_i \omega_i \, e^{-\epsilon_i/kT}$	$(\text{p.f.}) = \sum_i \omega_i \, e^{-\epsilon_i/kT}.$

The equivalence of the methods I and II (a) has already been discussed in some detail. That the method II (a) should itself be in exact accord with the rigorous analysis of method II (b) simply shows that the two approximations introduced in the second method, namely,

  (i) the technique of picking out the greatest term, and

  (ii) the use of Stirling's theorem,

exactly *annul* each other: so that the result, instead of being, as we should have expected, merely thermodynamically equivalent with that of an algebraically exact treatment, is actually completely identical therewith.

5. So far we have evaluated the partition function, (P.F.), only for an assembly of N identical, independent, localized systems. We have shown that it can be summed exactly, by purely algebraic methods. The same is true, of course, without further analysis, of the partition function for an assembly of N identical, independent, non-localized systems, i.e. for a perfect gas. We have immediately

$$(\text{P.F.}) = \sum_{(\sum_i n_i = N)} \frac{1}{\prod_i n_i!} \prod_i \omega_i^{n_i} e^{-\sum_i n_i \epsilon_i / kT}$$

$$= \frac{(\text{p.f.})^N}{N!}, \tag{29}$$

where $\qquad (\text{p.f.}) = \sum_i \omega_i e^{-\epsilon_i / kT}.$

But not all partition functions, (P.F.), can be summed exactly, in this algebraic way. When direct summation is impossible we have to fall back on the technique of method II(a), or some modification of this technique. As an illustration of a case in which the complete summation is impracticable, we may consider the problem of the equilibrium between a pure condensed phase, represented by an Einstein model, and a vapour phase which can be treated as a perfect gas. For this purpose we return to the specialized notation of Chapter XIII, and the reader should refer again to the table of results at the beginning of Chapter XIV.

Introducing degeneracies ϖ_i and ω_i for the sake of completeness, we start from the formula already obtained when discussing this problem in Chapter XIII, namely

$$\Omega = \sum_{(m_i, n_i)} \frac{M!}{\prod_i m_i!} \frac{1}{\prod_i n_i!} \prod_i \varpi_i^{m_i} \prod_i \omega_i^{n_i}$$

where the distribution numbers m_i and n_i are subject to the conditions

$$\sum_i m_i + \sum_i n_i = X$$

and $\qquad \sum_i m_i \eta_i + \sum_i n_i \epsilon_i = E.$

Then from the definition

$$(\text{P.F.}) = \sum_j \Omega_j e^{-E_j / kT},$$

we have at once

$$(\text{P.F.}) = \sum_{(m_i, n_i)} \frac{M!}{\prod_i m_i!} \frac{1}{\prod_i n_i!} \prod_i \varpi_i^{m_i} \prod_i \omega_i^{n_i} e^{-(\sum_i m_i \eta_i + \sum_i n_i \epsilon_i)/kT}, \tag{30}$$

where the only restriction on the distribution numbers is simply

$$\sum_i m_i + \sum_i n_i = X. \tag{31}$$

If instead of the single restriction (31) we had the two restrictions

$$\sum_i m_i = M \quad \text{and} \quad \sum_i n_i = N \tag{32}$$

then, as a little thought will show, the r.h.s. of (30) would factorize into

$$\left[\sum_{(\sum_i m_i = M)} \frac{M!}{\prod_i m_i!} \prod_i \varpi_i^{m_i} e^{-\sum_i m_i \eta_i / kT} \right] \left[\sum_{(\sum_i n_i = N)} \frac{1}{\prod_i n_i!} \prod_i \omega_i^{n_i} e^{-\sum_i n_i \epsilon_i / kT} \right]$$

which, by the results (28) and (29) above, is identical with

$$\left[\sum_i \varpi_i e^{-\eta_i / kT} \right]^M \frac{\left[\sum_i \omega_i e^{-\epsilon_i / kT} \right]^N}{N!}.$$

Since we have only the restriction (31), instead of the two restrictions (32), we infer at once that (30) yields

$$(\text{P.F.}) = \sum_{(M+N=X)} (\text{p.f.})_c^M \frac{(\text{p.f.})_g^N}{N!}, \tag{33}$$

where

$$(\text{p.f.})_c = \sum_i \varpi_i e^{-\eta_i / kT} \quad \text{and} \quad (\text{p.f.})_g = \sum_i \omega_i e^{-\epsilon_i / kT}.$$

Unfortunately we can get no further than equation (33) by purely algebraic means. The restriction $M+N = X$ reduces the r.h.s. to a finite sum which cannot be tidied up at all. Consequently we have now to fall back on the familiar, and entirely legitimate, method of picking out the greatest term in this sum, which leads to formulae for the equilibrium values of M and N identical with those obtained in Chapter XIII. There is no need to discuss this last stage in the problem again here.

6. By now it should be sufficiently clear that the second fundamental formula of statistical mechanics, which we may call the isothermic formula,

$$F(T, V, N) = -kT \ln(\text{P.F.}),$$

where

$$(\text{P.F.}) = \sum_i \Omega_i(E_i, V, N) e^{-E_i / kT},$$

will lead to results identical with those obtained from the first, or adiabatic, fundamental formula

$$S(E, V, N) = k \ln \Omega(E, V, N)$$

(where Ω is the number of distinct complexions of the assembly corresponding to the given values of E, V, and N) in the case of all problems with which we have so far dealt. Evidently the new method provides a bridge between mechanics and thermo-dynamics at least as dependable as that to which we have previously been accustomed. In fact, since, because the distri-bution numbers are now subject to only one restrictive condition instead of two, we can sometimes sum the partition function, (P.F.), by purely algebraic methods, the new bridge may be described as a more elegant structure than the old one. But it has still to be shown to provide a wider thoroughfare; we have still to show that the new method is more powerful than the old one in that with it we can successfully tackle problems which would be quite intractable, or prohibitively difficult, simply with the old technique.

We shall attempt this task in the next chapter. But since we must, for the purpose, choose a somewhat difficult problem it will be possible, within the scope of this book, only to give an approxi-mate, or partial, solution of that problem. Whenever it is possible to give an incomplete specification of the state of an assembly by means of distribution numbers which are themselves adequate to determine the energy of the assembly, either of the two methods under discussion can be applied: and both will, of course, produce the same final formulae. It is only when such distribution numbers cannot be defined, or can be defined only with very great difficulty, that the new method has marked advantages of strength, as well as elegance, over the old one. Such a case is provided by the problem of imperfect gases, and it is to the problem of an assembly of N identical, non-localized systems between which there are forces of interaction that we now turn.

EXAMPLES

1. Show that the equation (P.F.) = (p.f.)^N for an assembly of N identical, independent, localized systems follows at once from the factorization property of partition functions. (Chapter V, § 5.)

2. Show that the greatest term in the sum on the r.h.s. of equation (33) corresponds to values of M and N which satisfy the equations

$$N = (\text{p.f.})_g/(\text{p.f.})_c \quad \text{and} \quad M+N = X.$$

3. For the problem of adsorption, discussed in § 6 of Chapter XIII, prove that the partition function (P.F.) is given, precisely, by the coefficient of λ^X in the expansion of

$$[1+\lambda(\text{p.f.})_a]^{M_s} e^{\lambda(\text{p.f.})_g}$$

in ascending powers of λ.

(This cannot be found explicitly: but see Chapter XVII.)

4. Writing $\dfrac{\Omega_i e^{-E_i/kT}}{(\text{P.F.})} = p_i$, show that $S = -k \sum_i p_i \ln p_i$.

IMPERFECT GASES

1. In approaching the problem of imperfect gases, it is convenient to consider first the classical evaluation of the partition function, (P.F.), for a perfect gas. We have already, in the last chapter, dealt with a perfect gas (i.e. an assembly of independent, non-localized systems) in the notation of quantum mechanics, and found that

$$(\text{P.F.}) = \frac{1}{N!}(\text{p.f.})^N, \tag{1}$$

where (p.f.) is the partition function for a single system of the assembly. In the notation of classical mechanics, therefore, we shall expect to find

$$(\text{P.F.}) = \frac{1}{N!}\left[\frac{1}{h^n}\int_{(2n)}...\int e^{-\epsilon(q_1, q_2,...,q_n; p_1, p_2,...,p_n)/kT}\,dq_1...dq_n\,dp_1...dp_n\right]^N, \tag{2}$$

where $q_1,..., q_n$ are coordinates specifying the configuration and position in space of any one system in the assembly, and $p_1,..., p_n$ are the conjugate momentum variables. There is no real need for further proof of equation (2), but an outline of the completely classical argument (retaining the factors $1/h$ for tidiness) will help both in introducing a notation that is, necessarily, somewhat elaborate and in providing a simple background against which to view the more difficult problem involving non-independent systems.

We shall confine attention to the case of structureless point masses, each of mass m, moving freely in a volume V. Then, from first principles (see equation (22), Chapter IV)

$$(\text{P.F.}) = \frac{1}{h^{3N}}\int_{(6N)}...\int e^{-E(q_1,...,q_{3N}; p_1,...,p_{3N})/kT}\,dq_1...dq_{3N}\,dp_1...dp_{3N}, \tag{3}$$

where the $6N$-fold phase-integral has to be taken over all distinguishable complexions of the assembly. For the $3N$ spacial coordinates, q, we shall use the x, y, and z coordinates of each of the N systems (relative to some fixed set of rectangular axes): the $3N$

conjugate momental coordinates are then determined automatically and require no further specification.

Now only distinct complexions of the assembly are to be counted in evaluating the r.h.s. of (3); and we have already seen, in Chapter IV, that due to the indistinguishability of its systems an assembly of N identical, non-localized, particles will take up every distinct complexion $N!$ times as the coordinates, q and p above, assume, successively, all the values of which they are capable. Thus, if the integral on the r.h.s. of (3) is to have its obvious interpretation (without any rider being attached to the effect that only distinguishable complexions are to be counted), we must divide the r.h.s. of (3) by $N!$ to obtain

$$(P.F.) = \frac{1}{h^{3N}} \frac{1}{N!} \underset{(6N)}{\int \dots \int} e^{-E(q_1, \dots, q_{3N}; p_1, \dots, p_{3N})/kT} \, dq_1 \dots dq_{3N} \, dp_1 \dots dp_{3N}, \tag{3'}$$

where now the variables q and p take all the values of which they are physically capable. In other words, the integral on the r.h.s. of (3') differs from that on the r.h.s. of (3) in that the integral in (3') is the phase integral for N *numbered* systems, while the integral in (3) is the phase integral for N *indistinguishable* systems.

For each point mass the energy, which is entirely kinetic, is given (see Chapter IV) by

$$\epsilon(q, p) = \frac{1}{2m}(p_x^2 + p_y^2 + p_z^2),$$

and therefore, for the energy of the whole assembly, we have

$$E = \frac{1}{2m}(p_{x_1}^2 + p_{y_1}^2 + p_{z_1}^2 + p_{x_2}^2 + p_{y_2}^2 + \dots + p_{z_N}^2)$$

$$= \frac{1}{2m} \sum_{i=1}^{3N} p_i^2. \tag{4}$$

Introducing, as a shorthand notation, the symbol $d\tau$ in place of $dxdydz$, equation (3') thus becomes

$$(P.F.) = \frac{1}{h^{3N}} \frac{1}{N!} \int \dots \int e^{-\sum_i p_i^2/2mkT} \, dp_1 \, dp_2 \dots dp_{3N} \, d\tau_1 \, d\tau_2 \dots d\tau_N.$$

The r.h.s. factorizes, to give

$$(\text{P.F.}) = \frac{1}{h^{3N}} \frac{1}{N!} \left(\prod_{i=1}^{3N} \int_{-\infty}^{\infty} e^{-p_i^2/2mkT} dp_i \right) \int \dots \int d\tau_1 d\tau_2 \dots d\tau_N$$

$$= \frac{1}{h^{3N}} \frac{1}{N!} \prod_{i=1}^{3N} (2\pi mkT)^{\frac{1}{2}} \int \dots \int d\tau_1 d\tau_2 \dots d\tau_N$$

$$= \frac{1}{N!} \left(\frac{2\pi mkT}{h^2} \right)^{3N/2} \int \dots \int d\tau_1 d\tau_2 \dots d\tau_N \tag{5}$$

$$= \frac{1}{N!} \left(\frac{2\pi mkT}{h^2} \right)^{3N/2} V^N, \tag{6}$$

since the spacial coordinates of each particle are restricted to the volume V.

Consequently, $\quad (\text{P.F.}) = \dfrac{1}{N!}(\text{p.f.})^N$

where $\quad\quad\quad\quad (\text{p.f.}) = \left(\dfrac{2\pi mkT}{h^2} \right)^{\frac{3}{2}} V,$

i.e. where (p.f.) is the partition function for a point particle, of mass m, confined to a volume V: which completes the classical demonstration of equation (1) for the present problem.

2. We are now in a much better position to begin the discussion of the statistical theory of an imperfect gas, i.e. of an assembly of non-localized systems having interaction forces between them. We shall again assume that the systems of the assembly are essentially structureless particles, i.e. we shall suppose that in the absence of the interaction forces the partition function for the assembly would be given by equation (6). We shall also assume that these interaction forces are what are known in mechanics as additive, central, conservative forces. These two assumptions are not essential, in their entirety, to the present theory of imperfect gases. But we shall make them here for the sake of simplicity, and should notice that they restrict the applicability of the resulting equations, as they stand, to such gases of inert spherical atoms as argon, neon, krypton, and so on.

The assumption about the interaction forces made above implies that they produce, or are produced by, an interaction *potential*

energy which is the sum of contributions 'between' each pair of
systems in the assembly. More precisely, if two systems, numbered
i and j say, are at a distance r_{ij} apart, the assumption we have
made is that the interaction between these two systems gives rise
to a potential energy, U_{ij} say, whose magnitude depends only on
the distance r_{ij}. Thus we may write, for the potential energy of
the interaction directly between these two systems,

$$U_{ij} = U(r_{ij}). \qquad (7)$$

Now there are interaction forces between all the systems of the
assembly; and all the systems are alike, so in each case the interaction forces depend on the mutual distance in the same way.
Consequently the total potential energy of the assembly, which
depends, of course, on the spacial configuration of the systems of
the assembly, is the sum of expressions of the form (7) for *every
pair of systems* in the assembly. We may therefore write, for the
total potential energy, U, of the assembly

$$U = U(r_{ij}) \text{ for all pairs of systems in the assembly}$$

$$= \tfrac{1}{2} \sum_{i \neq j} U(r_{ij}) \qquad (8)$$

$$= \sum_{i>j} U(r_{ij}). \qquad (8')$$

The factor $\tfrac{1}{2}$ has to be introduced in (8) since otherwise we should
count each interaction energy twice: once for the pair (ij) and again
for the pair (ji). The convention $i > j$ in (8′) secures the same
unique counting of each pair of systems, and will be used below
as it provides a rather neater notation.

The total energy of the assembly is now the sum of the kinetic
energy given by (4) and the potential energy given by (8′). Thus
we now have

$$E = \frac{1}{2m} \sum_{i=1}^{3N} p_i^2 + \sum_{i>j=1}^{N} U(r_{ij}),$$

and this expression for E has to be introduced into the phase-
integral on the r.h.s. of (3′). Since the expression for U is entirely
independent of the momental coordinates, p, the factorization
of this phase-integral as far as the momental coordinates are

concerned proceeds exactly as before, so that we now obtain, instead of (5), the equation

$$(\text{P.F.}) = \frac{1}{N!}\left(\frac{2\pi m \boldsymbol{k} T}{h^2}\right)^{3N/2} \int \cdots \int e^{-\sum_{i>j} U(r_{ij})/\boldsymbol{k}T}\, d\tau_1\, d\tau_2 \ldots d\tau_N. \quad (9)$$

We shall write (9) as

$$(\text{P.F.}) = \left(\frac{2\pi m \boldsymbol{k} T}{h^2}\right)^{3N/2} \frac{Q_N}{N!},$$

where

$$Q_N = \int \cdots \int e^{-\sum_{i>j} U(r_{ij})/\boldsymbol{k}T}\, d\tau_1\, d\tau_2 \ldots d\tau_N. \quad (10)$$

And the crux of the problem is the evaluation of the configurational integral, Q_N.

3. The key to the evaluation of Q_N is the simple device of writing

$$e^{-U(r_{ij})/\boldsymbol{k}T} \equiv 1 + f(r_{ij}). \quad (11)$$

Before seeing how this enables the integral (10) to be broken up in a manageable way, we must digress a little from the main

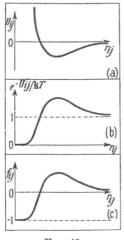

FIG. 40.

analysis to examine the nature of this new function $f(r_{ij})$ which, for short, we shall write as f_{ij}. Of course f_{ij} depends on the temperature T as well as on the distance r_{ij}: but it is with the latter dependence that we are now concerned.

As a function of r_{ij}, the potential energy, U_{ij}, will necessarily have a form similar to that shown in Fig. 40 (a). Qualitatively, this curve is very like that given in Fig. 10 for the potential-energy function of a diatomic molecule: but since the present systems are presumably not capable of uniting to form permanent molecules the minimum in the present potential-energy curve will be much more shallow than that in the curve of Fig. 10.

The function $\exp(-U_{ij}/\boldsymbol{k}T)$ will then, schematically, have the form shown in Fig. 40 (b); and f_{ij}, which is simply

$$\exp(-U_{ij}/\boldsymbol{k}T) - 1,$$

will have the form shown in Fig. 40 (c).

For our present purposes only one property of this particular functional behaviour of f_{ij} with the distance r_{ij} is important, namely the fact that f_{ij} vanishes when r_{ij} is large compared with the effective range of the interaction forces. Now interatomic forces have an effective range of perhaps 20 A; and we conclude that if two systems, i and j, are at an appreciably greater distance apart, then the corresponding function f_{ij} is effectively zero. More colloquially, we may say that f_{ij} vanishes unless the two systems i and j are 'close together'.

4. We are now in a position to tackle the integral on the r.h.s. of equation (10). Using the substitution (11), we have

$$Q_N = \int \ldots \int \prod_{i>j} (1+f_{ij}) \, d\tau_1 \, d\tau_2 \ldots d\tau_N \qquad (12)$$

and we can expand the product to obtain

$$Q_N = \int \ldots \int \left(1 + \sum_{i>j} f_{ij} + \ldots\right) d\tau_1 \, d\tau_2 \ldots d\tau_N \qquad (13)$$

where the terms not written down explicitly involve products of two or more of the functions f. At this point we shall deal only with the first two terms in the bracket on the r.h.s. of (13), returning to the other terms, not yet written down, in the next section.

Integration of the first term, unity, gives just V^N (see equation (6)). This is, of course, in accordance with the fact that the f's vanish when there are no interatomic forces, in which case we must obtain the well-known partition function for a perfect gas (equation (6)). It also shows that the terms involving the f's may be regarded as *correction* terms, modifying the partition function for a perfect gas in accordance with the imperfection produced by the forces between the systems. Consequently it is tempting to suppose that, to a first approximation, when the deviations from ideal behaviour are small (i.e. at sufficiently low pressures) the appropriate correction to (P.F.) is that produced by the terms involving one f-function only, i.e. that the first approximation to the partition function for an imperfect gas is obtained from the terms written down explicitly in (13). Unfortunately, for our convenience, this natural supposition is not true: for although all the subsequent terms are *individually* smaller than those containing one f-function only, there are also a great many more of them. We shall therefore have to consider all the terms in (13) explicitly, and only make approximations later when we are quite sure that they are valid.

Turning now to the second term, or group of terms, on the r.h.s. of (13), before examining how many terms there are in this group, we should first observe that they all have the same value. In other words

$$\int \dots \int f_{ij}\,d\tau_1\,d\tau_2 \dots d\tau_N \tag{14}$$

is independent of the suffixes i and j. This statement hardly calls for proof but, in detail, we have

$$\int \dots \int f_{ij}\,d\tau_1\,d\tau_2 \dots d\tau_j \dots d\tau_i \dots d\tau_N = \iint f_{ij}\,d\tau_i\,d\tau_j \underset{(N-2)}{\int \dots \int} \prod_{k \neq i,j} d\tau_k$$

$$= \iint f_{ij}\,d\tau_i\,d\tau_j\,V^{N-2}$$

and $$\iint f_{ij}\,d\tau_i\,d\tau_j = \iint f_{kl}\,d\tau_k\,d\tau_l,$$

since f_{kl} is the same function of the distance r_{kl} as is f_{ij} of the distance r_{ij}.

We can indeed say more than this about the integral (14), for $\iint f_{ij}\,d\tau_i\,d\tau_j$ can itself be expressed in a simpler form, on account of the property of f_{ij} portrayed in Fig. 40 (c). We have

$$\iint f_{ij}\,d\tau_i\,d\tau_j = \int \left(\int f_{ij}\,d\tau_i \right) d\tau_j$$

and since f_{ij} vanishes except when i and j are close together, the inner integral here is effectively independent of the position in

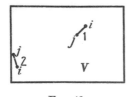

Fig. 41.

space of the system j. It would, of course, be entirely independent of the position of j, whatever the form of the function f_{ij}, except for the boundary condition imposed by the walls of the container of volume V. With both systems confined to the given volume V, $\int f_{ij}\,d\tau_i$ is independent of the position of the system j *unless j is itself very close to the boundary wall* (compare the relative positions 1 and 2 in Fig. 41). Only when j is very close to the walls of V do the boundary conditions affect the evaluation of the integral $\int f_{ij}\,d\tau_i$: in all other cases f_{ij} vanishes before the boundary conditions become effective. If we can neglect the contribution of positions like 2 in comparison with that of positions like 1, then

$$\int \left(\int f_{ij} \, d\tau_i \right) d\tau_j = V \int f(r_{ij}) \, d\tau_i. \tag{15}$$

Using spherical polar coordinates to express the position of i relative to j, we have

$$\int f(r_{ij}) \, d\tau_i = \int_0^\infty f(r) 4\pi r^2 \, dr \tag{16}$$

whence, from (15),

$$\iint f(r_{ij}) \, d\tau_i d\tau_j = V 4\pi \int_0^\infty f(r) r^2 \, dr. \tag{17}$$

In (16) and (17) we have written $f(r)$ in place of $f(r_{ij})$. The upper limit of integration is taken as infinity since in any case $f(r)$ vanishes when r is greater than the effective range of the inter-action forces.

Now the above neglect of contributions from configurations of the type 2, in comparison with those from configurations of the type 1, is perfectly legitimate. For the number of configurations of the type 2 will be proportional to A, the surface area of the containing walls: so that contributions from these configurations will affect the partition function in some way depending on the area A. But, in general, the thermodynamic properties of a gas are *extensive* properties, depending simply on the volume V: it is only when *capillary* effects are involved that the surface area A is of importance. Consequently for physical conditions in which capillary effects can be neglected, which are the only physical conditions in which we are here interested, the above procedure is permissible and equation (17) is valid.

Finally we have to ask, How many terms are there in the sum $\sum_{i>j} f_{ij}$ in (13), each of which will give to the partition function a contribution equal to the r.h.s. of equation (17)? The answer is immediate, for the number of different pairs of suffixes which we can pick from the numbers 1, 2,..., N is simply

$$\frac{N(N-1)}{2}.$$

Consequently equation (13) becomes

$$Q_N = \left[V^N + \frac{N(N-1)}{2} V^{N-1} \, 4\pi \int\limits_0^\infty f(r) r^2 \, dr + \dots \right]. \tag{18}$$

We have, however, still to examine the nature of the remaining terms, as yet unspecified, on the r.h.s. of equation (18).

5. Before, however, proceeding to examine these other, unspecified, terms in (18) let us first deduce the consequences of a partition function given by equation (18) as it stands, assuming that *the second term in* (18) *is small compared with the first term* (V^N).

If we write, for short,

$$\tfrac{1}{2} \int\limits_0^\infty 4\pi r^2 f(r) \, dr = b$$

and replace $N(N-1)$ by N^2 (which is legitimate, since N is very large) then, on the basis of (18), we have

$$
\begin{aligned}
\text{(P.F.)} &= \left(\frac{2\pi m kT}{h^2}\right)^{3N/2} \frac{Q_N}{N!} \\
&= \left(\frac{2\pi m kT}{h^2}\right)^{3N/2} \frac{V^N}{N!} \left[1 + \frac{N^2 b}{V} + \dots \right],
\end{aligned} \tag{19}
$$

whence

$$
\begin{aligned}
F &= -kT \ln(\text{P.F.}) \\
&= -NkT \ln\left(\frac{2\pi m kT}{h^2}\right)^{3/2} - NkT \ln V + NkT \ln N - \\
&\qquad\qquad - NkT - kT \ln\left[1 + \frac{N^2 b}{V} + \dots \right]
\end{aligned}
$$

and

$$
\begin{aligned}
P &= -\left(\frac{\partial F}{\partial V}\right)_{T,N} \\
&= \frac{NkT}{V} + kT \frac{\partial}{\partial V} \ln\left[1 + \frac{N^2 b}{V} + \dots \right] \\
&= \frac{NkT}{V} + \frac{kT\left(-\dfrac{N^2 b}{V^2}\right)}{1 + \dfrac{N^2 b}{V} + \dots},
\end{aligned}
$$

i.e., since we are assuming $N^2b/V \ll 1$ and ignoring the unspecified terms,

$$P = \frac{NkT}{V} - kT\frac{N^2b}{V^2} + \cdots,$$

or

$$PV = NkT\left(1 - \frac{Nb}{V} + \cdots\right). \tag{20}$$

But although, under the conditions stated, this equation is formally correct, physically it is not very useful. For if

$$\frac{N^2b}{V} \ll 1, \quad \text{then} \quad \frac{Nb}{V} \ll \frac{1}{N},$$

and so the second term in (20) is totally negligible compared with the first (unity) and altogether devoid of physical significance.

Nevertheless equation (20) is important. For, although as yet we have no firm ground for believing so, it is actually valid for sufficiently large V even when the second term in (20) is not negligible compared with unity. In fact equation (20), written in the equivalent form

$$P = kT\left(\frac{1}{v} - \frac{b}{v^2} + \cdots\right), \tag{21}$$

gives correctly the first two coefficients in the expansion of P in ascending powers of $1/v$, where v is the volume per *molecule* of the gas. This expansion is known as the *virial* expansion, and the coefficients of successive powers of $1/v$ are called virial coefficients. But if b/v^2 is not negligible compared with $1/v$, then the second term in (19) is certainly enormous compared with the first, i.e. the contribution from the terms $\sum\limits_{i>j} f_{ij}$ in (13) altogether swamps the contribution from the term unity. And this is, in fact, even more true of later terms in the expansion: terms which we must now consider in more detail.

6. The complete evaluation of Q_N on the basis of the expansion (13) presents very little difficulty once we properly appreciate the physical significance of the successive terms. The first term in (13), unity, leads, by itself, to the theory of a perfect gas, and so appertains to a physical state of the assembly in which interactions between the particles can be ignored. Each of the single

terms, f_{ij}, corresponds to a state of the assembly in which the interaction between the systems i and j is significant whereas all other interactions can be ignored. Likewise a term such as $f_{ij}f_{jk}$, which will certainly arise in the expansion of (12), will correspond to a state of the assembly in which the interactions between the systems i and j and the systems j and k are significant while all other interactions (including that between i and k) can be ignored: and so on.

Since a factor f_{ij} vanishes unless i and j are close together, it is convenient to say that a term involving the factor f_{ij} corresponds to a state of collision between the systems i and j. Thus the first term in (13) corresponds to a state of the assembly in which there are *no* collisions, and *each* of the terms f_{ij} corresponds to a state of the assembly in which there is just *one* collision.[†] Similarly, a term like $f_{ij}f_{kl}$ corresponds to a state of the assembly in which there are *two* collisions, namely significant interactions between the systems i and j and between the systems k and l.

It is convenient to refer to systems between which the interactions are significant as forming a *cluster* of systems. Thus a term f_{ij} corresponds to just one cluster of just two systems. A term $f_{ij}f_{kl}$, in which all four suffixes are different, corresponds to two such clusters, whilst a term $f_{ij}f_{jk}$, with a repeated suffix, pertains to a cluster of three systems (the systems i, j, and k). Now if the product $\prod_{i>j}(1+f_{ij})$ is expanded completely, we shall get a series of terms (connected by plus signs) each of which corresponds to a certain division of the systems into mutually exclusive clusters. The absence of a particular suffix from any such term simply means that the corresponding system is not joined (through an f-factor) to any other system: we may say that it forms an *isolated* system. Thus, strictly speaking, the term $f_{ij}f_{jk}$ corresponds to one cluster of three systems (i, j, and k) and $N-3$ isolated systems.

---

† The assumption that the first term in (19) is greater than the second implies that it is more likely that the assembly behaves as if there are *no* collisions between the systems than as if there is just one collision (between *any* two of its systems). It is not surprising that the physical effect of the possibility of this single collision (derived in (30)) should be entirely negligible!

Altogether there are N systems: and as far as Q_N is concerned they are distinguishable systems, since they have the suffixes 1, 2,..., N attached to them. We can divide them up into mutually exclusive clusters in a large number of ways. Suppose that, in a particular specification of the assembly, there are

$$\left.\begin{array}{l} n_1 \text{ isolated systems} \\ n_2 \text{ clusters of 2 systems} \\ n_3 \text{ clusters of 3 systems} \\ \quad . \qquad . \qquad . \qquad . \\ n_l \text{ clusters of } l \text{ systems} \\ \quad . \qquad . \qquad . \qquad . \\ \text{and so on.} \end{array}\right\} \qquad (22)$$

Let us fix attention on a particular distribution of the systems according to this specification, and suppose, for example, that in this particular distribution the systems numbered i, j, and k form one of the clusters of 3 systems. This can be secured through the presence of

$$f_{ij}f_{jk} \quad \text{or} \quad f_{ik}f_{jk} \quad \text{or} \quad f_{ij}f_{ik} \quad \text{or} \quad f_{ij}f_{jk}f_{ik}$$

in the corresponding term in the expansion of $\prod_{i>j}(1+f_{ij})$: consequently several such terms correspond to the same particular distribution of the systems into clusters. But we can add all these terms together, and then take out the factor

$$(f_{ij}f_{jk}+f_{ik}f_{jk}+f_{ij}f_{ik}+f_{ij}f_{jk}f_{ik}),$$

since the suffixes i, j, and k do not occur again in these terms.

Now $\qquad f_{ij}f_{jk}+f_{ik}f_{jk}+f_{ij}f_{ik}+f_{ij}f_{jk}f_{ik} = \sum\left(\prod_{p>q}f_{pq}\right),$

terms on the r.h.s. being consistent with a single cluster of 3 systems, p and q being restricted to the values i, j, and k. And, by the argument of paragraph 4 above,

$$\iiint \sum\left(\prod_{p>q}f_{pq}\right) d\tau_i\, d\tau_j\, d\tau_k = VB_3$$

(single cluster of the 3 systems, i, j, and k)

where, provided there are no capillary effects, B_3 is independent of V. Furthermore, B_3 is independent of the particular suffixes i, j, and k: any cluster of 3 systems will give rise to a factor VB_3

in the corresponding term in Q_N. Consequently, extending this argument, each particular distribution of the systems in accordance with the specification (22) will produce the contribution

$$V^{n_1}(VB_2)^{n_2}(VB_3)^{n_3}...(VB_l)^{n_l}... \tag{23}$$

towards Q_N, where†

$$B_l = \frac{1}{V} \int...\int_{(l)} \sum \left(\prod_{p>q} f_{pq} \right) d\tau_1 d\tau_2...d\tau_l$$

(single cluster of l systems)

$$= \int...\int_{(l-1)} \sum \left(\prod_{p>q} f_{pq} \right) d\tau_1 d\tau_2...d\tau_{l-1}$$

(single cluster of l systems).

(Since the particular suffixes do not matter, we have chosen to call them $1, 2,..., l$.) We can make (23) more symmetrical by writing $B_1 \equiv 1$, and then (23) becomes

$$(VB_1)^{n_1}(VB_2)^{n_2}...(VB_l)^{n_l}... \quad \text{or} \quad \prod_l (VB_l)^{n_l}. \tag{23'}$$

The expression (23') exhausts the terms in $\prod_{i>j} (1+f_{ij})$ which are consistent with any particular distribution of the systems into clusters in accordance with the specification (22). Consequently,

$$Q_N = \sum_{(n_l)} g(n_l) \prod_l (VB_l)^{n_l}, \tag{24}$$

where $g(n_l)$ stands for the number of ways in which N numbered systems can be divided up into n_1 isolated systems, n_2 clusters of 2 systems and so on, i.e. divided up according to the specification (22).

The next step is the relatively simple one of writing down an explicit expression for $g(n_l)$. The formula, which is an immediate extension of combinatory formulae with which we are already familiar, is

$$g(n_l) = \frac{N!}{\prod_l n_l! \prod_l (l!)^{n_l}}. \tag{25}$$

† Note: b, of § 5 above, is given by $B_2 = 2b$.

To prove this, we observe that we can imagine the N numbered systems arranged in order (say in a straight line) in $N!$ ways. Against this order we can divide the systems into groups according to the specification (22) (say by taking the first n_1 systems as the isolated systems, the next $2n_2$ systems, in successive pairs, as forming the n_2 binary clusters, the next $3n_3$ systems, in successive triplets, as forming the n_3 ternary clusters, and so on). But no order of sequence has to be attached to the n_l groups each containing l systems: so we have to divide by $n_l!$. And similarly no order of sequence has to be attached to the l systems contained in any one of these groups (e.g. it makes no difference whether we say i, j, and k form a cluster or j, k, and i, or any other permutation of these three suffixes); so we have to divide by $l!$ for every cluster of l systems. This leads directly to the expression (25).

Finally, we observe that the numbers n_l are restricted by the condition that there are just N systems in the assembly, i.e. by the equation

$$\sum_l l n_l = N. \tag{26}$$

Combining the equations (24), (25), and (26), we thus obtain

$$Q_N = \sum_{[\Sigma \, l n_l = N]} \frac{N!}{\prod_l n_l! \prod_l (l!)^{n_l}} \prod_l (V B_l)^{n_l},$$

or

$$\frac{Q_N}{N!} = \sum_{[\Sigma \, l n_l = N]} \frac{1}{\prod_l n_l!} \prod_l \left(\frac{V B_l}{l!} \right)^{n_l},$$

or

$$\frac{Q_N}{N!} = \sum_{[\Sigma \, l n_l = N]} \frac{1}{\prod_l n_l!} \prod_l (V b_l)^{n_l}, \tag{27}$$

where†

$$b_l = \frac{1}{l!} B_l.$$

The last step here is merely a matter of convenience. But we

† Note: b of § 5 above is the same as b_2.

may notice that b_l can be given a semi-physical meaning, since, explicitly,

$$Vb_l = \frac{1}{l!} \int \cdots \int_{(l)} \sum \left(\prod_{p>q} f_{pq} \right) d\tau_1 d\tau_2 \ldots d\tau_l$$

(single cluster of l numbered systems)

$$= \int \cdots \int_{(l)} \sum \left(\prod_{p>q} f_{pq} \right) d\tau_1 d\tau_2 \ldots d\tau_l \qquad (28)$$

(single cluster of l *indistinguishable* systems).

We shall refer to the expression (28) again later. At the moment it is sufficient to observe that, with Vb_l given by (28), equation (27) is exact, i.e. there is an *algebraic identity* between the right-hand sides of equations (12) and (27). That the above discussion should have been given in semi-physical language is quite irrelevant: it has merely helped us to group the terms in Q_N in a convenient way, to which we might equally well have been led by purely mathematical considerations. The only *physical* assumption which we have made (but not yet used) is that the quantities b_l, given by (28), are independent of V. Equation (27) is valid whether or not this physical condition is fulfilled, but when it is fulfilled the subsequent derivation of the thermodynamic properties of the assembly is greatly simplified. And we have seen that the quantities b_l will indeed be independent of V provided that capillary effects, dependent on the surface area of the assembly, can be ignored.

7. Unfortunately, owing to the restrictive condition (26), we cannot sum the r.h.s. of (27) explicitly, by purely algebraic methods, and so at this stage we must have recourse to the familiar technique of picking out the greatest term in the sum concerned, on the assumption that only this greatest term is of any importance. It is convenient to deal with (P.F.) itself, rather than with Q_N, and by equations (9) and (10) we have

$$(\text{P.F.}) = \left(\frac{2\pi mkT}{h^2} \right)^{3N/2} \frac{Q_N}{N!}.$$

Replacing N by $\sum_l l n_l$, this gives

$$(\text{P.F.}) = \sum_{[\Sigma\, l n_l = N]} \frac{1}{\prod_l n_l!} \prod_l \left[\left(\frac{2\pi m \boldsymbol{k} T}{h^2}\right)^{3l/2} V b_l\right]^{n_l}$$

$$= \sum_{[\Sigma\, l n_l = N]} \frac{1}{\prod_l n_l!} \prod_l (V g_l)^{n_l}, \qquad (29)$$

where g_l stands for $\left(\dfrac{2\pi m \boldsymbol{k} T}{h^2}\right)^{3l/2} b_l$.

I.e. $\qquad\qquad (\text{P.F.}) = \sum_{(n_l)} \mathfrak{T}(n_l),$

where $\qquad\qquad \mathfrak{T}(n_l) = \dfrac{1}{\prod_l n_l!} \prod_l (V g_l)^{n_l}, \qquad (30)$

and the quantities n_l are subject to

$$\sum_l l n_l = N. \qquad (26)$$

Using Stirling's theorem we obtain, from (30),

$$\delta \ln \mathfrak{T} = - \sum_l \ln n_l\, \delta n_l + \sum_l \ln(V g_l)\, \delta n_l \qquad (31)$$

where, from (26), $\qquad\qquad \sum_l l\, \delta n_l = 0. \qquad (32)$

Consequently the values of n_l, denoted by n_l^*, which make $\mathfrak{T}(n_l)$ greatest are given by the equations (found by adding $\alpha(32)$ to (31)),

$$\ln(V g_l) + \alpha l - \ln n_l^* = 0 \quad (l = 1, 2, \ldots),$$

whence $\qquad n_l^* = \lambda^l V g_l, \quad \text{where} \quad \lambda = e^\alpha. \qquad (33)$

Introducing these values into (30), and equating (P.F.) to $\mathfrak{T}(n_l^*)$, we thus find

$$\ln(\text{P.F.}) = - \sum_l n_l^* [l \ln \lambda + \ln(V g_l)] + \sum_l n_l^* + \sum_l n_l^* \ln(V g_l)$$

$$= \sum n_l^* - N \ln \lambda,$$

whence $\quad F = -\boldsymbol{k} T \ln(\text{P.F.})$

$$= N \boldsymbol{k} T \ln \lambda - \boldsymbol{k} T \left(\sum n_l^*\right). \qquad (34)$$

The thermodynamic equation, $P = -(\partial F/\partial V)_{N,T}$, applied to (34), now gives

$$P = -\frac{N \boldsymbol{k} T}{\lambda} \frac{\partial \lambda}{\partial V} + \boldsymbol{k} T \sum_l \frac{\partial n_l^*}{\partial V}$$

but, from (33), $\dfrac{\partial n_l^*}{\partial V} = l\lambda^{l-1}\dfrac{\partial\lambda}{\partial V}\,Vg_l + \lambda^l g_l$

since g_l is assumed independent of V. Consequently

$$P = -\frac{NkT}{\lambda}\frac{\partial\lambda}{\partial V} + kT\sum_l \frac{ln_l^*}{\lambda}\frac{\partial\lambda}{\partial V} + kT\sum_l \frac{n_l^*}{V}$$

$$= \frac{kT}{V}\sum_l n_l^*,$$

i.e. $PV = kT\sum_l n_l^*.$ (35)

Combining the equations (35) and (34), we obtain

$$G = F + PV$$
$$= NkT\ln\lambda,$$

which identifies λ with the absolute activity of a system in the assembly. But for our present purposes the important equations are (35), (33), and (26), namely,

$$PV = kT\sum_l n_l^*,$$ (35)

where $n_l^* = \lambda^l V g_l = \lambda^l V\left(\dfrac{2\pi mkT}{h^2}\right)^{3l/2} b_l$ (33)

and $\sum_l ln_l^* = N.$ (26′)

8. On putting the values of n_l^* given by the equation (33) into the equation (26′), we obtain

$$\sum_l l\lambda^l V g_l = N$$

or, dividing by V and writing $V/N = v$,

$$g_1\lambda + 2g_2\lambda^2 + 3g_3\lambda^3 + \ldots = \frac{1}{v}.$$ (36)

The l.h.s. of (36) is a power-series in λ of which the coefficients lg_l are (according to our basic physical assumption) independent of v. Consequently if v is sufficiently large, i.e. if the gas is at a sufficiently low pressure, λ must be small and given, to a first approximation, by

$$\lambda = \frac{1}{g_1 v} = \left(\frac{h^2}{2\pi mkT}\right)^{3/2}\frac{N}{V}$$

(which is, of course, the absolute activity of a perfect gas of structureless particles). We are, however, here interested in the *second* approximation to λ, which we can find by assuming

$$\lambda = \frac{a_1}{v} + \frac{a_2}{v^2} + \dots,$$

and substituting this expression into equation (36). This gives

$$g_1\left(\frac{a_1}{v} + \frac{a_2}{v^2} + \dots\right) + 2g_2\left(\frac{a_1}{v} + \frac{a_2}{v^2} + \dots\right)^2 + \dots - \frac{1}{v} = 0,$$

whence, equating to zero the coefficients of $\frac{1}{v}$ and $\frac{1}{v^2}$, we obtain

$$a_1 g_1 = 1,$$
$$a_2 g_1 + 2a_1^2 g_2 = 0,$$

giving $\qquad a_1 = 1/g_1 \quad \text{and} \quad a_2 = -2g_2/g_1^3.$

Hence, for sufficiently large v,

$$\lambda = \frac{1}{g_1 v} - \frac{2g_2}{g_1^3 v^2} + \dots. \tag{37}$$

Now, combining (35) and (33), we have

$$PV = kT(\lambda V g_1 + \lambda^2 V g_2 + \dots),$$

i.e. $\qquad\qquad P = kT(\lambda g_1 + \lambda^2 g_2 + \dots). \tag{38}$

So finally, substituting from (37) into (38), we find

$$P = kT\left\{g_1\left(\frac{1}{g_1 v} - \frac{2g_2}{g_1^3 v^2} + \dots\right) + g_2\left(\frac{1}{g_1^2 v^2} + \dots\right) + \dots\right\}$$

$$= kT\left(\frac{1}{v} - \frac{g_2}{g_1^2 v^2} + \dots\right).$$

But, returning to the definition of g_l, we have

$$\frac{g_2}{g_1^2} = b_2 = b = \tfrac{1}{2}\int_0^\infty 4\pi r^2 f(r)\, dr$$

and our equation for P, expanded in successive powers of $1/v$, commences

$$P = kT\left(\frac{1}{v} - \frac{b}{v^2} + \dots\right),$$

which is precisely the same as our former result, equation (21).

With this strict derivation of the expression for the second virial coefficient we must end our present discussion of the full statistical treatment of an imperfect gas. We shall, however, refer again briefly to the above equations in the next chapter. It is possible, by the method of successive approximations to λ outlined in this section, to derive expressions for the third, fourth, and later coefficients in the virial expansion

$$P = kT \sum_{n=1}^{\infty} \frac{c_n}{v^n},$$

but the algebra is tedious and the resulting formulae involve rather elaborate combinations of the cluster-integrals b_l. Actually Mayer has shown that the general virial-coefficient, c_n, can be expressed as a single integral having a simpler form than any of the cluster-integrals b_l; but this extension of the theory is certainly outside the scope of the present book.

The theory of imperfect gases, to which this chapter must serve only as an introduction, is, in the author's opinion, the most outstanding achievement yet attained in the whole field of statistical mechanics. The work, begun by Ursell in 1927, was taken much further by Mayer and his collaborators in America ten years later and has since been added to by Kahn, Born, Fuchs, and others. Detailed application of the general formulae has yet to be made: but formally the classical problem of an imperfect gas, and of a mixture of imperfect gases, has been solved.

9. It seems inappropriate to conclude a chapter on the theory of imperfect gases without at least a passing reference to the well-known van der Waals equation, which may be written in the form[†]

$$\left(P + \frac{N^2 a_1}{V^2}\right)(V - N a_2) = NkT, \tag{39}$$

where a_1 and a_2 are positive constants. This equation, although of considerable usefulness in discussing the behaviour of imperfect (i.e. actual) gases empirically, has little theoretical foundation. For the model (involving binary collisions) from which it is

[†] We use a_1 and a_2, instead of the more customary a and b, since we are already using $-b$ for the second virial-coefficient.

generally derived can be shown to break down completely long before the interesting critical conditions occur which the equation itself is most famed for predicting. Nevertheless it is instructive to examine the nature of the second virial-coefficient on the basis of van der Waals's equation and to see in what circumstances this agrees with the value found by the full statistical treatment.

Solving equation (39) for P, and expanding the result in successive powers of N/V, we have

$$P = \frac{kT}{v-a_2} - \frac{a_1}{v^2}$$

$$= \frac{kT}{v}\left(1 + \frac{a_2}{v} + \ldots\right) - \frac{a_1}{v^2}$$

$$= kT\left\{\frac{1}{v} + \frac{1}{v^2}\left(a_2 - \frac{a_1}{kT}\right) + \ldots\right\}, \tag{40}$$

so that, on the basis of van der Waals's equation, the second virial-coefficient is given by $a_2 - a_1/kT$. If this is to agree with the result found above, equation (21), we require

$$a_2 - \frac{a_1}{kT} = -b = -2\pi \int_0^\infty r^2 f(r)\, dr$$

$$= 2\pi \int_0^\infty r^2(1 - e^{-U(r)/kT})\, dr.$$

The equations (40) and (21) will, therefore, agree as far as the second virial-coefficient is concerned provided that the interatomic potential $U(r)$ is such that

$$2\pi \int_0^\infty r^2(1 - e^{-U(r)/kT})\, dr = a_2 - \frac{a_1}{kT}, \tag{41}$$

where a_1 and a_2 are positive constants.

We shall not attempt to discuss in detail the restrictions imposed on $U(r)$ by the condition (41), for the problem is in any case rather an artificial one. But it is worth noting that if $U(r)$ has the form shown in Fig. 42, where U_0 is sufficiently small for $\exp(-U(r)/kT)$ to be replaced by $1-U(r)/kT$ when $r > r_0$, then

$$2\pi \int_0^\infty r^2(1-e^{-U(r)/kT})\,dr = 2\pi \int_0^{r_0} r^2\,dr + 2\pi \int_{r_0}^\infty \frac{r^2 U(r)}{kT}\,dr$$

and the r.h.s. can be identified with $a_2 - a_1/kT$.

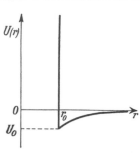

FIG. 42.

The potential field depicted in Fig. 42 is that appropriate to a model of the gas in which the atoms are regarded as rigid spheres, of diameter r_0, acting on each other with weak attractive forces. Such a model, therefore, gives a second virial-coefficient of the same form, i.e. having the same temperature dependence, as that implied by van der Waals's equation. Indeed, in this case, we have

$$a_2 = 2\pi \int_0^{r_0} r^2\,dr = \tfrac{2}{3}\pi r_0^3 = 4v_0 \quad \text{where} \quad v_0 = \tfrac{4}{3}\pi\left(\frac{r_0}{2}\right)^3,$$

i.e. where v_0 is the volume of one of the rigid atomic spheres.

EXAMPLES

1. Prove that the third virial-coefficient, c_3, is given by

$$c_3 = \frac{4g_2^2 - 2g_3 g_1}{g_1^4} = 4b_2^2 - 2b_3 = -\frac{1}{3V}\int\int\int f_{12}f_{23}f_{31}\,d\tau_1\,d\tau_2\,d\tau_3.$$

2. Show that for a binary gas-mixture consisting of N_A A-systems and N_B B-systems we have (with the obvious notation, and subject to the same assumptions as in this chapter)

$$\frac{Q_{N_A N_B}}{N_A!\,N_B!} = \sum_{\substack{(\Sigma l n_{lm} = N_A \\ \Sigma m n_{lm} = N_B)}} \frac{\prod (Vb_{lm})^{n_{lm}}}{\prod n_{lm}!},$$

where n_{lm} and b_{lm} refer to clusters containing l indistinguishable A-systems and m indistinguishable B-systems. ($b_{00} = 0$, $b_{01} = b_{10} = 1$.) Deduce the equation

$$PV = kTV(\lambda_A g_{10} + \lambda_B g_{01} + \lambda_A \lambda_B g_{11} + \lambda_A^2 g_{20} + \lambda_B^2 g_{02} + ...),$$

where λ_A and λ_B are given by

$$N_A = V(\lambda_A g_{10} + \lambda_A \lambda_B g_{11} + 2\lambda_A^2 g_{20} + ...),$$
$$N_B = V(\lambda_B g_{01} + \lambda_A \lambda_B g_{11} + 2\lambda_B^2 g_{02} + ...),$$

and
$$g_{lm} = \left(\frac{2\pi m_A kT}{h^2}\right)^{3l/2} \left(\frac{2\pi m_B kT}{h^2}\right)^{3m/2} b_{lm}.$$

Hence derive the virial expansion

$$P = kT \left(\frac{1}{v} - \frac{1}{v^2}(x_A^2 b_{20} + x_A x_B b_{11} + x_B^2 b_{02}) + ...\right),$$

where

$$v = V/(N_A + N_B), \quad x_A = N_A/(N_A + N_B), \quad x_B = N_B/(N_A + N_B)$$

$$b_{20} = \tfrac{1}{2}\int_0^\infty 4\pi r^2 f_{AA}(r)\, dr, \quad b_{11} = \int_0^\infty 4\pi r^2 f_{AB}(r)\, dr, \quad b_{02} = \tfrac{1}{2}\int_0^\infty 4\pi r^2 f_{BB}(r)\, dr.$$

GRAND PARTITION FUNCTIONS

1. So far we have considered two of the fundamental formulae of statistical mechanics, namely

$$S = k \ln \Omega, \qquad \Omega = \Omega(E, V, N) \qquad \text{(I)}$$

and

$$F(T, V, N) = -kT \ln(\text{P.F.}), \qquad (\text{P.F.}) = \sum_i \Omega_i e^{-E_i/kT}. \qquad \text{(II)}$$

We have seen that these two routes, or bridges, between mechanics and thermodynamics, lead to precisely the same territory, i.e. essentially they are equivalent structures although the second, or isothermal, bridge is more elegant and more easily crossed than the first, rather narrow, adiabatic one.

The advantages of formula (II), compared with formula (I), were clearly seen in the simple example of an assembly of N independent, identical, localized systems. Formula (I) led to

$$\Omega = \sum_{(n_i)} \frac{N!}{\prod_i n_i!}, \qquad (1)$$

where

$$\sum_i n_i = N \qquad (2)$$

and

$$\sum_i n_i \epsilon_i = E. \qquad (3)$$

We had to proceed by picking out the greatest term in the sum on the r.h.s. of (1), subject to the two restrictive conditions, (2) and (3). On the other hand formula (II), applied to the same problem, led to

$$(\text{P.F.}) = \sum_{(n_i)} \frac{N!}{\prod_i n_i!} e^{-\sum_i n_i \epsilon_i/kT}, \qquad (4)$$

where

$$\sum_i n_i = N, \qquad (2)$$

and we were able to sum the r.h.s. of (4) forthwith, purely algebraically. This advantage is due, of course, to the welcome loss of the restrictive condition, (3), expressing the constancy of the total energy of the assembly.

We have, however, also met with cases in which the remaining

restrictive condition, expressing the fact that the total number
of systems in the assembly is fixed, continues to impede purely
algebraic progress. This happened in the example discussed in
paragraph 5 of Chapter XV, and again in the theory of imperfect
gases developed in the last chapter (see equation (27), Chapter
XVI). The question therefore arises, Can we get rid of the remaining restrictive condition, typified by (2) above, and obtain a third
fundamental formula of statistical mechanics for which any distribution numbers that may be introduced are entirely unencum-
bered by restrictive conditions of any kind? If so, then this third
fundamental formula should provide an even better bridge,
between mechanics and thermodynamics, than either of those
which we have already explored.

As already suggested, in the introductory paragraph to Chapter
XV, there is such a third bridge, and one of great strength. We
shall proceed in this chapter to construct it, and to illustrate its
usefulness by considering again some of the problems to which we
have already applied methods based on the formulae (I) and (II)
above.

2. Our immediate problem, then, is to get rid of restrictive
conditions of the kind typified in equation (2); and it is convenient
to use the particular example of an assembly of N independent,
identical, localized systems in considering how this can be done.

A clue to the correct procedure is afforded by examining the
formal side of the transition, which we have already made, from
formula (I) to formula (II). Starting with Ω, we construct (P.F.)
by multiplying Ω by $e^{-E/kT}$ and then summing over all values of
E. Now $-1/kT$ was, in the first method, equal to the quantity β
with which we multiplied the restrictive condition $\sum_i n_i \epsilon_i = E$ in

applying the method of Lagrange's undetermined multipliers to
pick out the greatest term in Ω. Thus in passing from formula (I)
to formula (II), and getting rid of the restrictive condition
$\sum_i n_i \epsilon_i = E$, we have

   (i) multiplied Ω by $e^{\beta E}$,
   (ii) summed over all values of E,
   (iii) given β its physical meaning, $-1/kT$.

These observations at once suggest that an entirely analogous procedure might be fruitful in getting rid of the restrictive condition $\sum_i n_i = N$. Indeed they suggest that we should

(i) multiply (P.F.) by $e^{\alpha N}$,
(ii) sum over all values of N,
(iii) give α its physical meaning, μ/kT.

Here, of course, α is the quantity with which we formerly multiplied the restrictive condition $\sum_i n_i = N$ in applying the method of Lagrange's undetermined multipliers to pick out the greatest term in Ω, and μ is the chemical potential of a system in the assembly.

We shall denote the result of these three operations by the symbol (G.P.F.), an abbreviation for the words *Grand Partition Function*. Thus, quite formally,

$$(\text{G.P.F.}) = \sum_{(N)} (\text{P.F.})_N \, e^{N\mu/kT} \qquad (5)$$

or

$$(\text{G.P.F.}) = \sum_{(N)} (\text{P.F.})_N \lambda^N, \quad \text{where} \quad \lambda = e^{\mu/kT}, \qquad (5')$$

$$= \sum_{(E,N)} \Omega(E, V, N) e^{-E/kT} \lambda^N. \qquad (5'')$$

Now equation (5) may, as we hope, provide a useful function of the *mechanical* properties of the assembly, but we have still to link this function with some *thermodynamical* property of the assembly. If the expression on the r.h.s. of (5) is to form the r.h.s. of an equation akin to (I) or (II), what thermodynamic function is to replace S or F on the l.h.s. of this equation?

The answer is suggested by supposing that only the greatest term in the sum on the r.h.s. of (5') makes any significant contribution to the (G.P.F.). If we write

$$(\text{G.P.F.}) = \sum_{(N)} T(N),$$

where

$$T(N) = (\text{P.F.})_N \lambda^N,$$

then

$$\ln T(N) = \ln(\text{P.F.})_N + N \ln \lambda$$

and the value of N for which $T(N)$ is a maximum is given by

$$\frac{\partial \ln(\text{P.F.})}{\partial N} + \ln \lambda = 0.$$

But
$$\frac{\partial \ln(\text{P.F.})}{\partial N} = -\frac{1}{kT}\frac{\partial F}{\partial N} = -\frac{\mu}{kT},$$

and therefore the greatest term in the (G.P.F.) is the term for which $\ln\lambda = \mu/kT$, where μ is the chemical potential of a system in the assembly as calculated by method II. Our previous experience in comparing method II with method I ought to have prepared us for this result, which suggests that to pick out the greatest term in the (G.P.F.), while not inevitably a necessary procedure, is at least a valid one. And if we can equate (G.P.F.) with $T_{\max}$, then

$$(\text{G.P.F.}) = (\text{P.F.})_{N^*}e^{N^*\mu/kT},$$

i.e.
$$kT\ln(\text{G.P.F.}) = kT\ln(\text{P.F.})_{N^*} + N^*\mu$$
$$= -F + G$$
$$= PV.$$

These considerations, therefore, lead us to suppose that a third fundamental formula of statistical mechanics may be provided by the equations

where
$$\left.\begin{array}{l} PV = kT\ln(\text{G.P.F.}) \\ (\text{G.P.F.}) = \sum_{(N)} (\text{P.F.})_N \, \lambda^N \end{array}\right\}, \qquad (\text{III})$$

and where $(\text{P.F.})_N$ stands for the partition function, as already defined, for an assembly of N systems (in a volume V and at temperature T) and λ is the equilibrium value of the absolute activity of (a system in) the assembly.

Before discussing the equations (III), one further comment in the vein of the argument of the present section can usefully be made. It is that the familiar equations (see equation (23), Chapter XV),

$$\ln N + \alpha + \beta\epsilon_i - \ln n_i = 0, \quad i = 1, 2, \dots$$

can equally well be regarded as

(a) giving the values of n_i^* which make $\dfrac{N!}{\prod\limits_i n_i!}$ a maximum subject to

$$\sum_i n_i = N,$$
$$\sum n_i \epsilon_i = E,$$

(b) giving the values of n_i^* which make $\dfrac{N!}{\prod\limits_i n_i!} e^{\beta \sum\limits_i n_i \epsilon_i}$ a maximum,

subject to

$$\sum_i n_i = N,$$

or (c) giving the values of n_i^* which make $\dfrac{N!}{\prod\limits_i n_i!} e^{\beta \sum\limits_i n_i \epsilon_i} e^{\alpha \sum\limits_i n_i}$ a maximum.

And the sum, for all values of n_i, of the expression in (c) is (for the problem of an assembly of N independent, identical, localized systems) the quantity to which we have given the name grand partition function.

3. The first important observation that has to be made on the content of the equations (III) concerns the nature, or identity, of the *independent variables* occurring in the grand partition function itself.

In the case of Ω, the independent variables are E, V, and N: which we have already seen are appropriate to the thermodynamic function S.

In the case of (P.F.), the independent variables are T, V, and N: which we have, likewise, seen are appropriate to the thermo-dynamic function F.

It is evident, from equation (5), that T and V remain independent variables as far as (G.P.F.) is concerned; but—since we sum over all values of N in forming (G.P.F.)—the variable N no longer enters explicitly into the final function. In place of N, however, we now have, as a new independent variable, either the chemical potential μ (equation (5)) or the absolute activity λ (equation (5′)). And it does not matter whether we regard T, V, and μ or T, V, and λ as independent variables, since λ and μ are related by the equation $\ln \lambda = \mu/\boldsymbol{k}T$.

The grand partition function itself, therefore, is an explicit function of the three variables T, V, and μ or T, V, and λ. We must now inquire whether these variables are appropriate to the thermodynamic function PV on the l.h.s. of equation (III).

The product of the pressure and the volume of a thermo-dynamical assembly is very possibly a quantity with which the reader is not well acquainted. But it is shown in Appendix I, § c that, quite generally, for any single component assembly

$$d(PV) = S\,dT + P\,dV + N\,d\mu, \tag{6}$$

which reveals at once that T, V, and μ are just the independent variables most appropriate to the thermodynamic function PV. In fact

$$\left(\frac{\partial PV}{\partial T}\right)_{V,\mu} = S, \qquad \left(\frac{\partial PV}{\partial V}\right)_{\mu,T} = P, \quad \text{and} \quad \left(\frac{\partial PV}{\partial \mu}\right)_{T,V} = N, \quad (7)$$

so that, knowing PV as an explicit function of T, V, and μ, we can at once, by simple differentiation, calculate the other thermodynamic properties of the assembly.

Actually, however, the quantity with which we wish to have to deal is not PV itself, but (G.P.F.) which is related to PV through the equation

$$PV = kT \ln(\text{G.P.F.}).$$

And for (G.P.F.) the variables T, V, and λ are even more convenient than the variables T, V, and μ. For since

$$\mu = kT \ln \lambda,$$

we have
$$d\mu = k \ln \lambda \, dT + kT \, d\ln \lambda$$

and therefore

$$\begin{aligned}
d(PV) &= (S + Nk \ln \lambda)\, dT + P\, dV + NkT\, d\ln \lambda \\
&= \left(S + \frac{N\mu}{T}\right) dT + P\, dV + NkT \frac{d\lambda}{\lambda} \\
&= (TS + G)\frac{dT}{T} + P\, dV + NkT \frac{d\lambda}{\lambda} \\
&= (E + PV)\frac{dT}{T} + P\, dV + NkT \frac{d\lambda}{\lambda} \quad (8)
\end{aligned}$$

since $E - TS = F = G - PV$. And from equation (8) we have

$$\left(\frac{\partial PV}{\partial T}\right)_{V,\lambda} = \frac{E + PV}{T}, \qquad \left(\frac{\partial PV}{\partial V}\right)_{\lambda,T} = P, \qquad \left(\frac{\partial PV}{\partial \lambda}\right)_{T,V} = \frac{NkT}{\lambda}, \quad (9)$$

whence, introducing the equation $PV = kT \ln(\text{G.P.F.})$ into (9), we obtain at once

$$\frac{\partial}{\partial T}[kT \ln(\text{G.P.F.})] = \frac{E}{T} + k \ln(\text{G.P.F.}),$$

i.e.
$$kT \frac{\partial}{\partial T} \ln(\text{G.P.F.}) = \frac{E}{T},$$

i.e.
$$E = kT^2 \frac{\partial}{\partial T} \ln(\text{G.P.F.})$$

and
$$P = kT \frac{\partial}{\partial V} \ln(\text{G.P.F.})$$

(10)

and
$$N = \lambda \frac{\partial}{\partial \lambda} \ln(\text{G.P.F.})$$

(G.P.F.) being a function of T, V, and λ. These equations are considerably simpler than those which result from the equations (7) on regarding (G.P.F.) as an explicit function of T, V, and μ, and will form the basis of our subsequent work with grand partition functions.

The last of the equations (10) can be written

$$\bar{N} = \lambda \frac{\partial}{\partial \lambda} \ln \left(\sum_{(N)} (\text{P.F.})_N \lambda^N \right),$$

(10')

where on the r.h.s. we have written the explicit form of the (G.P.F.) and on the l.h.s. we have written $\bar{N}$ in place of N in order to avoid a confusion of notation. (The symbols N in equation (10) and $\bar{N}$ in (10') both stand for the equilibrium number of systems in the assembly when its volume is V, the temperature T, and the absolute activity of a system is λ.) Now (10') gives

$$\bar{N} = \frac{\sum_{(N)} N(\text{P.F.})_N \lambda^N}{\sum_{(N)} (\text{P.F.})_N \lambda^N},$$

(10'')

which shows that the term $(\text{P.F.})_N \lambda^N$ in the (G.P.F.) is proportional to the probability that there are in fact N systems in the assembly when T, V, and λ are given.

4. We must next verify that these new equations lead to the results obtained by methods (I) and (II) for some of the problems already discussed in earlier chapters. We shall give the equations with a minimum of comment.

(i) *A perfect gas*

Since
$$(\text{P.F.})_N = \frac{(\text{p.f.})^N}{N!}$$

we have
$$(\text{G.P.F.}) = \sum_{(N)} \frac{(\text{p.f.})^N \lambda^N}{N!},$$

i.e.
$$(\text{G.P.F.}) = \exp[\lambda(\text{p.f.})]. \tag{11}$$

This is an algebraic identity. Since $(\text{p.f.}) = Vg(T)$ for a non-localized system,
$$\ln(\text{G.P.F.}) = \lambda Vg(T). \tag{11'}$$

The equations (10) now give
$$E = \lambda VkT^2 g'(T), \qquad P = \lambda kTg(T), \quad \text{and} \quad N = \lambda Vg(T),$$

whence
$$PV = NkT \quad \text{and} \quad E = NkT^2 \frac{d}{dT} \ln g(T) = NkT^2 \frac{\partial}{\partial T} \ln(\text{p.f.})$$

which are results with which we are already familiar.

The criticism, which may be made on physical grounds, that for fixed V the model of a perfect gas must break down for sufficiently large N (and we have summed over all values of N) is, formally, a valid one. But that some terms in (G.P.F.) have been evaluated incorrectly does not matter at all provided that these terms do not pertain to the equilibrium state of the assembly.

(ii) *Condensed phase: Einstein model*

Since
$$(\text{P.F.}) = (\text{p.f.})^N$$

we have
$$(\text{G.P.F.}) = \sum_{(N)} (\text{p.f.})^N \lambda^N,$$

i.e.
$$(\text{G.P.F.}) = \frac{1}{1 - \lambda(\text{p.f.})} \quad \text{provided } \lambda(\text{p.f.}) < 1. \tag{12}$$

The equations (10) for E and N now give
$$E = \frac{\lambda(\text{p.f.})}{1 - \lambda(\text{p.f.})} \bar{\eta}, \quad \text{where} \quad \bar{\eta} = kT^2 \frac{\partial}{\partial T} \ln(\text{p.f.}),$$

and
$$N = \frac{\lambda(\text{p.f.})}{1 - \lambda(\text{p.f.})},$$

whence $E = N\bar{\eta}$, as we should expect, and
$$\lambda(\text{p.f.}) = \frac{N}{1+N}. \tag{13}$$

Since for a real assembly N, though very large, is finite, the condition $\lambda(\text{p.f.}) < 1$ in (12) is strictly satisfied; but for all practical purposes, for any macroscopic assembly

$$\lambda(\text{p.f.}) = 1. \tag{14}$$

The equation (10) for P gives $P = NkT\dfrac{\partial \ln(\text{p.f.})}{\partial V}$, just as if we were using methods (I) or (II).

The equation $PV = kT \ln(\text{G.P.F.})$, however, gives, using (13),

$$PV = -kT \ln[1-\lambda(\text{p.f.})] = kT \ln(1+N),$$

and though N is large, $\ln N$ is, thermodynamically, quite negligible. This shows that the present treatment possesses the familiar fundamental weakness of neglecting the volume of the condensed phase. We shall refer to this matter again in the last section of this chapter.

(iii) *Crystal-gas equilibrium*

Equation (33) of Chapter XV, i.e.

$$(\text{P.F.}) = \sum_{(M+N=X)} (\text{p.f.})_c^M \frac{(\text{p.f.})_g^N}{N!}, \tag{15}$$

was obtained algebraically. We now have

$$(\text{G.P.F.}) = \sum_{(X)} (\text{P.F.})_X \lambda^X = \sum_{M,N} (\text{p.f.})_c^M \frac{(\text{p.f.})_g^N}{N!} \lambda^{M+N}$$

$$= \left(\sum_M (\text{p.f.})_c^M \lambda^M\right)\left(\sum_N \frac{(\text{p.f.})_g^N \lambda^N}{N!}\right) = \frac{\exp[\lambda(\text{p.f.})_g]}{1-\lambda(\text{p.f.})_c}, \tag{16}$$

showing that the grand partition function for the assembly which is capable of forming two phases is the product of the grand partition functions for the two phases separately.

Further discussion of this problem is unnecessary. But it should be noted that for two phases in equilibrium P, T, and λ are the same for both phases, and therefore the physical requirement $V = V_1 + V_2$, combined with the fundamental equation

$$PV = kT \ln(\text{G.P.F.}),$$

leads at once to the result $(\text{G.P.F.}) = (\text{G.P.F.})_1(\text{G.P.F.})_2$, of which equation (16) is simply a particular instance.

(iv) *Imperfect gas*

Equation (29) of Chapter XVI, i.e.

$$(\text{P.F.}) = \sum_{\substack{(\Sigma l n_l = N)}} \frac{1}{\prod_l n_l!} \prod_l (Vg_l)^{n_l}, \qquad (17)$$

was an algebraic identity. We now have

$$(\text{G.P.F.}) = \sum_{(n_l)} \frac{1}{\prod_l n_l!} \prod_l (Vg_l)^{n_l} \lambda^{\Sigma l n_l}$$

$$= \sum_{(n_l)} \frac{1}{\prod_l n_l!} \prod_l (\lambda^l Vg_l)^{n_l}$$

$$= \prod_l \sum_{(n_l)} \frac{(\lambda^l Vg_l)^{n_l}}{n_l!} = \prod_l \exp[\lambda^l Vg_l],$$

i.e. $$(\text{G.P.F.}) = \exp\Big[\sum_l \lambda^l Vg_l\Big]. \qquad (18)$$

The equations (10), applied to (18), now produce at once the equations (36) and (38) of Chapter XVI which were previously obtained only by the laborious technique of picking out the greatest term on the r.h.s. of (17).

5. The next two examples with which we shall continue to illustrate the grand partition function method of statistical mechanics involve multi-component assemblies and therefore demand a slight extension of our general theory.

If the assembly contains several components, distinguished by the suffixes $1, 2,..., m$, then the immediate extension of equation $(5'')$ is simply

$$(\text{G.P.F.}) = \sum_{(N_1,...N_m;E)} \Omega(E, V, N_1,..., N_m)e^{-E/kT}\lambda_1^{N_1} \lambda_2^{N_2}...\lambda_m^{N_m}, \quad (19)$$

where $\lambda_1,..., \lambda_m$ are the absolute activities of the components $1,..., m$, respectively. The justification of (19) lies in the corresponding extension of the thermodynamic formula (6), i.e.

$$d(PV) = S\,dT + P\,dV + \sum N_i\,d\mu_i.$$

In place of the single equation for N in (10) we now have m such equations

$$N_i = \lambda_i \frac{\partial}{\partial \lambda_i} \ln(\text{G.P.F.}) \quad (i = 1, 2,..., m), \qquad (20)$$

but otherwise everything is unchanged. Proceeding to the further illustrative examples, we have

(v) *Perfect mixed crystal: Raoult's law*

Considering just the condensed phase we have, in the notation of Chapter XIV,

$$(\text{P.F.})_{M_A, M_B} = \frac{(M_A + M_B)!}{M_A! \, M_B!} [(\text{p.f.})_A^c]^{M_A} [(\text{p.f.})_B^c]^{M_B}.$$

This is an algebraic identity, as the reader should confirm by the methods of Chapter XV. Then

$$(\text{G.P.F.}) = \sum_{(M_A, M_B)} \frac{(M_A + M_B)!}{M_A! \, M_B!} [(\text{p.f.})_A^c]^{M_A} [(\text{p.f.})_B^c]^{M_B} \lambda_A^{M_A} \lambda_B^{M_B}$$

$$= \sum_M \sum_{(M_A + M_B = M)} \frac{(M_A + M_B)!}{M_A! \, M_B!} [\lambda_A (\text{p.f.})_A^c]^{M_A} [\lambda_B (\text{p.f.})_B^c]^{M_B}$$

$$= \sum_M [\lambda_A (\text{p.f.})_A^c + \lambda_B (\text{p.f.})_B^c]^M \quad \text{(binomial theorem)}$$

i.e.
$$(\text{G.P.F.}) = \frac{1}{1 - \lambda_A (\text{p.f.})_A^c - \lambda_B (\text{p.f.})_B^c}. \tag{21}$$

The equations (20) now give

$$M_A = \frac{\lambda_A (\text{p.f.})_A^c}{1 - \lambda_A (\text{p.f.})_A^c - \lambda_B (\text{p.f.})_B^c}, \quad M_B = \frac{\lambda_B (\text{p.f.})_B^c}{1 - \lambda_A (\text{p.f.})_A^c - \lambda_B (\text{p.f.})_B^c}, \tag{22}$$

and for $M_A + M_B$ to be physically significant (say 10^{23}) we require

$$\lambda_A (\text{p.f.})_A^c + \lambda_B (\text{p.f.})_B^c \approx 1. \tag{23}$$

Equation (23), with $\approx$ replaced by $=$, may be regarded as a chemical equation of state for the condensed phase. Equations (22) and (23) then give

$$\frac{M_A}{M_A + M_B} = \lambda_A (\text{p.f.})_A^c, \quad \frac{M_B}{M_A + M_B} = \lambda_B (\text{p.f.})_B^c,$$

equations which lead (§ 2, Chapter XIV) directly to Raoult's law.

(vi) *Combining gases: Law of Mass Action*

Considering the problem of dissociative equilibrium of the type $A + B \rightleftarrows AB$ previously discussed in paragraph 4 of Chapter XI, and using the same notation:

$$(\text{G.P.F.}) = \sum \frac{1}{N_1! \, N_2! \, N_{12}!} \frac{N_1!}{\prod_i n_i^a!} \frac{N_2!}{\prod_i n_i^b!} \frac{N_{12}!}{\prod_i n_i^{ab}!} e^{-E(n_i^a, n_i^b, n_i^{ab})/kT} \lambda_A^{N_A} \lambda_B^{N_B},$$

where

$$N_A = N_1 + N_{12} = \sum_i n_i^a + \sum_i n_i^{ab}, \quad N_B = N_2 + N_{12} = \sum_i n_i^b + \sum_i n_i^{ab}$$

and

$$E(n_i^a, n_i^b, n_i^{ab}) = \sum_i n_i^a \epsilon_i^a + \sum_i n_i^b \epsilon_i^b + \sum_i n_i^{ab} \epsilon_i^{ab}.$$

Summing over N_A and N_B implies an unrestricted summation over the distribution numbers n_i^a, n_i^b, n_i^{ab}: consequently

$$(\text{G.P.F.}) = \sum_{(n)} \frac{\prod_i (e^{-\epsilon_i^a/kT}\lambda_A)^{n_i^a} \prod_i (e^{-\epsilon_i^b/kT}\lambda_B)^{n_i^b} \prod_i (e^{-\epsilon_i^{ab}/kT}\lambda_A\lambda_B)^{n_i^{ab}}}{\prod_i n_i^a! \; \prod_i n_i^b! \; \prod_i n_i^{ab}!}$$

$$= \prod_i \left(\sum_{(n_i^a)} \frac{(e^{-\epsilon_i^a/kT}\lambda_A)^{n_i^a}}{n_i^a!} \right)(\ldots)(\ldots)$$

$$= \prod_i \exp[e^{-\epsilon_i^a/kT}\lambda_A] \prod_i \exp[e^{-\epsilon_i^b/kT}\lambda_B] \prod_i \exp[e^{-\epsilon_i^{ab}/kT}\lambda_A\lambda_B]$$

$$= \exp\left[\lambda_A \sum_i e^{-\epsilon_i^a/kT}\right] \exp\left[\lambda_B \sum_i e^{-\epsilon_i^b/kT}\right] \exp\left[\lambda_A\lambda_B \sum_i e^{-\epsilon_i^{ab}/kT}\right]$$

i.e. $$(\text{G.P.F.}) = \exp[\lambda_A(\text{p.f.})_A + \lambda_B(\text{p.f.})_B + \lambda_A\lambda_B(\text{p.f.})_{AB}]. \quad (24)$$

The equations (20) and (10) now give

$$N_A = \lambda_A(\text{p.f.})_A + \lambda_A\lambda_B(\text{p.f.})_{AB},$$
$$N_B = \lambda_B(\text{p.f.})_B + \lambda_A\lambda_B(\text{p.f.})_{AB} \quad (25)$$

and $$E = \lambda_A(\text{p.f.})_A \bar{\epsilon}_a + \lambda_B(\text{p.f.})_B \bar{\epsilon}_b + \lambda_A\lambda_B(\text{p.f.})_{AB}\bar{\epsilon}_{ab}, \quad (26)$$

where each $\bar{\epsilon}$ is given by $\bar{\epsilon} = kT^2 \dfrac{\partial}{\partial T}\ln(\text{p.f.})$.

From (25) and (26) it follows physically that

$$N_1 = \lambda_A(\text{p.f.})_A, \quad N_2 = \lambda_B(\text{p.f.})_B, \quad \text{and} \quad N_{12} = \lambda_A\lambda_B(\text{p.f.})_{AB}, \quad (27)$$

whence we at once obtain the law of mass action

$$\frac{N_{12}}{N_1 N_2} = \frac{(\text{p.f.})_{AB}}{(\text{p.f.})_A(\text{p.f.})_B}.$$

Moreover, substituting from (27) into (24), we have

$$PV = kT(N_1 + N_2 + N_{12}) \quad \text{(equation (2), Chapter XII)}:$$

this equation can also be obtained from the formula

$$\frac{P}{kT} = \frac{\partial \ln(\text{G.P.F.})}{\partial V},$$

remembering that $(\text{p.f.})_A$, $(\text{p.f.})_B$, and $(\text{p.f.})_{AB}$ are all of the form $Vg(T)$.

For dissociative equilibrium of the type $A + A \rightleftarrows A_2$ we find

$$(\text{G.P.F.}) = \exp[\lambda_A(\text{p.f.})_A + \lambda_A^2(\text{p.f.})_{A_2}]$$

and a mere extension of the analysis allowing for association of the A's into molecules A_l of any order l leads to

$$(\text{G.P.F.}) = \exp\left[\sum_l \lambda_A^l(\text{p.f.})_{A_l} \right] \tag{28}$$

(cf. equation (28), Chapter XII). There is a close similarity between equations (28) and (18), but they are not identical since $(\text{p.f.})_{A_l}$ and $V g_l$ have not quite the same meaning. Actually equation (18) is exact, whereas equation (28) is only approximate since roughly speaking, it ignores the volume of phase-space taken up by the species in the assembly. But when interaction potentials are such as to allow the formation of physically stable 'permanently' associated species the deviations from Boyle's law are of a much higher order than are those for an ordinary 'imperfect' gas and equation (28) can satisfactorily be used in place of equation (18).

6. In all the above examples we have been able to construct the grand partition function exactly, from first principles, using no mathematical techniques other than those of straightforward, and fairly simple, algebra. Herein lies the elegance and strength of the grand partition function method. Indeed the author knows of no problem in statistical mechanics as yet satisfactorily solved in which recourse to picking out the greatest term in an otherwise intractable sum is necessary when the grand partition function method is used. But for a condensed phase represented by an Einstein model our discussion so far has been somewhat cursory; and before ending this chapter on grand partition functions we must examine the condensed phase problem rather more carefully.

If the equations, $(\text{P.F.}) = (\text{p.f.})^N$, where $(\text{p.f.}) = \sum_i \varpi_i e^{-\eta_i/kT}$, pertaining to the Einstein model of a condensed phase, are to be physically appropriate to the condensed state then it is necessary that each energy, η, and its degeneracy, ϖ, must depend not on the total volume, V, of the assembly but on the *specific volume*, V/N. For, clearly, doubling the content of the assembly by doubling both N and V (e.g. considering two grams of liquid instead of one) will not significantly alter the permissible energies of a system within that part of the assembly originally under consideration. Consequently, for such an Einstein model

$$(\text{P.F.}) = [f(v, T)]^N, \quad \text{where} \quad v = V/N,$$

and

$$(\text{G.P.F.}) = \sum_{(N)} \boldsymbol{T}_N, \quad \text{where} \quad \boldsymbol{T}_N = f\left(\frac{V}{N}, T\right)^N \lambda^N, \qquad (29)$$

so that, V being fixed, we *cannot* perform the summation over N (a point which was deliberately obscured in example (ii) above by suppressing any mention of the volume, V).

Assuming, however, that only the greatest term on the r.h.s. of (29) makes any significant contribution to the sum, we have

$$\ln \boldsymbol{T}_N = N \ln f\left(\frac{V}{N}, T\right) + N \ln \lambda$$

and

$$\frac{\partial \ln \boldsymbol{T}_N}{\partial N} = \ln f\left(\frac{V}{N}, T\right) - N \frac{V}{N^2} \frac{\partial \ln f(v, T)}{\partial v} + \ln \lambda,$$

so that the maximum term corresponds to $V/N = v^*$, where

$$v^* \frac{\partial \ln f(v^*, T)}{\partial v^*} - \ln f(v^*, T) = \ln \lambda, \qquad (30)$$

and

$$(\text{G.P.F.}) = f(v^*, T)^{N^*} \lambda^{N^*}, \qquad (31)$$

where $N^* = V/v^*$ and v^* is given by (30).

The equations (10) applied to (31) now give

$$E = N^* k T^2 \frac{\partial}{\partial T} \ln f(v^*, T) = N^* \begin{pmatrix} \text{average energy of system in} \\ \text{Einstein model corresponding} \\ \text{to } v = v^* \end{pmatrix},$$

$$\frac{P}{k T} = N^* \frac{\partial}{\partial V} \ln f\left(\frac{V}{N^*}, T\right) = \frac{\partial}{\partial v^*} \ln f(v^*, T), \qquad (32)$$

and

$$N = N^*.$$

Of these equations (32) is the most important since combining (30) and (32) we find

$$\lambda f(v^*, T) = e^{P v^*/k T}$$

(see equation (44), Chapter XIII), in contrast with equation (14) above.

We thus see that our previous, and rather uncritical, discussion of the (G.P.F.) for a condensed phase was incorrect in so far as it neglected Pv^*/kT. Nevertheless the (G.P.F.)'s so constructed are quite adequate for most purposes. We may call them quasi grand partition functions. Results derived from them become formally correct if in them we replace λ by $\lambda e^{-Pv/kT}$, F by G, and E by H (the heat content, given by $E+PV$). In Table XI, summarizing typical grand partition functions, with which we conclude this chapter, quasi grand partition functions are distinguished by an asterisk. Results included in the table and not already proved are left as examples for the reader.

TABLE XI

	Assembly	*Grand partition function*
(a)	Perfect gas, one component	(G.P.F.) $= \exp[\lambda(\text{p.f.})]$
(b)	Condensed phase, Einstein model	(G.P.F.)* $= 1/[1-\lambda(\text{p.f.})]$
(c)	Crystal-gas equilibrium	(G.P.F.)* $= \exp[\lambda(\text{p.f.})_g]/[1-\lambda(\text{p.f.})_c]$
(d)	Immobile adsorption: independent systems	(G.P.F.) $= [1+\lambda(\text{p.f.})_a]^{M_s}$
(e)	Perfect mixed crystal	(G.P.F.)* $= 1/[1-\lambda_A(\text{p.f.})_A - \lambda_B(\text{p.f.})_B]$
(f)	Dissociative equilibrium in gas phase	(G.P.F.) $= \exp[\lambda_A(\text{p.f.})_A + \lambda_B(\text{p.f.})_B + \lambda_A\lambda_B(\text{p.f.})_{AB}]$
(g)	Imperfect gas	(G.P.F.) $= \exp\left[\sum_l \lambda^l V g_l\right]$
(h)	Dimerization in one-component condensed phase	(G.P.F.)* $= 1/[1-\lambda(\text{p.f.})_1 - \lambda^2(\text{p.f.})_2]$
(i)	Dimerization in otherwise perfect solution	(G.P.F.)* $= 1/[1-\lambda_u(\text{p.f.})_1 - \lambda_u^2(\text{p.f.})_2 - \lambda_v(\text{p.f.})_v]$

EXAMPLES

1. Derive the results (d), (h), and (i) above, and in each case show that these grand partition functions lead to the equations already obtained by method (I) or (II).

2. Derive the formulae

$$(\text{G.P.F.})_{\text{E.B.}} = 1/\prod_i (1-\lambda e^{-\epsilon_i/kT}), \qquad (\text{G.P.F.})_{\text{F.D.}} = \prod_i (1+\lambda e^{-\epsilon_i/kT})$$

for the grand partition functions appropriate to assemblies of systems, each capable of energies $\epsilon_1, \epsilon_2, ..., \epsilon_i, ...$, obeying Einstein-Bose and Fermi-Dirac statistics, respectively. (See Chapter III, § 3.)

REGULAR, BUT NON-PERFECT, SOLUTIONS

1. HAVING now a fairly complete picture of the technical equipment of statistical mechanics, we shall end this introductory survey of statistical methods by considering some of the contributions made to the theory of binary solutions during the last ten or twelve years. It will be possible to touch on only two or three of the simpler problems in this field, which is notoriously difficult and very extensive. Nevertheless, it is hoped that the following rather discursive account of certain aspects of this work will serve to introduce the reader to a wide range of current literature.

In Chapter XIV, Raoult's law was derived for a model assembly which may or may not give a good description of any particular binary solution. The important characteristics of the model, without which the statistical treatment would not lead to Raoult's law, were

(i) that the systems of the assembly can be regarded as *independent* systems, the partition function, (p.f.), for any one of them being entirely unaffected by either the bulk composition of the binary solution or the local composition of the solution in its immediate neighbourhood, and

(ii) that the number of spacial arrangements of N_A A-systems and N_B B-systems is given by the permutational expression†

$$\frac{(N_A+N_B)!}{N_A!\,N_B!}. \tag{1}$$

Moreover, it was evident, physically, that implicit in these postulates are the assumptions

(a) that the systems move in potential fields which are not sensibly affected by the composition (either gross or local) of the solution, and

(b) that the A-systems and B-systems are of roughly the same size and shape,

† Although we are concerned with condensed phases, we shall in this chapter use the more customary symbols N_A and N_B instead of M_A and M_B.

—we noted a possible exception to (b), but this need not concern us further here.

Exactly similar postulates characterized the model from which we derived Langmuir's adsorption isotherm equation. The 'binary solution' now comprises adsorbed atoms and vacant lattice-sites—which could be, but are not, occupied by an adsorbed system. The parallelism is enforced by comparing the equations

$$\theta = \frac{\lambda(\text{p.f.})_a}{1+\lambda(\text{p.f.})_a} \quad \text{and} \quad \frac{N_A}{N_A+N_B} = \frac{\lambda_A(\text{p.f.})_A}{\lambda_B(\text{p.f.})_B+\lambda_A(\text{p.f.})_A}.$$

Explicitly, the assumptions in the adsorption problem are that adsorbed systems do not interfere with each other, either geometrically or due to intermolecular forces.

But, of course, comparatively few physical or chemical assemblies actually satisfy these requirements. Binary solutions satisfying Raoult's law for all concentrations (often called *ideal* solutions, though the word *perfect* is, perhaps, preferable)† are the exception, rather than the rule. This means that the assumptions (a) and (b) are generally too restrictive and that a statistical theory of solutions based on a more comprehensive model is required.

Considerable progress has, indeed, been made towards the removal of assumptions (a) and (b) and their replacement by less restrictive conditions. But just as the statistical mechanics of imperfect gases is mathematically more difficult than that of perfect (or ideal) gases, so also every attempt to extend the scope of the model on which our theory of binary solutions is based leads to an increase in the mathematical complexity of the theory itself. Some of these mathematical difficulties have not yet been overcome, and an exact statistical theory for the new model is then impracticable. Failing an exact theory, we have to be content to derive *approximate* statistical theories, which are probably strictly valid for no particular model at all, but which may be sufficiently good to give us an *indication* of the true implications of the new model concerning the thermodynamical properties of the assembly. Naturally an approximation of the mathematical validity of which we can form some estimate will be more valuable than any *ad hoc* simplification of the theory having no particular range of validity (e.g. as a *theory*—as distinct from a

† *Ideal* can then be used to signify 'ideally dilute'.

semi-empirical formula—the first two terms of the virial expansion are of more value than van der Waals's equation as an approximation to the true statistical theory of an imperfect gas).

After this rather lengthy introduction, we turn to consider some of the models used to represent non-perfect binary solutions, and approximate methods employed to deal with the otherwise intractable mathematics.

2. When the condensed phase (crystal or liquid) contains only one type of system (atom or molecule), then the use of an Einstein model to represent this phase is equivalent to writing the partition function in the form

$$(\text{P.F.}) = \left[\left(\frac{2\pi m k T}{h^2} \right)^{\frac{3}{2}} J(T) \int e^{-\psi(r)/kT} \, d\tau \right]^N, \qquad (2)$$

where $J(T)$ is the factor in the partition function (p.f.) for the internal vibrations and rotations of a system (supposed independent of the rest of its motion) and $\psi(r)$ denotes the potential energy of the system when displaced a distance r (or (x, y, z)) from its mean position.

For a perfect solution (leading to Raoult's law) comprising N_A A-systems and N_B B-systems, the generalization of (2) is simply

$$(\text{P.F.}) = \left[\left(\frac{2\pi m_A k T}{h^2} \right)^{\frac{3}{2}} J_A(T) \int e^{-\psi_A(r)/kT} \, d\tau \right]^{N_A} \times$$

$$\times \left[\left(\frac{2\pi m_B k T}{h^2} \right)^{\frac{3}{2}} J_B(T) \int e^{-\psi_B(r)/kT} \, d\tau \right]^{N_B} g(N_A, N_B), \quad (3)$$

where $g(N_A, N_B)$ is a factor given by the number of arrangements of N_A A-systems and N_B B-systems on the lattice sites of the crystal or mean positions in the liquid phase. We shall write (3) as

$$(\text{P.F.}) = [f_A(T, v)]^{N_A} [f_B(T, v)]^{N_B} g(N_A, N_B), \qquad (3')$$

where v, the specific volume of the whole assembly (supposed independent of N_A/N_B) enters through the potential functions ψ. For a perfect solution, as we have already said, $g(N_A, N_B)$ is given by (1), and (3') becomes

$$(\text{P.F.}) = [f_A(T, v)]^{N_A} [f_B(T, v)]^{N_B} \frac{(N_A + N_B)!}{N_A! \, N_B!}. \qquad (4)$$

The expression on the r.h.s. of (4) leads immediately to Raoult's law.

But the assumption, which we have made, that the fields $\psi(\boldsymbol{r})$ are independent of the composition of the phase is not likely to be correct, i.e. to give a model with properties approximating closely to those of most solutions of chemistry or metallurgy.

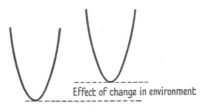

Effect of change in environment

Fig. 43.

Clearly the average field in which any atom (or molecule) of such a solution vibrates will depend, usually, on the kind of atoms which are surrounding it.

Retaining, for the present, assumption (*b*), we seek, then, to modify assumption (*a*) so as to take some account of the specific influence which the environment will exert on the potential field within which any particular system moves as a whole.

Almost all theoretical work to date has been based on the assumption that the modifying influence of the environment is merely to add a *constant* (whose value depends on the nature of the environment) to the potential $\psi(\boldsymbol{r})$ *without changing its form as a function of* $\boldsymbol{r}$ (see Fig. 43). This is probably a legitimate first step towards a more elaborate theory, though its validity has not yet received sufficient investigation.

The simplest case to consider now is that in which each system is roughly spherical and has the same number of (nearest) neighbours in the solution. Denoting this coordination number by z, and assuming further that

each AA pair of neighbours contributes w_{AA} to the energy,

each BB pair of neighbours contributes w_{BB} to the energy, and

each AB pair of neighbours contributes w_{AB} to the energy, then the 'configurational' energy of the assembly is given by

$$E_{\text{config}} = N_{AA}w_{AA} + N_{BB}w_{BB} + N_{AB}w_{AB}, \qquad (5)$$

where N_{AA} = number of AA pairs of neighbours, and so on. But, on counting up all the neighbours of the N_A A-systems, we have

$$2N_{AA} + N_{AB} = zN_A$$

and similarly

$$2N_{BB} + N_{AB} = zN_B. \qquad (6)$$

Consequently,

$$E_{\text{config}} = \tfrac{1}{2}zN_A w_{AA} + \tfrac{1}{2}zN_B w_{BB} + N_{AB}(w_{AB} - \tfrac{1}{2}w_{AA} - \tfrac{1}{2}w_{BB})$$
$$= E_A^c + E_B^c + wN_{AB}, \qquad (7)$$

where E_A^c = 'configurational' energy of N_A A-systems in a condensed phase of A-systems only,

E_B^c = 'configurational' energy of N_B B-systems in a condensed phase of B-systems only,

and $w = w_{AB} - \tfrac{1}{2}w_{AA} - \tfrac{1}{2}w_{BB}$ = energy gained on mixing, per creation of an AB pair of neighbours.

The rest of the energy of the assembly, over and above E_{config}, is vibrational, rotational, etc., and may be supposed included in the partition functions $f_A(T, v)$ and $f_B(T, v)$. Therefore, on these new assumptions, we have

$$(\text{P.F.}) = \sum_{(N_{AB})} f_A^{N_A} f_B^{N_B} g(N_A, N_B, N_{AB}) e^{-(E_A^c + E_B^c + wN_{AB})/kT}, \qquad (8)$$

where

$g(N_A, N_B, N_{AB})$ = number of arrangements of N_A A-systems and N_B B-systems so that there are altogether N_{AB} pairs of AB neighbours.

A solution for which the partition function is given by equation (8) is known as a *regular* solution.

3. Equation (8) may be written

$$(\text{P.F.}) = (f_A^{N_A} e^{-E_A^c/kT})(f_B^{N_B} e^{-E_B^c/kT}) \sum_{(N_{AB})} g(N_A, N_B, N_{AB}) e^{-wN_{AB}/kT},$$

whence the Helmholtz free energy of the assembly is given by

$$F = -kT \ln(\text{P.F.}) = F_A + F_B + \Delta F,$$

where

$$F_A = -kT \ln(f_A^{N_A} e^{-E_A^c/kT}) = -kT \ln(f_A e^{-\frac{1}{2}zw_{AA}/kT})^{N_A}$$

   = free energy of N_A systems of condensed phase of pure
      A-component,

$$F_B = -kT \ln(f_B^{N_B} e^{-E_B^c/kT}) = -kT \ln(f_B e^{-\frac{1}{2}zw_{BB}/kT})^{N_B}$$

   = free energy of N_B systems of condensed phase of pure
      B-component,

and

$$\Delta F = -kT \ln\left(\sum_{(N_{AB})} g(N_A, N_B, N_{AB}) e^{-wN_{AB}/kT} \right) \tag{9}$$

   = gain in free energy on mixing the two pure components.

The equations for F_A and F_B need not detain us: the factors
involving the configurational energy of a pure phase should be
absorbed into the partition functions f_A and f_B in order to obtain
formulae strictly comparable with equations (2) and (4) above.
It is, however, rather more convenient in the present work to
adjust the energy-zeros for f_A and f_B so that the terms involving
w_{AA} and w_{BB} appear explicitly: which we have done.

Equation (9), for ΔF, forms the basis of the present problem.
From it, by means of the Gibbs–Helmholtz equation, we derive

$$\Delta E = w \frac{\sum_{(N_{AB})} N_{AB} g(N_A, N_B, N_{AB}) e^{-wN_{AB}/kT}}{\sum_{(N_{AB})} g(N_A, N_B, N_{AB}) e^{-wN_{AB}/kT}}, \tag{10}$$

but to proceed further we have to evaluate the 'configurational
partition function'

$$(\text{P.F.})_{\text{config}} = \sum_{(N_{AB})} g(N_A, N_B, N_{AB}) e^{-wN_{AB}/kT}, \tag{11}$$

and here the mathematical difficulties begin.

The r.h.s. of (11) has not as yet been evaluated accurately
except for the very simple case of linear arrangements of the A's
and B's in a straight line (or in two or three such lines side by
side). The whole difficulty is due to our not having an explicit
mathematical formula available for $g(N_A, N_B, N_{AB})$ for any two-
or three-dimensional lattice array (coordination number z). Quite
recently very considerable progress has indeed been made, by

Onsager, Wannier, and others, in dealing with the two-dimensional problem; but even this is not yet completely solved, and the mathematical difficulties are very formidable. Consequently at this point we have, at present, to resort to approximate methods.

4. Although we do not know $g(N_A, N_B, N_{AB})$ for any particular (non-linear) lattice with coordination number z, we do know that

$$\sum_{(N_{AB})} g(N_A, N_B, N_{AB}) = \frac{(N_A + N_B)!}{N_A!\, N_B!}, \tag{12}$$

and

$$\frac{\sum_{(N_{AB})} N_{AB}\, g(N_A, N_B, N_{AB})}{\sum_{(N_{AB})} g(N_A, N_B, N_{AB})} = z\, \frac{N_A\, N_B}{N_A + N_B}. \tag{13}$$

The proof of (12) is immediate: for if we are not interested in the value of N_{AB} then the number of arrangements of the systems is simply given by (1). In proving (13), we observe first that the l.h.s. gives simply the average value of N_{AB} when $w = 0$, i.e. when there is random mixing of the A- and B-systems. We shall, therefore, denote the l.h.s. of (13) by $\overset{\ominus}{N}_{AB}$. We then consider two neighbouring lattice-sites, say (i) and (ii). In evaluating $\overset{\ominus}{N}_{AB}$ the mixing is random, and consequently:

the probability of A on (i) $= \dfrac{N_A}{N_A + N_B}$,

the probability of B on (ii) $= \dfrac{N_B}{N_A + N_B}$,

and therefore

the probability of $A(\text{i})B(\text{ii}) = \dfrac{N_A\, N_B}{(N_A + N_B)^2}$.

Similarly,

the probability of $B(\text{i})A(\text{ii}) = \dfrac{N_A\, N_B}{(N_A + N_B)^2}$.

Therefore the probability that the pair of sites (i)(ii) contributes to $\overset{\ominus}{N}_{AB}$ is

$$\frac{2N_A\, N_B}{(N_A + N_B)^2}.$$

But there are $\frac{1}{2}z(N_A+N_B)$ pairs of neighbouring sites in the whole lattice. Therefore,

$$\overset{\ominus}{N}_{AB} = \frac{1}{2}z(N_A+N_B)\frac{2N_A N_B}{(N_A+N_B)^2} = z\frac{N_A N_B}{N_A+N_B}, \tag{13'}$$

which proves equation (13).

Now the first approximation made to (11), which we may associate with the names of Bragg and Williams (though other authors have used it independently) is obtained by *replacing all values of N_{AB} in (11) by $\overset{\ominus}{N}_{AB}$*. In this way we obtain

$$(\text{P.F.})_{\text{config}} = \sum_{(N_{AB})} g(N_A, N_B, N_{AB})e^{-w\overset{\ominus}{N}_{AB}/kT}$$

$$= \frac{(N_A+N_B)!}{N_A! N_B!}\exp\left(-zw\frac{N_A N_B}{N_A+N_B}\frac{1}{kT}\right),$$

whence

$$\Delta F = zw\frac{N_A N_B}{N_A+N_B} - kT\ln\frac{(N_A+N_B)!}{N_A! N_B!},$$

$$\Delta S = k\ln\frac{(N_A+N_B)!}{N_A! N_B!} \quad \text{(as for random mixing)}, \tag{14}$$

$$\Delta E = zw\frac{N_A N_B}{N_A+N_B} \quad (= w\overset{\ominus}{N}_{AB}). \tag{15}$$

Using x to denote the mole fraction, $N_A/(N_A+N_B)$, (14) and (15) become

$$\Delta S = -(N_A+N_B)k\{x\ln x+(1-x)\ln(1-x)\} \tag{14'}$$

and

$$\Delta E = (N_A+N_B)zwx(1-x), \tag{15'}$$

and as functions of the mole fraction, x, ΔS and ΔE have the forms shown in Fig. 44.

When $w > 0$, ΔF, given by $\Delta E - T\Delta S$, can have the double-minimum form shown in Fig. 44 (c), with the physical significance that the solution will then separate into two different (complementary) concentrations—as indicated by the dotted line. (Note: $w > 0$ implies that $AA+BB$ is energetically more stable than $2AB$; which accords with the possibility of phase separation in this case.)

In terms of partial vapour-pressures, we have

$$kT \ln \frac{p_A}{p_A^0} = \mu_A - \mu_A^0 = \left(\frac{\partial \Delta F}{\partial N_A}\right)_{N_B, T}$$

$$= zw\frac{N_B}{N_A + N_B} - zw\frac{N_A N_B}{(N_A + N_B)^2} + kT \ln \frac{N_A}{N_A + N_B}$$

$$= zw(1-x)^2 + kT \ln x,$$

i.e.

$$p_A = p_A^0\, x e^{zw(1-x)^2/kT}. \left.\vphantom{\begin{array}{c}1\\1\end{array}}\right\} \qquad (16)$$

Similarly,

$$p_B = p_B^0(1-x)e^{zwx^2/kT}.$$

Here p_A^0 and p_B^0 refer to pure condensed phases of the A and B species, respectively.

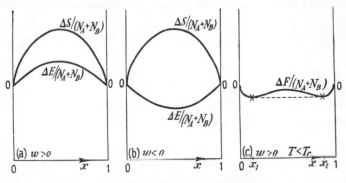

Fig. 44.

It is left to the reader to show that the equations (16) imply everywhere positive deviations from Raoult's law if $w > 0$, and negative deviations from Raoult's law if $w < 0$.

Straightforward differentiation now gives

$$\frac{\partial p_A}{\partial x} = \frac{p_A}{x}\frac{2zw}{kT}\left(\frac{kT}{2zw} - x(1-x)\right)$$

$$= \frac{p_A}{x}\frac{2zw}{kT}\left\{\frac{kT}{2zw} - \frac{1}{4} + \left(x - \frac{1}{2}\right)^2\right\} \qquad (17)$$

so that the equation $\partial p_A/\partial x = 0$ has two roots, symmetrical with respect to $x = \frac{1}{2}$, provided that

$$\frac{kT}{2zw} < \frac{1}{4}, \quad \text{i.e. provided that} \quad kT < \frac{zw}{2}.$$

It follows thermodynamically (see Appendix V) that separation into two phases, differing in concentration, will occur at temperatures below a temperature of critical mixing given by

$$kT_c = \tfrac{1}{2}zw. \tag{18}$$

Thus, in outline, we have derived the properties of the partition function based on Bragg and Williams's approximation. In particular, positive and negative w (heats of mixing) imply positive and negative deviations, respectively, from Raoult's law; and there is a temperature of critical mixing given by equation (18). To some extent we have certainly extended the perfect-solution model to take account of a possible heat of mixing, but it may be doubted whether equations (16) and (18) more than very qualitatively describe attributes of a regular solution defined by the partition function (11). For equation (14) shows that although we allow for a possible heat of mixing, nevertheless we assume that the A and B systems still undergo completely random mixing (either in the whole assembly if there is no phase separation, or in each separate phase if there is). Indeed, we have assumed that *all* arrangements of the systems correspond to the *same* configurational energy, $w\overset{\ominus}{N}_{AB}$. But this is in contradiction with equation (11), according to which some configurations will be energetically much more favourable, and so more probable, than others. In fact, according to equation (11), the entropy of mixing for a regular solution will depend on the temperature. A better approximation to the partition function (11) is, therefore, required if the resulting thermodynamical equations are to do justice to the mechanical model underlying our concept of a regular solution.

5. At this point it is convenient to digress and consider the exact treatment of a one-dimensional array. This was first given by Ising (1925) in connexion with an analogous problem in the theory of ferromagnetism.

We require the number of arrangements of N_A A-systems and N_B B-systems, in a straight line, for which there are N_{AB} AB (or BA) 'links', or pairs of neighbours. We shall assume (justifiably) that N_A and N_B are so large that we can neglect 'end' effects.

Then, since each unbroken succession of A-systems begins and ends with an AB link, in any such arrangement the N_A A-systems are divided into $N_{AB}/2$ groups, each containing at least one system (see Fig. 45).

Let the left-hand member of each A-group be marked with a star. Then the division of the A's into groups is entirely specified

Fig. 45.

by the placing of $N_{AB}/2$ stars on $N_{AB}/2$ of the N_A A-systems. This can be done in

$$\frac{N_A!}{\left(\dfrac{N_{AB}}{2}\right)!\left(N_A-\dfrac{N_{AB}}{2}\right)!}$$

ways.

Similarly, let the right-hand member of each B-group be marked with a star. This completely specifies the B-groups, which can, therefore, be specified in

$$\frac{N_B!}{\left(\dfrac{N_{AB}}{2}\right)!\left(N_B-\dfrac{N_{AB}}{2}\right)!}$$

ways.

If now we arrange that the ith A^*-system immediately follows the ith B^*-system, then we have uniquely specified the arrangement of the A's and B's in a straight line. For given N_{AB}, therefore, the number of such arrangements is

$$\frac{N_A!}{\left(\dfrac{N_{AB}}{2}\right)!\left(N_A-\dfrac{N_{AB}}{2}\right)!}\frac{N_B!}{\left(\dfrac{N_{AB}}{2}\right)!\left(N_B-\dfrac{N_{AB}}{2}\right)!}. \qquad (19)$$

(Actually twice this would be more precise, since we could equally well suppose that the ith B-group immediately followed the ith

A-group. But a numerical factor of this kind is entirely unimportant.) Consequently,

$$(\text{P.F.})_{\text{config}} = \frac{N_A! \, N_B!}{(N_A - \tfrac{1}{2}N_{AB})! (N_B - \tfrac{1}{2}N_{AB})! \left[\left(\dfrac{N_{AB}}{2} \right)! \right]^2} e^{-N_{AB} w / kT}. \quad (20)$$

We can now proceed to pick out the greatest term in the sum on the r.h.s. of (20). But, since the corresponding (G.P.F.) can be evaluated explicitly, it is more elegant to use the grand partition function method. Strictly there is no such thing as (G.P.F.)$_{\text{config}}$, and so we must return to the full expression for (P.F.) which, by (20), is

$$(\text{P.F.}) = \sum_{(X)} \frac{N_A!}{X!(N_A - X)!} \frac{N_B!}{X!(N_B - X)!} f_A^{N_A} f_B^{N_B} e^{-E_A^c/kT} e^{-E_B^c/kT} y^{2X},$$

where $X = \tfrac{1}{2} N_{AB}$ and $y = e^{-w/kT}$. Then, since

$$E_A^c = w_{AA} N_A \quad \text{and} \quad E_B^c = w_{BB} N_B \quad (z = 2)$$

we have

$$(\text{G.P.F.}) = \sum_{(N_A, N_B, X)} \frac{N_A!}{X!(N_A - X)!} \frac{N_B!}{X!(N_B - X)!} \times$$
$$\times y^{2X} (f_A e^{-w_{AA}/kT})^{N_A} (f_B e^{-w_{BB}/kT})^{N_B} \lambda_A^{N_A} \lambda_B^{N_B}$$
$$= \sum_{(N_A, N_B, X)} \frac{N_A!}{X!(N_A - X)!} \frac{N_B!}{X!(N_B - X)!} y^{2X} \boldsymbol{\lambda}_A^{N_A} \boldsymbol{\lambda}_B^{N_B}, \quad (21)$$

where $\boldsymbol{\lambda}_A = f_A e^{-w_{AA}/kT} \lambda_A$ and $\boldsymbol{\lambda}_B = f_B e^{-w_{BB}/kT} \lambda_B$. Therefore,

$$(\text{G.P.F.}) = \sum_{(X)} y^{2X} \boldsymbol{\lambda}_A^X \boldsymbol{\lambda}_B^X \sum_{(N_A)} \frac{N_A!}{X!(N_A - X)!} \boldsymbol{\lambda}_A^{N_A - X} \times$$
$$\times \sum_{(N_B)} \frac{N_B!}{X!(N_B - X)!} \boldsymbol{\lambda}_B^{N_B - X}$$
$$= \sum_{(X)} y^{2X} \boldsymbol{\lambda}_A^X \boldsymbol{\lambda}_B^X (1 - \boldsymbol{\lambda}_A)^{-(X+1)} (1 - \boldsymbol{\lambda}_B)^{-(X+1)}$$

(by the binomial theorem, see Appendix II, § c)

$$= \frac{1}{(1 - \boldsymbol{\lambda}_A)(1 - \boldsymbol{\lambda}_B)} \sum_{(X)} \left\{ \frac{\boldsymbol{\lambda}_A \boldsymbol{\lambda}_B y^2}{(1 - \boldsymbol{\lambda}_A)(1 - \boldsymbol{\lambda}_B)} \right\}^X$$
$$= \frac{1}{(1 - \boldsymbol{\lambda}_A)(1 - \boldsymbol{\lambda}_B) \left\{ 1 - \dfrac{\boldsymbol{\lambda}_A \boldsymbol{\lambda}_B y^2}{(1 - \boldsymbol{\lambda}_A)(1 - \boldsymbol{\lambda}_B)} \right\}},$$

i.e.
$$(\text{G.P.F.}) = \frac{1}{(1-\lambda_A)(1-\lambda_B)-\lambda_A\lambda_B y^2}. \tag{22}$$

This surprisingly simple and striking result can be generalized to include more than two species; but our present purpose is to deduce the thermodynamic properties of the assembly. Since, at constant temperature,

$$\lambda_A\frac{\partial}{\partial\lambda_A} = \lambda_A\frac{\partial}{\partial\lambda_A} \quad \text{and} \quad \lambda_B\frac{\partial}{\partial\lambda_B} = \lambda_B\frac{\partial}{\partial\lambda_B},$$

we have†

$$\overline{N}_A = -\lambda_A\frac{\partial}{\partial\lambda_A}\ln[(1-\lambda_A)(1-\lambda_B)-\lambda_A\lambda_B y^2],$$

i.e.
$$\left.\begin{aligned}\overline{N}_A &= \frac{\lambda_A(1-\lambda_B)+\lambda_A\lambda_B y^2}{(1-\lambda_A)(1-\lambda_B)-\lambda_A\lambda_B y^2}\\[2mm] \overline{N}_B &= \frac{\lambda_B(1-\lambda_A)+\lambda_A\lambda_B y^2}{(1-\lambda_A)(1-\lambda_B)-\lambda_A\lambda_B y^2}\end{aligned}\right\}. \tag{23}$$
and

Moreover, from (21) (see end of § 3, Chapter XVII),

$$2\overline{X} = \overline{N}_{AB} = y\frac{\partial}{\partial y}\ln(\text{G.P.F.}),$$

whence, from (22),

$$\overline{N}_{AB} = \frac{2\lambda_A\lambda_B y^2}{(1-\lambda_A)(1-\lambda_B)-\lambda_A\lambda_B y^2}. \tag{24}$$

But, from equations (6),

$$\left.\begin{aligned}\overline{N}_A &= \overline{N}_{AA}+\tfrac{1}{2}\overline{N}_{AB}\\ \overline{N}_B &= \overline{N}_{BB}+\tfrac{1}{2}\overline{N}_{AB}\end{aligned}\right\}. \tag{25}$$
and

Therefore, from (23) and (24),

$$\left.\begin{aligned}\overline{N}_{AA} &= \frac{\lambda_A(1-\lambda_B)}{(1-\lambda_A)(1-\lambda_B)-\lambda_A\lambda_B y^2}\\[2mm] \overline{N}_{BB} &= \frac{\lambda_B(1-\lambda_A)}{(1-\lambda_A)(1-\lambda_B)-\lambda_A\lambda_B y^2}\end{aligned}\right\} \tag{26}$$

and from (24) and (26) we obtain

$$\frac{\overline{N}_{AA}\,\overline{N}_{BB}}{(\overline{N}_{AB})^2} = \frac{(1-\lambda_A)(1-\lambda_B)}{4\lambda_A\lambda_B}y^{-4}. \tag{27}$$

† It is convenient to use $\overline{N}_A$ and $\overline{N}_B$, rather than N_A and N_B, to denote the equilibrium values of N_A and N_B.

But if we are dealing with a macroscopic thermodynamical assembly, $\overline{N}_A$ and $\overline{N}_B$ must be very large quantities. Therefore the denominator in (24) and (26) must (effectively) vanish, i.e. the assembly must satisfy the 'equation of state'

$$(1-\lambda_A)(1-\lambda_B) = \lambda_A \lambda_B y^2 \qquad (28)$$

(cf. discussion of Raoult's law in Chapter XVII). Equation (27) therefore becomes

$$\frac{\overline{N}_{AA}\,\overline{N}_{BB}}{(\overline{N}_{AB})^2} = \tfrac{1}{4}y^{-2}$$

i.e.
$$\frac{\overline{N}_{AA}\,\overline{N}_{BB}}{(\overline{N}_{AB})^2} = \tfrac{1}{4}e^{2w/kT}. \qquad (29)$$

With equation (29) we shall close the present discussion of this rather artificial one-dimensional problem. But this final equation is of considerable interest. It may be compared with the analogous equation derived from Bragg and Williams's approximation. Writing (see (25))

$$\overset{\ominus}{N}_{AA} = N_A - \tfrac{1}{2}\overset{\ominus}{N}_{AB} \quad \text{and} \quad \overset{\ominus}{N}_{BB} = N_B - \tfrac{1}{2}\overset{\ominus}{N}_{AB},$$

equation (13′) becomes

$$\frac{\overset{\ominus}{N}_{AA}\,\overset{\ominus}{N}_{BB}}{(\overset{\ominus}{N}_{AB})^2} = \frac{1}{4} \qquad (30)$$

—which clearly makes sense, since $\overset{\ominus}{N}_{AB}$ is the true average value of N_{AB} when $w = 0$. Thus, for the one dimensional problem with which we have been concerned in this section, equation (30), which epitomizes the Bragg and Williams approximation, is false in so far as it replaces by unity the factor $e^{2w/kT}$ on the r.h.s. of equation (29).

6. We are now in a position to appreciate an important approximate treatment of the real, three-dimensional,† regular-solution problem: it is due, chiefly, to Guggenheim. Guggenheim suggested, in effect, that equation (29) should form the basis of an approximate treatment of three-dimensional regular solutions: at any rate

† The two-dimensional problem is also 'real' in the theory of adsorption.

equation (29) should be preferable to equation (30), which under-lies the Bragg and Williams approximation.

Historically, this suggestion was made not by analogy with the correct solution of the corresponding one-dimensional problem but by analogy with the law of mass action for the reaction

$$AA + BB \rightarrow 2AB$$

in a gas phase, i.e. with the equation

$$\frac{N_{AA} N_{BB}}{(N_{AB})^2} = \frac{(\text{p.f.})_{AA}(\text{p.f.})_{BB}}{(\text{p.f.})^2_{AB}}. \tag{31}$$

And the analogy between (29) and (31) is very close: for if we destroy an AA and a BB pair of neighbours to form two AB pairs, then we increase the internal energy of the assembly by the amount $2w$; while with the AA link, and the BB link, there is associated a symmetry factor of 2 compared with an unsym-metrical AB link. For this reason Guggenheim refers to equation (29) as an equation of *quasi-chemical equilibrium*.

Dropping the unnecessary bars, we shall now show that the equations

$$\frac{N_{AA} N_{BB}}{(N_{AB})^2} = \tfrac{1}{4}e^{2w/kT}, \tag{29}$$

$$2N_{AA} + N_{AB} = zN_A,$$
$$2N_{BB} + N_{AB} = zN_B, \tag{6}$$

and, of course, $\qquad\qquad \Delta E = N_{AB}w \tag{32}$

suffice to determine the thermodynamic properties of the solution.

We start by calculating ΔE as a function of the temperature, T, and the mole fraction $x \ (= N_A/(N_A + N_B))$.

It is convenient to denote the quantity $\dfrac{(1/z)N_{AB}}{(N_A + N_B)}$ by the symbol ξ.

On account of the equations (6), equation (29) can then be written as $\qquad (x - \xi)(1 - x - \xi) = \xi^2 e^{2w/kT},$

whence, solving this quadratic for ξ, we obtain

$$\xi = \frac{-1 \pm \sqrt{\{4x(1-x)(e^{2w/kT} - 1) + 1\}}}{2(e^{2w/kT} - 1)}. \tag{33}$$

Now, on account of its physical meaning, we need $0 \leqslant \xi \leqslant \frac{1}{2}$: and this restricts us to the plus sign before the square root in (33).†
Consequently, by (32),

$$\frac{\Delta E}{N_A + N_B} = zw \frac{\sqrt{\{4x(1-x)(e^{2w/kT}-1)+1\}}-1}{2(e^{2w/kT}-1)}. \tag{34}$$

Having thus obtained ΔE as a function of x and T, we must next obtain ΔF as a function of x and T by integrating the Gibbs–Helmholtz equation, i.e. from the equation

$$\Delta F = -T \int^T \frac{\Delta E}{T^2} dT + \text{constant } T. \tag{35}$$

Substituting from (34) into (35), we have

$$\frac{\Delta F}{N_A + N_B} = -\frac{zwT}{2} \int^T \frac{\sqrt{\{4x(1-x)(e^{2w/kT}-1)+1\}}-1}{T^2(e^{2w/kT}-1)} dT + \text{constant } T, \tag{36}$$

and to integrate (36) it is convenient to put

$$4x(1-x)(e^{2w/kT}-1)+1 = t^2,$$

i.e.

$$4x(1-x)e^{2w/kT}\left(\frac{-2w}{k}\right)\frac{dT}{T^2} = 2t\, dt.$$

This gives

$$\frac{\Delta F}{N_A + N_B} = -\frac{zwT}{2} \int^t (t-1)\frac{4x(1-x)}{t^2-1}\left(\frac{-k}{w}\right)\frac{t\,dt}{t^2-1+4x(1-x)} +$$
$$+ \text{constant } T,$$

i.e.

$$\frac{\Delta F}{N_A + N_B} = \frac{zkT}{2} \int^t \frac{4x(1-x)t\,dt}{(t+1)[t-\sqrt{\{1-4x(1-x)\}}][t+\sqrt{\{1-4x(1-x)\}}]} +$$
$$+ \text{constant } T$$

$$= \frac{zkT}{2} \int^t \left[\frac{-1}{t+1} + \frac{\dfrac{4x(1-x)}{2[1+\sqrt{\{1-4x(1-x)\}}]}}{t-\sqrt{\{1-4x(1-x)\}}} + \right.$$
$$\left. + \frac{\dfrac{4x(1-x)}{2[1-\sqrt{\{1-4x(1-x)\}}]}}{t+\sqrt{\{1-4x(1-x)\}}} \right] dt + \text{constant } T. \tag{37}$$

† This is true whether $e^{2w/kT} > 1$ or < 1, i.e. whether $w > 0$ or < 0.

(Here we have used the partial fraction identity

$$\frac{u}{(u-a)(u-b)(u-c)}$$
$$= \frac{a(a-b)^{-1}(a-c)^{-1}}{(u-a)} + \frac{b(b-a)^{-1}(b-c)^{-1}}{(u-b)} + \frac{c(c-a)^{-1}(c-b)^{-1}}{(u-c)}$$

to express the integrand as the sum of three terms each of which is the differential coefficient of a simple logarithmic function of t.)
Thence, from (37),

$$\frac{\Delta F}{N_A + N_B} = \frac{zkT}{4} \left\{ \frac{4x(1-x)}{1+\sqrt{\{1-4x(1-x)\}}} \ln[t-\sqrt{\{1-4x(1-x)\}}] + \right.$$
$$\left. + \frac{4x(1-x)}{1-\sqrt{\{1-4x(1-x)\}}} \ln[t+\sqrt{\{1-4x(1-x)\}}] - 2\ln(t+1) \right\} +$$
$$+ \text{constant } T. \quad (38)$$

At this point it is convenient (but see below) to assume $N_A > N_B$. Then

$$\frac{4x(1-x)}{1+\sqrt{\{1-4x(1-x)\}}} = \frac{2N_B}{N_A+N_B}$$

and
$$\frac{4x(1-x)}{1-\sqrt{\{1-4x(1-x)\}}} = \frac{2N_A}{N_A+N_B}$$

and (38) becomes

$$\frac{\Delta F}{kT} = N_A \tfrac{1}{2} z \Big[\ln(\sqrt{\{4N_A N_B e^{2w/kT} + (N_A-N_B)^2\}} + N_A - N_B) -$$
$$- \ln(\sqrt{\{4N_A N_B e^{2w/kT} + (N_A-N_B)^2\}} + N_A + N_B) \Big] +$$
$$+ N_B \tfrac{1}{2} z \Big[\ln(\sqrt{\{4N_A N_B e^{2w/kT} + (N_A-N_B)^2\}} - N_A + N_B) -$$
$$- \ln(\sqrt{\{4N_A N_B e^{2w/kT} + (N_A-N_B)^2\}} + N_A + N_B) \Big] +$$
$$+ \text{constant}. \quad (39)$$

Our next task is to determine the 'constant' in equation (39); but before proceeding further the reader should verify that equation (38) again produces equation (39) on the assumption that $N_B > N_A$.

To fix the constant in (39) we observe that, since this constant is independent of T, we can find it provided that we know the value of ΔF for some particular temperature. Now the simplest temperature to take is a very large temperature, for which w/kT

can be ignored: for in this case we have random mixing and ΔF is given by

$$\frac{\Delta F}{kT} = -\ln\frac{(N_A+N_B)!}{N_A!\,N_B!} = N_A\ln\frac{N_A}{N_A+N_B}+N_B\ln\frac{N_B}{N_A+N_B}. \quad (40)$$

And when w/kT can be ignored, (39) becomes

$$\frac{\Delta F}{kT} = N_A\tfrac{1}{2}z\{\ln 2N_A-\ln 2(N_A+N_B)\}+$$
$$+N_B\tfrac{1}{2}z\{\ln 2N_B-\ln 2(N_A+N_B)\}+\text{constant.} \quad (41)$$

Equating the r.h.s.'s of (40) and (41), we thus find

$$\text{constant} = -N_A\frac{z-2}{2}\ln\frac{N_A}{N_A+N_B}-N_B\frac{z-2}{2}\ln\frac{N_B}{N_A+N_B}.$$

Thus, finally, Guggenheim's equation of quasi-chemical equilibrium yields

$$\frac{\Delta F}{kT} = N_A\tfrac{1}{2}z\Big[\ln(\sqrt{\{4N_AN_B\,e^{2w/kT}+(N_A-N_B)^2\}}+N_A-N_B)-$$
$$-\ln(\sqrt{\{4N_AN_B\,e^{2w/kT}+(N_A-N_B)^2\}}+N_A+N_B)-$$
$$-\frac{z-2}{z}\ln\frac{N_A}{N_A+N_B}\Big]+$$
$$+N_B\tfrac{1}{2}z\Big[\ln(\sqrt{\{4N_AN_B\,e^{2w/kT}+(N_A-N_B)^2\}}-N_A+N_B)-$$
$$-\ln(\sqrt{\{4N_AN_B\,e^{2w/kT}+(N_A-N_B)^2\}}+N_A+N_B)-$$
$$-\frac{z-2}{z}\ln\frac{N_B}{N_A+N_B}\Big]. \quad (42)$$

And from equation (42) all further thermodynamic properties of the assembly can at once be deduced.

7. The equations

$$kT\ln\frac{p_A}{p_A^0} = \mu_A-\mu_A^0 = \left(\frac{\partial\Delta F}{\partial N_A}\right)_{N_B}$$

and

$$kT\ln\frac{p_B}{p_B^0} = \mu_B-\mu_B^0 = \left(\frac{\partial\Delta F}{\partial N_B}\right)_{N_A}$$

give (as can be verified without difficulty)

$$\ln\frac{p_A}{p_A^0} = \tfrac{1}{2}z(\text{first quantity in [ ] in (42)})$$

and

$$\ln\frac{p_B}{p_B^0} = \tfrac{1}{2}z(\text{second quantity in [ ] in (42)}).$$

Thus, in terms of the mole fraction, x,

$$\ln\frac{p_A}{p_A^0} = \tfrac{1}{2}z\left[\ln(\sqrt{\{4x(1-x)e^{2w/kT}+(2x-1)^2\}}+2x-1)- \\ -\ln(\sqrt{\{4x(1-x)e^{2w/kT}+(2x-1)^2\}}+1)-\frac{z-2}{z}\ln x\right]$$

and

$$\ln\frac{p_B}{p_B^0} = \tfrac{1}{2}z\left[\ln(\sqrt{\{4x(1-x)e^{2w/kT}+(2x-1)^2\}}-2x+1)- \\ -\ln(\sqrt{\{4x(1-x)e^{2w/kT}+(2x-1)^2\}}+1)-\frac{z-2}{z}\ln(1-x)\right]$$

$$\left.\vphantom{\begin{array}{c}a\\a\\a\\a\end{array}}\right\},\quad (43)$$

from which it can be proved that, just as in the case of the Bragg and Williams approximation, positive w implies everywhere positive deviations from Raoult's law and negative w implies everywhere negative deviations from Raoult's law.

In paragraph 4 above, we saw that the Bragg and Williams approximation predicted the occurrence, when $w > 0$, of phase-separation at temperatures below a certain critical mixing temperature, T_c. Examining the present approximation for the same possibility, we find, by straightforward differentiation (followed by an algebraic factorization) that $\partial p_A/\partial x$ vanishes if and only if†

$$\sqrt{\{4x(1-x)e^{2w/kT}+(2x-1)^2\}} = \frac{z}{z-2}. \qquad (44)$$

Now equation (44) implies

$$(2x-1)^2(1-e^{2w/kT})+e^{2w/kT} = \left(\frac{z}{z-2}\right)^2,$$

i.e.

$$(2x-1)^2 = \frac{\{z/(z-2)\}^2-e^{2w/kT}}{1-e^{2w/kT}}. \qquad (44')$$

The l.h.s. of (44′) always lies between 0 and 1: but we must discuss separately the two cases, $w < 0$ and $w > 0$.

Case (i), $w < 0$. $e^{2w/kT} < 1$.

Then (44′) can be satisfied (for some x) provided

$$0 < \frac{\{z/(z-2)\}^2-e^{2w/kT}}{1-e^{2w/kT}} < 1.$$

But this is impossible, since the numerator of this fraction is

---

† The same is true, of course, of $\partial p_B/\partial x$.

necessarily greater than the denominator. Consequently $\partial p_A/\partial x$ does not vanish for any x (at any temperature), and phase-separation does not occur.

Case (ii), $w > 0$. $e^{2w/kT} > 1$.

Then (44') can be satisfied (for some x) provided

$$0 < \frac{e^{2w/kT} - \{z/(z-2)\}^2}{e^{2w/kT} - 1} < 1,$$

i.e. provided

$$e^{2w/kT} > \left(\frac{z}{z-2}\right)^2,$$

i.e.

$$\frac{w}{kT} > \ln\frac{z}{z-2}. \tag{45}$$

Consequently, if $T < T_c$, where T_c is given by

$$kT_c = w\Big/\ln\frac{z}{z-2}, \tag{46}$$

then phase-separation occurs at some concentration.

Actually for $T = T_c$, $\partial p_A/\partial x = 0$ (twice) at $x = \frac{1}{2}$: so a solution with composition $x = \frac{1}{2}$ will separate into two phases whose compositions differ progressively from $x = \frac{1}{2}$ as the temperature is reduced below T_c. A solution with initial composition $x \neq \frac{1}{2}$ will start to separate into two phases when $T = T_c(x) < T_c$. We shall not here attempt to evaluate $T_c(x)$: this requires graphical methods, and is best done by plotting the isothermals (42)—see Fig. 44(c) and Appendix V.

Here we must leave the discussion of the approximate treatment of a regular solution based on Guggenheim's equation of quasi-chemical equilibrium. Qualitatively the partial vapour-pressure curves so calculated are not unlike those derived from the Bragg and Williams approximation, though there are quantitative differences as is, of course, evidenced by the difference between equations (18) and (46) for the critical mixing temperature.

Of the two approximations this second one is certainly the better: it gives a temperature-dependent entropy of mixing and, moreover, provides the exact solution in the (artificial) one-dimensional case: which the Bragg and Williams approximation does not. And here we should observe that according to equation (46) there is no finite critical temperature when $z = 2$: a result emphasized by Ising in connexion with the analogous ferromagnetic problem.

Nevertheless, it is only an approximate treatment of the underlying regular solution problem. Kirkwood, indeed, has shown that for plane square $(z = 4)$ or simple cubic $(z = 6)$ lattices, the expansion in ascending powers of w/kT of the r.h.s. of equation (42) agrees with the strict requirements of equation (9) up to and including† the terms in $(w/kT)^3$, but not further. Moreover the recent work by Wannier and Onsager, though incomplete, strongly suggests that for a plane square lattice $(z = 4)$ the critical temperature, T_c, is given correctly by the equation

$$\sinh\frac{w}{kT_c} = 1. \tag{47}$$

Comparing, for $z = 4$, the predictions of the three equations (18), (42), and (47), we have

$$\frac{w}{kT_c} = 0\!\cdot\!50 \quad \text{(Bragg and Williams)},$$

$$\frac{w}{kT_c} = 0\!\cdot\!69 \quad \text{(Guggenheim)},$$

$$\frac{w}{kT_c} = 0\!\cdot\!88 \quad \text{(correct)}.$$

The comparison probably gives a fair indication of the relative validities of the two approximations which we have discussed in the present chapter.

Finally, it should be noted that equation (9) necessarily implies that ΔF, as a function of x, is symmetrical about $x = \frac{1}{2}$. This important feature of the regular solution model has been preserved in both of the above approximate treatments.

8. So far in this chapter we have dealt only with attempts to relax the first of the two physical assumptions underlying the concept of a perfect solution—assumption (a) of paragraph 1 above. Any relaxation of the second of these assumptions, (b) above, so as to allow solvent and solute species to differ markedly

† This refers to $\Delta F/kT$.

in size or shape, gives rise to statistical problems even more formidable than those with which we have been here concerned. It is possible within the scope of this book only to indicate very qualitatively the nature of some of the obstacles encountered, and one or two of the conclusions apparently established, in this important, but decidedly difficult, field.

Practically all the truly statistical, as distinct from thermodynamical, work so far attempted has been based on the assumption that the spacial configurations of the solvent and solute species may be enumerated against the background of a quasi-crystalline structure in the condensed phase, i.e. assuming at least a definite coordination number in the condensed phase. The simplest problem would then seem to be that of a binary solution, with no heat of mixing, in which one species is just twice the size of the other: i.e. in which each solute system, say, occupies two neighbouring lattice-sites compared with a solvent system, which occupies just one lattice-site. All the permissible configurations having the same energy, the problem is then only the combinatorial one of enumerating the number, $g(N_{AA}, N_B)$, of arrangements of N_{AA} AA-systems† and N_B B-systems on a lattice of $2N_{AA} + N_B$ sites, having coordination-number z.

However, no exact mathematical expression for $g(N_{AA}, N_B)$ is known, and so even in this simplest problem approximate methods must be used. We shall not enter into these approximations here, but merely assert that several independent lines of attack all lead to the same conclusion, namely that the partial vapour-pressure curves for such a solution will show everywhere *small negative deviations* from Raoult's law. And if the solute species occupy three or four neighbouring lattice-sites, instead of just two, and again there is no heat of mixing, then the small negative deviations from Raoult's law would seem to be rather larger than in the case of the double- and single-molecule problem.

If the problem for zero heat of mixing can be regarded as solved, then some account can be taken of interaction-energies, i.e. of a non-zero heat of mixing, by an extension of the quasi-chemical

---

† AA emphasizes that each such system occupies two sites: but the notation has no further molecular significance.

equilibrium method already discussed in this chapter. The reader is referred, in this connexion, to a recent paper by Guggenheim, listed in the bibliography (Appendix VII).

Perhaps the most important solutions of physical chemistry, however, in which solvent and solute molecules differ markedly in size, are solutions of polymers in simple solvents. If the polymer molecules are flexible as is often, indeed usually, the case, then an additional difficulty is introduced into the statistical theory. For even if there is only *one* solute molecule, i.e. just one polymer molecule surrounded by solvent molecules, we do not now know the number of possible configurations of this limitingly dilute solution. At first sight we may be tempted to say that if the polymer consists of n sub-species, or monomer units, then the number of such configurations when one end of the polymer is kept fixed is simply $z(z-1)^{n-2}$: for there are apparently z ways of laying down the first link and then $(z-1)$ ways of laying down each succeeding link. But this ignores the fact that many of the configurations so enumerated must be ruled out since they imply that more than one unit of the polymer can occupy the same position in the quasi-lattice structure. It is this ability of a long flexible molecule to 'get in its own way' which so complicates the statistical theory of polymer solutions. Nor is this self-obstruction unimportant: indeed the late W. J. C. Orr, responsible for some of the best work on these problems, has shown that excluding these forbidden configurations may reduce the corresponding entropy by as much as 10 or 20 per cent. But for further details the reader must be referred to the original papers: since these have not yet been summarized in standard treatises a short list of appropriate references is given in the bibliography (Appendix VII).

EXAMPLES

1. In the problem of immobile adsorption, let there be an interaction energy, $-w$, between each pair of adsorbed atoms. ($w > 0$ corresponds to attraction between the adsorbed systems.) Show that the Bragg and Williams approximation leads to

$$(\text{P.F.})_a = \frac{M_s!}{M!(M_s-M)!}\,(\text{p.f.})_a^M\,e^{zwM^2/2M_s kT},$$

whence the adsorption isotherms are given by

$$P = \frac{\theta}{1-\theta} e^{-zw\theta/kT} \frac{kT \, g(T)}{(\text{p.f.})_a}$$

where $g(T) = (\text{p.f.})_g / V$.   (Fowler's adsorption isotherms.)

2. Show that, when $w > 0$, Fowler's isotherms predict critical conditions below a critical adsorption temperature given by $kT_c = zw/4$: and that when $w < 0$ there are no such critical conditions.   (Consider $(\partial \ln P / \partial \theta)_T$.)

3. Show that the partial vapour-pressures given by equations (43) satisfy the Duhem–Margules equation.   (Equation (22), Chapter XIV.)

4. Prove that the quasi-chemical approximation is equivalent to assuming that $g(N_A, N_B, N_{AB})$ is given by

$$\left[\frac{N_A! \, N_B!}{\left(N_A - \dfrac{N_{AB}}{z}\right)! \left(N_B - \dfrac{N_{AB}}{z}\right)! \left(\dfrac{N_{AB}}{z}!\right)^2} \right]^{z/2} \left[\frac{(N_A + N_B)!}{N_A! \, N_B!} \right]^{1-z/2}. \quad \text{(Chang.)}$$

STATISTICAL MECHANICS, THERMODYNAMICS, AND PHYSICAL MODELS

1. OUR introductory survey of the methods of statistical mechanics is now practically complete. In this final chapter we shall attempt, very briefly, to set the two disciplines of statistical mechanics and thermodynamics in their proper mutual perspective. Anything like a complete discussion of the foundations of statistical mechanics is certainly outside our present scope, but it is hoped that these final paragraphs may serve as some introduction, however inadequate, to the fuller treatments to be found in standard treatises (see Bibliography†). For this reason we shall proceed to introduce one or two technical terms which have, hitherto, been avoided.

In the previous chapters we have recognized three alternative statistical methods, summarized in the equations

$$S(E, V, N) = k \ln \Omega, \qquad \text{where} \qquad \Omega = \Omega(E, V, N) \qquad \text{(I)}$$

$$F(T, V, N) = -kT \ln(\text{P.F.}), \text{where} \quad (\text{P.F.}) = \sum_i \Omega_i e^{-E_i/kT} \qquad \text{(II)}$$

$$PV(T, V, \lambda) = kT \ln(\text{G.P.F.}), \text{where (G.P.F.)} = \sum_{(E,N)} \Omega e^{-E/kT} \lambda^N. \text{(III)}$$

In using all three methods, Ω is to be evaluated on the basis of the hypothesis (b) of Chapter II (or its classical counterpart); and in all three methods internal distribution functions for the assembly are derived on the assumption (see hypothesis (b) of Chapter II, §1 of Chapter XV and §3 of Chapter XVII) that any term in Ω, (P.F.) or (G.P.F.) is proportional to the probability of occurrence of the corresponding state, or condition, of the assembly concerned.

The three methods, (I), (II), and (III), are said, in statistical terminology, to be based on the concepts of the *micro-canonical ensemble*,‡ *canonical ensemble*, and *grand-canonical ensemble*,

† In this connexion the reader is especially referred to Tolman's magnificent book, *The Principles of Statistical Mechanics*.

‡ Sometimes called *petit ensemble*.

respectively, of Willard Gibbs. But we shall not examine these concepts further here.

In the first of these methods, and sometimes also in the second, we had generally to proceed by picking out the greatest of a large number of terms, each corresponding to a large number of distinct states of the assembly, but only the greatest of them contributing appreciably to Ω, or (P.F.). Normally this was entirely justifiable mathematically, but for an assembly of non-localized systems that we obtain the right result for Ω in this way is entirely fortuitous, since in deriving the result we use Stirling's theorem to handle $\sum \ln n_i!$ and then find that n_i^* is a very small number—strictly 0 or 1, but since we have treated n_i as a continuous variable we actually obtain a very small fraction (see paragraph 3, Chapter III). Historically, this difficulty was first successfully avoided by Darwin and Fowler. The Darwin–Fowler method is based on the micro-canonical ensemble, i.e. on Ω, but rests on the fact that Ω is itself

$$\text{the coefficient of } x^E y^N \text{ in } \sum_{(E,N)} \Omega(E, V, N) x^E y^N,$$

and we have already seen that this sum, which is simply the grand partition function with x in place of $e^{-1/kT}$ and y in place of λ, can generally be evaluated in closed† algebraic form—in fact for a perfect gas the sum is simply $\exp\left[y \sum_i \omega_i x^{\epsilon_i}\right]$. This coefficient can then be evaluated, asymptotically for large E and N, by a perfectly valid analytic method, the so-called *method of steepest descents*; but since this entails complex variable analysis we cannot pursue the matter further. The results obtained are identical with those with which we are already familiar.

The Darwin–Fowler method is of great elegance, but ceases to be necessary if we adopt the grand partition function approach. And the grand partition function method is certainly valid, whatever the statistics, for thermodynamical assemblies.

2. Application of these statistical methods to particular assemblies, either simple or composite, has frequently yielded results

† Certain summations, analogous to partition functions (p.f.), do remain but cause no trouble.

which might have been predicted thermodynamically but actually came directly out of the statistical treatment. For instance, the fact that systems which can be found in several different phases possess, for the equilibrium state of the composite assembly concerned, the same chemical potential in each phase was discovered by applying method (I) to determine the internal distribution of the systems among the various phases in which they could occur (see Chapter XIII). This at once raises the question of how much thermodynamics need be assumed to supplement the equations of statistical mechanics. And the strict answer is, *none*.

Throughout the past chapters we have looked upon statistical mechanics as a bridge, or set of bridges, between mechanics and thermodynamics, and we have consciously built these bridges 'from both ends'. But the hypothesis (b) of Chapter II, amplified to the extent of explicitly stating (see Chapter V) that physical measurements give average or 'equilibrium' values of internal distribution functions, is a sufficient basis not only for specifically statistical results but also for all the equations of equilibrium thermodynamics.

Thus, underlying method (I) is the assumption that

the measurable properties of any assembly, for which E, V, and N are 'given', are found by averaging over all distinct, accessible,†
complexions (quantum mechanically, stationary states; classically,
descriptions in phase space) of the assembly 'without fear or
favour'.   (a).

The total number of these complexions, $\Omega(E, V, N)$, has the property that if we write‡

$$d \ln \Omega = -\beta \, dE + \gamma \, dV - \alpha \, dN \qquad (1)$$

then β is the same for all assemblies which can interchange energy and α is the same for all assemblies which can interchange systems.§ It can similarly be shown that if two assemblies are separated by a partition, through which they can exchange energy and which is itself capable of movement, then this partition will adjust itself

---

† For the significance of the qualification 'accessible' see Chapter VII, § 6 and Chapter IX, § 4.

‡ Notation chosen to conform with usage earlier in the book.

§ For brevity, the argument is outlined for one-component assemblies only.

so that γ is the same for both the assemblies. Such arguments allow us to conclude that equation (1) is merely another form, *using different symbols*, of the well-known *thermodynamical* equation

$$dS = \frac{1}{T} dE + \frac{P}{T} dV - \frac{\mu}{T} dN. \tag{2}$$

Comparison of the equations (1) and (2) merely enables us to give to the symbols Ω, α, β, γ names such as entropy, temperature, etc., with which we are already familiar: it does not add anything more to the content of equation (1).

Analogous arguments apply also to the methods (II) and (III). And it can further be shown that the three methods are essentially equivalent, in that if the hypothesis (*a*) above is justified then so also, usually, are the statistical methods (II) and (III) (which, at first sight, appear to rest on quite different statistical presuppositions). We have already had considerable evidence, and some demonstration of this in earlier chapters: but for a full treatment the reader is referred to the two references to Tolman in the Bibliography.

In this book we have dealt only with *equilibrium* statistical mechanics, and consequently have been concerned only with equilibrium thermodynamics. But such well-known laws of non-equilibrium thermodynamics as the increasing property of entropy in irreversible changes are also in fact implied in (the suitable non-equilibrium extension of) the fundamental statistical hypothesis (*a*) above. The proof of this is the content of the famous Boltzmann H-theorem, a full treatment of which will be found in Tolman's book. Here we can only assert that all thermodynamics, whether equilibrium or not, may be regarded, logically, as an offshoot of statistical mechanics based on the assumption (*a*), or its suitable non-equilibrium extension.

In the early days of statistical theory it was hoped that just as the equations of thermodynamics follow logically from the assumption (*a*) above, so also it might be possible to show that the assumption (*a*) itself, i.e. the equal *a priori* probability of all conceivable complexions of an assembly, was a logical consequence of the exact laws of Newtonian or quantum mechanics. But this

is now realized to be a false, indeed (bearing in mind the 'reversible' nature of the equations of mechanics and the 'directional' content of the second law of thermodynamics) an unreasonable, hope. We can only say that statistical mechanics, based on the hypothesis (*a*) above, forms a natural *extension*—indeed, the only natural extension at all possible for its purpose—of mechanics (whether classical or quantal). The extra postulate, of equal *a priori* probabilities, is required, since, to quote from Tolman:†
'*Without* this postulate there would be nothing to correspond to the circumstance that nature does not have any tendency to present us with systems [assemblies] in conditions which we regard as mechanically entirely possible but statistically improbable...'.

3. Although, as we have just seen, the equations of pure thermodynamics are only a part of the corpus of statistical theory (and can be derived logically from the fundamental hypothesis of statistical mechanics in much the same way as the laws of conservation of energy and momentum in classical mechanics can be derived logically from Newton's laws of motion), they in no way lose their importance, or usefulness, on that account. Not only do they apply to any assembly whatever, however little we may know in detail of its microscopic structure, but they also provide a useful check on the validity, or consistency, of approximate statistical treatments.

Moreover, there are problems of considerable practical interest which, whilst they can be solved accurately, are nevertheless based on certain *physical* approximations which appear, at first sight, to exclude a direct statistical attack. For example, throughout this book we have always treated solid or liquid phases on the basis of an Einstein model. For a pure, one component, phase the treatment is certainly formally correct (see § 1, Chapter XVIII): the real usefulness of the concept of an Einstein model is revealed in the theory of perfect and regular solutions. Recent work of Kirkwood in America and of Born and Green in this country offers hope of a more fundamental treatment of condensed phases, at the same level as the theory of imperfect gases outlined

† *The Principles of Statistical Mechanics*, p. 70.

in Chapter XVI, but for many practical purposes the Einstein model approach is likely to retain its value. And in dealing with Einstein models we have had frequently to appeal to the requirements of pure thermodynamics: as, for instance, when insisting that the partition function, (p.f.), for a system in a condensed phase depends on the specific volume, v, of the assembly and not on its total volume, V.

We shall conclude by discussing another case in which a physical approximation appears to exclude a direct statistical approach.

4. Fundamentally, statistical mechanics deals with mechanical pictures, or models, of physical assemblies: for example, with a perfect gas of structureless particles whose allowed energies are given by either classical mechanics or quantum theory. Thus, in particular, the possible energies themselves are purely mechanical concepts and may be supposed known when V and N are given. On the other hand, and less fundamentally, the most adequate simple description of a physical assembly may itself involve energy levels, or energy differences, *depending directly on the temperature.* Thus we might, for instance, in the problem of immobile adsorption, suppose that the heat of adsorption was directly dependent on the temperature of the surface concerned.

Since, at first sight, there is no room in fundamental statistical theory for temperature-dependent energy levels, thermodynamic considerations are now very helpful. Let us examine what pure thermodynamics has to say on this matter.

Fig. 46 (a) represents an assembly comprising a gaseous phase, assumed perfect, and an adsorbed phase, upon the surface S, which we shall suppose characterized by an adsorption energy $W(T)$ per adsorbed atom. If we take this assembly round the Carnot cycle indicated in Fig. 46 (b), in which AB and CD are isothermals and BC and DA are adiabatics; and then let T_1 and T_2 tend to coincidence and afterwards let the adiabatics (a) and (b) tend to coincidence, we find in this purely thermodynamic way that the assembly must satisfy the differential equation of state

$$\left(\frac{W(T)}{kT}+\frac{\gamma}{\gamma-1}\right)P\frac{\partial M}{\partial P}+T\frac{\partial M}{\partial T}=0, \tag{3}$$

where M denotes the number of adsorbed systems and γ is the ratio C_p/C_v for the gas concerned.

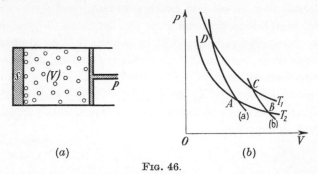

FIG. 46.

When W is a constant, independent of T, we can easily show that the differential equation (3) simply asserts that $M(P, T)$ is a function solely of the variable x given by

$$x = \frac{P}{T^{\gamma/(\gamma-1)}\exp(-W/kT)}. \qquad (4)$$

Of course not all functions of x are physically permissible; and actually Langmuir's adsorption isotherms correspond to

$$M(x) = M_s\frac{x}{x+A},$$

where M_s and A are constants.

On the other hand, in the general case when W is a function of T, the equation (3) asserts that $M(P, T)$ is a function solely of the variable y given by

$$y = \frac{P}{T^{\gamma/(\gamma-1)}\exp\left[-\int\limits_{T}^{T_0}\dfrac{W(T)}{kT^2}\,dT\right]}, \qquad (5)$$

where T_0 is a constant. Now, comparing the equations (4) and (5) we see that the energy W in (4) has been replaced in (5) by

$$-T\int\limits_{T_0}^{T}\frac{W(T)}{T^2}\,dT, \text{ i.e. by } \Delta F, \text{ where } W = -T^2\frac{\partial}{\partial T}\left(\frac{\Delta F}{T}\right),$$

i.e. where ΔF is the corresponding *free energy* change† related to W by the Gibbs–Helmholtz equation.

This result can be proved quite generally, and by more fully statistical methods, but in doing so the demands of pure thermodynamics have always to be kept in mind. It then appears that if an energy level ϵ occurring in a partition function, or Boltzmann factor,‡ depends directly on the temperature T then the expression $e^{-\epsilon/kT}$ should always be replaced by $e^{-\phi(T)/kT}$, where $\phi(T)$ is the Helmholtz free energy connected with the energy $\epsilon(T)$ through the Gibbs–Helmholtz equation

$$\epsilon(T) = -T^2 \frac{\partial}{\partial T}\left(\frac{\phi(T)}{T}\right). \tag{6}$$

This is necessary in order that the resulting equations may be thermodynamically correct.

Two comments on this result, which has considerable practical importance, may usefully be added. First, if we define the entropy $\sigma(T)$ by the equation $\phi(T) = \epsilon(T) - T\sigma(T)$, then

$$e^{-\phi(T)/kT} = e^{\sigma(T)/k}e^{-\epsilon(T)/kT},$$

i.e. $e^{-\phi(T)/kT} = \omega(T)e^{-\epsilon(T)/kT}$ where $\sigma(T) = k\ln\omega(T)$. (7)

Thus the new Boltzmann factor is indeed of the normal form, $\omega e^{-\epsilon/kT}$; but we now see that when ϵ depends directly on T so also must ω, and the functions $\epsilon(T)$ and $\omega(T)$ *are not independent*. For the equations (6) and (7) imply that

$$\frac{d\epsilon(T)}{dT} = kT\frac{d\ln\omega(T)}{dT} \tag{8}$$

(the reader should confirm this), and our equations will not be thermodynamically correct unless this condition is satisfied.

Secondly, formulae of the type

$$\eta = Ae^{-\Delta E/RT}, \tag{9}$$

where A is a constant, are of frequent occurrence in physical chemistry. When ΔE is a constant, independent of T, then

† The arbitrariness in ΔF due to the constant T_0 in (5) can usually be removed by suitable physical considerations.
‡ Single term $\exp(-\epsilon/kT)$.

$RT^2 \partial \ln \eta / \partial T = \Delta E$. If, however, ΔE varies with T, then (9) must be replaced by

$$\eta = A e^{-\Delta F / RT}, \tag{10}$$

but ΔE is still determined by the equation $RT^2 \partial \ln \eta / \partial T = \Delta E$. For we now have

$$RT^2 \partial \ln \eta / \partial T = -RT^2 \frac{d}{dT}\left(\frac{\Delta F}{RT}\right) = \Delta E,$$

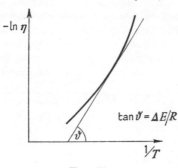

Fig. 47.

by the Gibbs–Helmholtz equation. Fig. 47 shows the well-known graphical construction for determining ΔE from values of $-\ln \eta$ plotted against $1/T$.

APPENDIX I

FUNDAMENTAL THERMODYNAMIC FORMULAE

(a) A THERMODYNAMIC system (i.e. statistical assembly) is characterized by certain extensive properties, e.g. its volume V, internal energy E, entropy S, etc., and by certain intensive properties, e.g. the external pressure P, the temperature T, and chemical potentials μ_i, etc. The extensive properties are directly proportional to the size of the assembly: in thermodynamics this is usually specified by the number of moles of substance concerned, whilst in statistical mechanics it is more convenient to use the number of microscopic systems for each component of the assembly. We shall here use N_i in this second, statistical, sense, i.e. to denote the number of systems of the ith component in the assembly. Intensive properties are independent of the size of the assembly.

If the numbers N_i are fixed then, by the first law of thermodynamics, in any small change of state the heat absorbed by the assembly, δQ, is equal to the change in the internal energy of the assembly plus the work done by the assembly against the external pressure, i.e.

$$\delta Q = dE + P\,dV, \tag{1}$$

whilst, if the change is reversible, then according to the second law of thermodynamics

$$\delta Q = T\,dS. \tag{2}$$

Combining (1) and (2) we have, for a small reversible change of state,

$$dE = T\,dS - P\,dV. \tag{3}$$

If now the numbers N_i are changed, then we must add to the r.h.s. of (3) terms proportional to the changes dN_i, so that (3) becomes

$$dE = T\,dS - P\,dV + \sum_i \mu_i\,dN_i. \tag{4}$$

Here we know only that the factors μ_i must be intensive properties of the assembly (since dE must be independent of the amount of substance originally present). We shall later see that the quantities μ_i are indeed the chemical potentials of the various components.

Finally, we may now suppose that the assembly is built up (from nothing) in such a way that the intensive properties remain constant throughout the process. Then, adding together equations of the form (4), and writing $\sum dE = E$, etc., we obtain

$$E = TS - PV + \sum_i \mu_i N_i, \tag{5}$$

which is the basic formula of thermodynamics.

Defining the Helmholtz free energy F and the Gibbs free energy G by the equations

$$F = E - TS \tag{6}$$

and

$$G = F + PV, \tag{7}$$

we thus obtain, from (5),

$$G = \sum_i \mu_i N_i \tag{8}$$

which identifies the quantities μ_i with the chemical potentials (or partial molar free-energies divided, in our nomenclature, by Avogadro's constant, N_0).

Equation (4) becomes equation (4) of Chapter I for single-component assemblies.

(*b*) To obtain equation (23) of Chapter II, we consider simultaneous small changes in all the quantities occurring in equation (6), so obtaining the formula

$$dF = dE - T\,dS - S\,dT$$

which, combined with equation (4), leads at once to

$$dF = -S\,dT - P\,dV + \sum_i \mu_i\,dN_i. \tag{9}$$

(*c*) To obtain equation (6) of Chapter XVII we combine equations (7) and (8) to give

$$PV = \sum_i \mu_i N_i - F$$

whence, for simultaneous small changes in all these quantities,

$$d(PV) = \sum_i N_i\,d\mu_i + \sum_i \mu_i\,dN_i - dF$$

which, by equation (9), gives

$$d(PV) = S\,dT + P\,dV + \sum_i N_i\,d\mu_i. \tag{10}$$

(*d*) Finally, on writing $d(PV) = P\,dV + V\,dP$, equation (10) leads to the formula

$$S\,dT - V\,dP + \sum_i N_i\,d\mu_i = 0.$$

We have not explicitly used this equation in the text.

COMBINATORIAL FORMULAE AND MULTINOMIAL THEOREM

(a) *Number of ways of dividing N distinct things into sets of n_1, n_2,..., n_k, where $\sum_i n_i = N$, with no particular order of arrangement in any set.*

The N things can be arranged in an ordered sequence in $N!$ ways: for the first in the sequence can be chosen in N ways (the objects being distinct), then the second in the sequence in $(N-1)$ ways (there being $N-1$ things left to choose from), the third in $(N-2)$ ways and so on, giving altogether $N(N-1)(N-2)...2.1 = N!$ ways of choosing the sequence.

Now the first n_1 items in this sequence may be regarded as forming the set of n_1 things, the next n_2 items as forming the set of n_2 things and so on $\left(\text{since } \sum_i n_i = N\right)$. Consequently, at first sight there are $N!$ ways of dividing the N things into groups of n_1, n_2,..., n_k.

But most of these $N!$ distributions differ from each other only in the sequence of the items within a given set. For instance, with all the last $N-n_1$ things in the sequence fixed, there are, by the above argument, $n_1!$ ways of forming the sequence which differ only in the order of the items in the first set. But we do not wish to distinguish arrangements within any particular set: so there are $N!/n_1!$ possibilities when the first set is unordered and all later sets are ordered. Similarly, there are $N!/n_1!\,n_2!$ possibilities when the first two sets are unordered and all later sets are ordered. Finally, there are

$$\frac{N!}{n_1!\,n_2!...n_k!}$$

possibilities of dividing N things into sets of n_1, n_2,..., n_k, where $\sum_i n_i = N$, with no particular order of arrangement in any set.

(b) *Multinomial Theorem.*

$$(x_1+x_2+...+x_k)^n = (x_1+x_2+...+x_k)(x_1+x_2+...+x_k)...(x_1+x_2+...+x_k) \tag{1}$$

there being altogether n bracket expressions on the r.h.s. of (1).

A term involving $x_1^{n_1} x_2^{n_2}...x_k^{n_k}$, where, necessarily, $\sum_i n_i = n$, is obtained by choosing n_1 brackets from which, on multiplication, we shall take the term x_1, n_2 brackets from which we shall take the term x_2, and so on. Having decided from which brackets the n_i terms x_i are to be taken we do not desire to lay down any particular sequence in which we shall multiply these n_i x_i's together: however we do so we shall obtain $x_i^{n_i}$ and we only have to do so once. Consequently the coefficient of $x_1^{n_1} x_2^{n_2}...x_k^{n_k}$ in the expansion of the r.h.s. of (1) is simply the number of ways in which we can divide

n things (the above brackets) into sets of n_1, n_2,..., n_k, where $\sum_i n_i = n$, and with no particular order of arrangement in any set, i.e., by (a), the coefficient of $x_1^{n_1} x_2^{n_2}...x_k^{n_k}$ is $n!/n_1!\,n_2!...n_k!$, so that, taking all possible choices of the numbers n_i,

$$(x_1 + x_2 + ... + x_k)^n = \sum_{\left(\sum_i n_i = n\right)} \frac{n!}{n_1!\,n_2!...n_k!} x_1^{n_1} x_2^{n_2}...x_k^{n_k}.$$

(c) The above multinomial theorem has been proved for n a positive integer. In Chapter XVIII, in deriving equation (22) from (21), we used the binomial theorem for a negative index, i.e.

$$(1+x)^{-n} = 1 - nx + \frac{n(n+1)}{2!} x^2 - \frac{n(n+1)(n+2)}{3!} x^3 + ... +$$
$$+ \frac{(-1)^s n(n+1)...(n+s-1)}{s!} x^s + ...,$$

in which the coefficient of x^s is

$$(-1)^s \frac{(n+s-1)!}{(n-1)!\,s!}.$$

We shall not prove this expansion here. It is valid when $-1 < x < 1$.

APPENDIX III

LAGRANGE'S UNDETERMINED MULTIPLIERS

QUITE generally, if we require stationary values of $f(x_1, x_2, ..., x_n)$ where the variables $x_1, ..., x_n$ have also to satisfy the equations $g_1(x_1, ..., x_n) = 0$, $g_2(x_1, ..., x_n) = 0$, ..., $g_k(x_1, ..., x_n) = 0$, where $k < n$, we may argue as follows.

For any small changes $\delta x_1, ..., \delta x_n$ in $x_1, ..., x_n$ we have

$$\delta f = \frac{\partial f}{\partial x_1}\delta x_1 + \frac{\partial f}{\partial x_2}\delta x_2 + ... + \frac{\partial f}{\partial x_n}\delta x_n,$$

$$\delta g_1 = \frac{\partial g_1}{\partial x_1}\delta x_1 + \frac{\partial g_1}{\partial x_2}\delta x_2 + ... + \frac{\partial g_1}{\partial x_n}\delta x_n,$$

$$\cdot \quad \cdot \quad \cdot \quad \cdot \quad \cdot \quad \cdot$$

$$\delta g_k = \frac{\partial g_k}{\partial x_1}\delta x_1 + \frac{\partial g_k}{\partial x_2}\delta x_2 + ... + \frac{\partial g_k}{\partial x_n}\delta x_n,$$

whence
$$(\delta f + \alpha_1 \delta g_1 + ... + \alpha_k \delta g_k) = \sum_{i=1}^{n}\left(\frac{\partial f}{\partial x_i} + \sum_{j=1}^{k}\alpha_j\frac{\partial g_j}{\partial x_i}\right)\delta x_i \tag{1}$$

for any values of $\alpha_1, \alpha_2, ..., \alpha_k$. And if the 'point' $(x_1 + \delta x_1, x_2 + \delta x_2, ..., x_n + \delta x_n)$ is also to satisfy $g_1 = g_2 = ... = g_k = 0$, then $\delta g_1 = \delta g_2 = ... = \delta g_k = 0$ and (1) becomes

$$\delta f = \sum_{i=1}^{n}\left(\frac{\partial f}{\partial x_i} + \sum_{j=1}^{k}\alpha_j\frac{\partial g_j}{\partial x_i}\right)\delta x_i. \tag{2}$$

Now the equations $\delta g_1 = 0$, $\delta g_2 = 0, ..., \delta g_k = 0$ may be regarded as giving $\delta x_1, \delta x_2, ..., \delta x_k$ in terms of $\delta x_{k+1}, \delta x_{k+2}, ..., \delta x_n$. If then we choose $\alpha_1, \alpha_2, ..., \alpha_k$ to satisfy

$$\frac{\partial f}{\partial x_i} + \sum_{j=1}^{k}\alpha_j\frac{\partial g_j}{\partial x_i} = 0 \quad (i = 1, 2, ..., k) \tag{3}$$

equation (2) becomes

$$\delta f = \sum_{i=k+1}^{n}\left(\frac{\partial f}{\partial x_i} + \sum_{j=1}^{k}\alpha_j\frac{\partial g_j}{\partial x_i}\right)\delta x_i, \tag{4}$$

and we can now choose all but one of the δx's in (4) to vanish, in which case

$$\delta f = \left(\frac{\partial f}{\partial x_i} + \sum_{j=1}^{k}\alpha_j\frac{\partial g_i}{\partial x_i}\right)\delta x_i,$$

and if f is stationary, δf must vanish for small but non-zero δx_i. Consequently

$$\frac{\partial f}{\partial x_i} + \sum_{j=1}^{k}\alpha_j\frac{\partial g_j}{\partial x_i} = 0 \quad (i = k+1, ... n). \tag{5}$$

Combining the equations (3) and (5) we have n equations

$$\frac{\partial f}{\partial x_i} + \sum_{j=1}^{k} \alpha_j \frac{\partial g_j}{\partial x_i} = 0 \quad (i = 1, 2, ..., n),$$

which, together with the k equations $g_j(x_1, ..., x_n) = 0, j = 1, 2, ..., k$, suffice to determine $x_1, x_2, ..., x_n$ and $\alpha_1, \alpha_2, ..., \alpha_k$.

APPENDIX IV

STIRLING'S FORMULA

STIRLING'S formula may be written

$$\lim_{N\to\infty} \frac{N!}{\sqrt{(2\pi)}N^{N+\frac{1}{2}}e^{-N}} = 1$$

or, more precisely,

$$N! \sim (2\pi)^{\frac{1}{2}}N^{N+\frac{1}{2}}e^{-N}\left\{1+O\left(\frac{1}{N}\right)\right\}$$

whence
$$\ln N! \sim (N+\tfrac{1}{2})\ln N - N + \tfrac{1}{2}\ln(2\pi) + O\left(\frac{1}{N}\right).$$

For the very large values of N in statistical mechanics ($\sim 10^{23}$) the less exact form
$$\ln N! \sim N\ln N - N$$

is good enough, and has been used throughout this book.

Table XII lists $\ln N!$, $N\ln N - N$, and $(N+\tfrac{1}{2})\ln N - N + \tfrac{1}{2}\ln(2\pi)$ for $N = 5, 10, 15, 20, 25$.

TABLE XII

N	$\ln N!$	$N\ln N - N$	$(N+\tfrac{1}{2})\ln N - N + \tfrac{1}{2}\ln(2\pi)$
5	4·8	3·0	4·8
10	15·1	13·0	15·1
15	27·9	25·6	27·9
20	42·3	39·9	42·3
25	58·0	55·5	58·0

APPENDIX V

THERMODYNAMICS OF BINARY SOLUTIONS

(a) *The Duhem–Margules equation.* The Duhem–Margules equation

$$\frac{x_A}{p_A}\frac{\partial p_A}{\partial x}+\frac{x_B}{p_B}\frac{\partial p_B}{\partial x}=0$$

follows from the Gibbs–Duhem thermodynamic equation

$$x_A\,d\mu_A+x_B\,d\mu_B=0 \tag{1}$$

on using the fact that for a perfect gas μ is of the form (equation (19), Chapter III)

$$\mu=kT(\ln p+a\ln T+b),$$

where a and b are constants and the changes in (1) are assumed to occur at constant temperature. The equation (1) itself is applied simply to the condensed phase: but systems in the condensed phase have the same chemical potential as in the vapour phase in equilibrium therewith.

Equation (1) is a particular case of the more general relationship

$$\sum_i N_i\,d\mu_i=-S\,dT+V\,dP, \tag{2}$$

which holds for the condensed phase and follows at once from equations (7), (8), and (9) of Appendix I. For from these equations we obtain

$$dG=-S\,dT+V\,dP+\sum_i \mu_i\,dN_i$$

and

$$dG=\sum \mu_i\,dN_i+\sum_i N_i\,d\mu_i,$$

whence (2) follows on equating the two right-hand sides.

For processes at constant temperature, T, and constant total pressure, P, (which, for a binary solution, is usually atmospheric pressure) (2) becomes

$$\sum N_i\,d\mu_i=0$$

which, for just two components reduces to (1) on dividing throughout by N_A+N_B.

Even when P is not strictly constant the term $V\,dP$ on the right-hand side of (2) is usually negligible compared with any particular term on the left-hand side, and consequently equation (1) is still effectively true.

(b) *Phase-Separation.* Writing

$$F=N_A\,\mu_A^0+N_B\,\mu_B^0+\Delta F(N_A,N_B) \tag{3}$$

we have

$$\mu_A-\mu_A^0=\left(\frac{\partial\Delta F}{\partial N_A}\right)_{N_B};\quad \mu_B-\mu_B^0=\left(\frac{\partial\Delta F}{\partial N_B}\right)_{N_A} \tag{4}$$

On the other hand, dividing (3) throughout by N_A+N_B, and writing $F/(N_A+N_B)=\mathrm{F}$, $N_A/(N_A+N_B)=x$, $N_B/(N_A+N_B)=(1-x)$, we have

$$\mathrm{F}=x\mu_A^0+(1-x)\mu_B^0+\Delta\mathrm{F}$$

where, since $\Delta \mathrm{F}$ is necessarily an intensive property of the condensed phase we can write

$$\mathrm{F} = x\mu_A^0 + (1-x)\mu_B^0 + \Delta \mathrm{F}(x) \qquad (3')$$
$$= \mathrm{F}^0 + \Delta \mathrm{F}(x).$$

Now $\mathrm{F}^0 = x\mu_A^0 + (1-x)\mu_B^0$ and is therefore a linear function of x (see Fig. 48 (i)). Moreover

$$\frac{d\mathrm{F}}{dx} = \mu_A^0 - \mu_B^0 + \frac{d\,\Delta \mathrm{F}}{dx}$$

(all differentiations being at constant temperature), so that plots of F and $\Delta \mathrm{F}$ as functions of x have gradients which differ everywhere by a constant

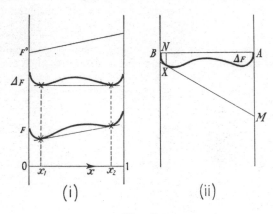

Fig. 48.

amount (equal to $\mu_A^0 - \mu_B^0$). Consequently if the curve $\Delta \mathrm{F}(x)$ has a double tangent so also has the curve $\mathrm{F}(x)$, and the points of contact, x_1 and x_2, are the same for both curves (Fig. 48 (i)).

Now, by (4)

$$\mu_A - \mu_A^0 = \frac{\partial[(N_A + N_B)\Delta \mathrm{F}(x)]}{\partial N_A}$$

$$= \Delta \mathrm{F}(x) + (N_A + N_B)\frac{d\,\Delta \mathrm{F}(x)}{dx}\left(\frac{\partial x}{\partial N_A}\right)_{N_B}$$

$$= \Delta \mathrm{F}(x) + \frac{N_B}{N_A + N_B}\frac{d\,\Delta \mathrm{F}}{dx}$$

$$= \Delta \mathrm{F}(x) + (1-x)\frac{d\,\Delta \mathrm{F}}{dx}. \qquad (5)$$

But, in Fig. 48 (ii), NX measures $\Delta \mathrm{F}$ and NA measures $(1-x)$. Therefore AM measures $\Delta \mathrm{F} + (1-x)\dfrac{d\,\Delta \mathrm{F}}{dx}$, i.e. $AM = \mu_A - \mu_A^0$ (a negative quantity in the case illustrated).

It follows that a double tangent of $F(x)$ touches the curve at points, x_1 and x_2, corresponding to two compositions of the solution for which the chemical potentials of the component A are equal. It is easy to show that the chemical potentials of the component B are also equal for these two compositions. It can also be shown that the parts of the curves lying between x_1 and x_2 correspond to thermodynamically unstable states of the solution, so that increasing x beyond x_1 results in phase separation into two conjugate phases with compositions x_1 and x_2. When the mole fraction x is increased beyond x_2 we again have a single, or homogeneous, phase.

In § 7 of Chapter XVIII we used as a criterion of critical conditions the vanishing of $\frac{\partial p_A}{\partial x}$, i.e. of $\frac{\partial \mu_A}{\partial x}$. On account of (5) this implies

$$\frac{d\,\Delta F}{dx} - \frac{d\,\Delta F}{dx} + (1-x)\frac{d^2\,\Delta F}{dx^2} = 0,$$

i.e. $\qquad \frac{d^2\,\Delta F}{dx^2} = 0$, since we can rule out the solution $x = 1$. $\qquad$ (6)

But it is evident from Fig. 48 (ii) that a double tangent to ΔF implies (at least) two points of inflexion of ΔF between x_1 and x_2, and at any point of inflexion $d^2\,\Delta F/dx^2 = 0$. Consequently equation (6) is a necessary criterion for the existence of a double tangent, i.e. for phase separation. It can also be shown to be a sufficient condition in the case of the symmetrical curves with which we are concerned in the theory of regular solutions.

APPENDIX VI

PHYSICAL CONSTANTS

THE values of fundamental physical magnitudes listed below are taken from the tables of R. T. Birge (1941) as given in his article, 'The General Physical Constants' published by the Physical Society[1] in *Reports on Progress in Physics*, vol. viii, 1941.

Velocity of light	$c = (2 \cdot 99776 \pm 0 \cdot 00004)10^{10}$ cm. sec.$^{-1}$
Electronic charge	$e = (4 \cdot 8025 \pm 0 \cdot 0010)10^{-10}$ e.s.u.
Planck's constant	$h = (6 \cdot 624 \pm 0 \cdot 002)10^{-27}$ erg sec.
Avogadro's number	$N_0 = (6 \cdot 0228 \pm 0 \cdot 0011)10^{23}$.
Joule equivalent	$J = (4 \cdot 1855 \pm 0 \cdot 0004)$ abs. joule cal$_{15}$.$^{-1}$
Boltzmann's constant	$\boldsymbol{k} = (1 \cdot 38047 \pm 0 \cdot 00026)10^{-16}$ erg deg.$^{-1}$
Electronic mass	$m = (9 \cdot 1066 \pm 0 \cdot 0032)10^{-28}$ gram.
Mass of ^{1}H atom	$m_{1_H} = (1 \cdot 67339 \pm 0 \cdot 00031)10^{-24}$ gram.
Standard atmosphere	$A = (1 \cdot 013246 \pm 0 \cdot 000004)10^6$ dyne cm.$^{-2}$

Note: 1 volt $= 10^8 c^{-1}$ e.s.u. and 1 joule $= 10^7$ ergs.

APPENDIX VII

BIBLIOGRAPHY

Introductory books containing useful sections on Statistical Mechanics

BORN, M., *Atomic Physics*. Blackie: 4th ed. 1946.

BUTLER, J. A. V., *Chemical Thermodynamics*. Appendix by W. J. C. Orr, Macmillan, 1946.

JEANS, SIR J., *An Introduction to the Kinetic Theory of Gases*. C.U.P., 1940.

KENNARD, E. H., *Kinetic Theory of Gases*, McGraw-Hill, 1938.

SLATER, J. C., *Introduction to Chemical Physics*. McGraw-Hill, 1939.
(The most completely statistical of the books listed in this section.)

Standard Treatises

FOWLER, R. H., and GUGGENHEIM, E. A., *Statistical Thermodynamics*. C.U.P., 1939.
(Indispensable to the serious student of physical chemistry: contains a masterly survey of applications of statistical formulae prior to its date of publication and an excellent introduction to chemical kinetics.)

MAYER, J. E., and MAYER, M. G., *Statistical Mechanics*. John Wiley & Sons, 1940.
(This deservedly popular book gives a very thorough account of the statistical mechanics of gaseous assemblies.)

TAYLOR, H. S., and GLASSTONE, S., *A Treatise on Physical Chemistry*, Vol. I, Chapters III and IV (by H. S. Taylor and J. G. Aston, respectively), D. Van Nostrand Co., 1942.
(Chiefly useful for references to papers more recent than those dealt with in Fowler and Guggenheim.)

TOLMAN, R. C., *The Principles of Statistical Mechanics*. O.U.P., 1938.
(Of primary interest to the theoretical physicist, the book gives a lucid and critical account of the foundations of statistical mechanics—see Chapter XIX above. Is not very much concerned with particular applications of statistical formulae.)

A Commentary on the Scientific Writings of J. Willard Gibbs, in two volumes, edited by ARTHUR HAAS. Yale University Press, 1936.
(Vol. II contains critical accounts, by A. HAAS and P. S. EPSTEIN, of Gibbs's contributions to statistical mechanics.)

LANDAU, L., and LIFSHITZ, E., *Statistical Physics*. O.U.P., 1938.
(Not easy reading: but concerned with thermodynamics and classical statistical mechanics applied to problems of physical chemistry. Includes useful work on fluctuation phenomena.)

More Specialized Books

FARKAS, A., *Light and Heavy Hydrogen*. C.U.P., 1935.
(The figures of Chapter VII above derive from numerical values tabulated in this monograph.)

HERZBERG, G., *Molecular Spectra and Molecular Structure*. I. Diatomic Molecules. Prentice Hall, 1939. II. Polyatomic Molecules. D. Van Nostrand Co., 1945.

SCHRÖDINGER, E., *Statistical Thermodynamics*. C.U.P., 1946.
(Stimulating: concerned largely with Einstein–Bose and Fermi–Dirac statistics: contains a useful account of the 'method of steepest descents'.)

Papers dealing with Grand Partition Functions

R. H. FOWLER, *Proc. Cambridge Phil. Soc.* **34**, 382 (1938).

E. A. GUGGENHEIM, *J. Chem. Phys.* **7**, 103 (1939).

R. C. TOLMAN, *Phys. Rev.* **57**, 1160 (1940).

See also,

CHANDRASEKHAR, S., *An Introduction to the Study of Stellar Structure*. The University of Chicago Press, 1939. Chapter X, 'The Quantum Statistics'.

Supplementary reading on the theory of solutions (Chapter XVIII)

E. A. GUGGENHEIM, 'Statistical Thermodynamics of Mixtures with Zero and Non-zero Energies of Mixing' (two papers). *Proc. Roy. Soc.* A **183**, 203–27 (1944).

W. J. C. ORR, 'Statistical Treatment of Polymer Solutions at Infinite Dilution'. *Trans. Faraday Soc.* **43**, 12–27 (1947).

(These papers give useful references to other recent work in this field.)

INDEX